S0-BBI-860

Estrangement and Relationship

Estrangement and Relationship

Experience with Schizophrenics

Francis A. Macnab

INDIANA UNIVERSITY PRESS
BLOOMINGTON & LONDON

To my Parents

FIRST PUBLISHED IN THE UNITED STATES IN 1966

LIBRARY OF CONGRESS CATALOG CARD NUMBER: 66-12730
MANUFACTURED IN THE UNITED STATES OF AMERICA

Contents

Foreword

I believe this book to be unique, in that it is the most ambitious, and the most successful, attempt by a theologian to bridge the gulf between theology and clinical psychiatry. The bridge in this study is constructed out of two main elements: first, Francis Macnab's remarkable capacity, clearly revealed in his book, for participation in a simple human sense with schizophrenics in a mental hospital; second, his wide-ranging scholarship, strongly polarized by the discipline of existential theory. No other theoretical position could, in my view, have achieved the successful integration of so diverse and often so dissociated domains of research and experience.

Psychiatrists unfamiliar with existential philosophy and theology will find here concise introductions to Heidegger, Buber, and Tillich as well as to the existential movement in psychiatry. Theologians and others will find a coherent digest of clinical psychiatric and psychotherapeutic theory and practice in relation to schizophrenia.

Francis Macnab's theoretical comprehensiveness, critical fairness, and practical humanity do not mean, of course, that his position lies outside controversy. In the context of the historical form of our alienation within our advanced industrial-technological world, the schizophrenic is estranged from men who are themselves already largely alienated from themselves, from one another, and from the material world. Some people can, perhaps, endure this state of affairs more easily than others. Some start to crumple, to suffocate, and to scream sooner than those of us who are slicker at strategems of compliance, equivocation, mystification, and compromise. Set in the context of the forms of social poison we all ingest, the destruction of our humanity we all undergo, the solitude we endure and perpetuate, the deadness we all endure as the price of our civilization, the schizophrenic who declares that he has an atom bomb inside him is not so much more estranged from reality than the man who would be better dead than Red. When the world has itself gone mad, we should not too readily suppose that it is just the schizophrenic who is 'the ruined man'.

The issues presented in this book are not merely the particular concern of a few specialists; they must be generally recognized as having critical importance for the understanding of the schizophrenic experience. And it should be borne in mind that in most countries of the world (including the United Kingdom and the United States of America) it is ten times more likely that a baby born today will in later life be admitted to a mental hospital than to a university.

The debate on the meaning of 'schizophrenia', the research undertaken upon it, and the disquisitions as to its occasion will continue. This book is a significant contribution to this debate.

R. D. LAING

London, 1965

Preface

Schizophrenia is one of the most complex and tragic conditions into which our human existence can fall. Even after centuries of civilization and decades of research, there are no ready answers. Although the methods of hospital care are now greatly improved, and the overall prospects are far less horrifying, the frequency of schizophrenic breakdown is of such an order that it is still ranked as one of the worst diseases of mankind. In launching into the work which this book describes, I am aware of the immensity of the problem, but the field is vast; and so many are in chains!

In schizophrenia, it seems that we are dealing with a corporate condition. It seems, too, that this corporate condition requires a corporate answer, or at least a corporate approach. Thus this work attempts to bring the insights of psychotherapy, theology and existentialism to this problem of schizophrenia. In it we will see something of man's existential fulfilment, and something of the tragic mode of his existential failure.

This book represents a considerably revised and shortened version of the thesis which was submitted to the University of Aberdeen as one of the requirements for the degree of Doctor of Philosophy. The work as it was originally presented was carried out under the supervision of Professor David Cairns, DD, Professor of Practical Theology, and Professor W. M. Millar, MD, Professor of Mental Health, both of the University of Aberdeen.

While it is necessary to say that I alone am responsible for the viewpoints expressed here, I wish to express my gratitude to these two men for their expert and conscientious weekly supervision, and for their close and practical interest in all phases of the work. It must be extremely rare for a research student to find in his supervisors such consistent academic and practical brilliance combined with such a friendly and personal concern. I owe a further debt to Professor Millar who, in addition to these many favours, readily made his hospital and clerical facilities available to me. It is fitting that the clinic and teaching centre of which I am now director is called in honour of these two men – The Cairnmillar Institute.

From the outset the work was a practical study which entailed a deep and intensive personal involvement with schizophrenic patients and their relatives. While this will have some implications for the overall problems of schizophrenia, it is immediately relevant to these people with whom it was most intimately concerned. I am conscious of my debt to them. I want to assure them that I have taken great care to conceal the facts about them which could identify them or cause them any more pain than that which they have already suffered. My involvement with these patients was subjected to careful weekly supervision and for this I am greatly indebted to Dr R. A. Y. Stewart, Physician Superintendent of Kingseat Hospital where the practical part of this work was done. I was accorded many generous favours from this hospital; I was granted access to its records and privileges, and Dr Stewart gave me invaluable guidance in many additional ways. I am also grateful to the staff of the hospital who were always co-operative and helpful. At the conclusion of the work, the Board of Management for the Aberdeen Mental Hospitals was very generous to me, and I should also like to make public acknowledgement of this fact.

FRANCIS A. MACNAB

The Cairnmillar Institute,
South Yarra, Victoria,
Australia.

Introduction

Schizophrenia – what is this strange condition, which could be the destiny of any one of us or all of us? What can we say of this madness which can lie dormant in the personality, but when provoked, can devastate a man's life and scatter his soul?

Relief and cure are urgent considerations in a condition of this kind. But there are deeper issues which carry us beyond the outward manifestations and external behaviour of this chaotic madness. We are forced to consider afresh the way a man lives in the world, the way he communicates to the world, and the way the world communicates to him. We have to consider the rapport and empathy that the one has for the other; and as well as considering the schizophrenic condition in the man, we might also consider the schizophrenic condition in his world. For the schizophrenic, schizophrenia is not some complicated disease of doubtful prognosis; for him this is – temporarily, permanently – his life, his way of speaking to his world, his way of finding some security in his world.

Schizophrenia therefore has far-reaching ramifications for man's whole existence, and has disturbing implications for any doctrine of a corporate salvation. Here we are dealing with the impoverishment of the person, his loss of contact with his world, and the breakdown in mutuality in human relationships. We are dealing with some of the extreme forms of estrangement and some of the most chaotic counterfeit attempts to find fulfilment. And what of the Christian message when all the normal channels of communication have broken down? The Christian Community may function well under some circumstances; but the tragedy is that the Christian Community is so often paralysed when faced with the schizophrenic, and so tends to exacerbate rather than cure the condition.

In this work, theological insights will be used or criticized wherever it is felt appropriate. In adopting this approach I am well aware that many questions may be asked. It seems to me that our knowledge and understanding of a condition can benefit greatly when light is thrown on it from different angles. The suggestion that any one approach or any one discipline has a priority or privilege can no longer be seriously made.

Psychiatry has made extraordinary progress as it has moved forward with its multidimensional approaches. It is true: it has directed its resources mainly to the relief and cure of the state of suffering and has tended to regard the illness from the standpoint of an organismal theory, interpreting maladaptations and malfunctioning in biological and socio-biological terms. Theology on the other hand has tended to remain remote from the actuality of mental suffering in its nature and cure. It has given its answers to suffering and mental illness generally, but often without any clear or first-hand knowledge derived from any personal involvement.

As we come to see how schizophrenia is concerned with the dialectical relationship between a man and his world, we will also begin to see the immense gain that psychiatry and theology could provide for each other.

In the present work for example, the need for us to go deeper than 'relief and cure' is repeatedly stressed. In some cases it is neither healthy nor appropriate simply to relieve tension or suffering. Greatest fulfilment may be found through sustained suffering. It will also be stressed that there is a need to understand the basic structures of our human existence so that we may see how mental illness destroys or distorts these structures.

In our development we are frequently involved in the enigmas and horrors of contradiction, irrationality and paradox. In our anxiety we may not be able to discover a clear concept of the self or of what it means 'to be'. Our relationships may be marked by uncertainty, and the distortions of others close to us may become our distortions. We become frightened and sensitive in our relationships. This may be followed by accumulating inadequacy in our attempts to relate to our world. It is out of situations such as these that schizophrenia may and does develop. In this schizophrenic condition we are thus able to preserve our life in the world while suspending our relationships with it.

The existentialist frame of reference can be very helpful. We become concerned for the schizophrenic's own experience, his experience of himself and his world, and the validity it has for him. We try to understand the basic structures surrounding the man and his world – 'the self-world polarity' – and his struggles to be. We see that his life, even as he becomes a schizophrenic, is his answer to this polarity of self and the world. We have to ask ourselves: Can we adequately appreciate the condition of schizophrenia and how it can become a particular person's way of living in the world unless we have attempted to understand and live what is involved in this basic polarity (self-world) of our human existence? It seems necessary that we should have some understanding of what man is, and what he is meant to be, before the concepts of recovery and cure can be meaningful.

We will see that in schizophrenia the basic self-world polarity has undergone drastic changes, and fluctuates chaotically from time to time. The schizophrenic has lost the consistency-of-relation, both with himself and with his world. He no longer experiences a sense of mutuality as we know it in human relationships. He is sensitive and afraid. He fears relationships, yet longs for them.

The self-world polarity is a polarity of relatedness. If we are to understand a person's way of relating himself to his world, then it is preferable that we should meet him in the dynamic process of his relating. (This 'participant-observer' approach is to be contrasted with the so-called 'scientific objectification' approach.) Likewise, if we are going to open to him the possibilities of fulfilment through relating, it is preferable to involve him in the actual experience of relating. In this work, therefore, emphasis has been placed upon meeting in small groups. In these the schizophrenic faced the possibilities arising from revealing who he was. He was turned towards his world and made aware of the possibilities of re-experiencing himself in the simple intimate relation of 'being-with' the other.

The group can assume a greater significance over and above being instrumental in relating one to the other. It is not only a means for therapy; it can become an end in itself. In the group the patient is directed beyond the preliminary issues of cure, to the ultimate issue of the *relationship* between himself and the other. Beyond its existential and biological primacy, the group has a warrant from theological doctrine. It is not in the individual *per se* that God sees the fulfilment of creation and the fulfilment of man. This fulfilment is found in the corporate relation of the community – one with the other – for God's redemption is a corporate redemption.

In the group situation, an attempt has been made to bring to the patient an awareness of the primacy of the self-world relation. There are possibilities here for him to move out from his isolated individuality and to participate courageously in the world. In schizophrenia, consistent spontaneity has been lost. In the group situation I have sought to revitalize spontaneity and creativeness; I have encouraged a break-away from the stereotyped patterns and the enclosed restricting behaviour so common in schizophrenia. Care was taken to preserve a balance lest spontaneity became chaotic, driven in every direction and in none. The patient, through participation with patients and therapist, was helped to regain the capacity to decide. Here we see that, although all decisions are not verbalized, they nevertheless arise out of, and participate in, a man's destiny.

In a work of this kind there is the tendency to talk too much about the patients and say very little about the therapist. So often our attention is directed towards our experience of the patient and in doing so, we tend to neglect the patient's experience of us. I believe that this kind of emphasis, in which the patient becomes the object of our observations, can lead to a most serious error and to a considerable distortion in our attitude and theoretical presuppositions. We tend to evade or overlook the significance of our contribution to the patient's behaviour and attitude at any particular time. While he sits in front of the therapist, the therapist, during that time at least, is a very important part of the patient's world. The patient wants to influence the therapist's judgement; he tries to divert his attention; he wants to impress or annoy; he would like to come closer or flee away. It may be any one of these or it may be a mixture of them all, but the fact cannot be overlooked that the therapist is a person in his world.

I found it was always necessary to be aware of the relationship and aware of myself in this relationship. In the groups I became sensitive to my own contribution to the group process, even when I said and did nothing. It was equally necessary for me to participate with little inhibition in the group process. I set out to meet with the schizophrenic. Aware of my preconceptions, I have attempted to 'be with him', and to understand some of his ways of self-realization and self-fulfilment.

In the beginning there was little more than casualness, self-preoccupation, or the striving for an exclusive relationship with me. This called for some structuring and catalytic activity whereby the individual could be turned to the group and the group turned to the individual. Often the group mood reflected my mood. I noted for example that when I was prevented from having my customary sleep in the bus which took me to the hospital each day, the mood of the group could be influenced by my tiredness. This was more noticeable when, in the middle of winter, the normal bus services were withdrawn and it was necessary for me to walk the last one and a half miles of the journey, sometimes in the rain, more often through deep snow.

In this work I was involved with two groups of patients and one group of their relatives. It was evident that the schizophrenic could not be understood apart from his family which, even in the advanced stages of the schizophrenic condition, was still a sensitive nexus in all his attempts to live in the world.

The first group of patients consisted of a small number of female patients, usually on their first admission to hospital, and regarded as being in the early (acute) phase of the schizophrenic illness. This was an open group, such that when one group was discharged, another was begun. There were four of these series within this group.

The second group consisted of six male patients, regarded as being in the chronic phase of the illness. All had been in hospital for a period of more than six years (one had been 17 years) and all were under 40 years of age. Both groups met four times a week for sessions of one hour.

The relatives' group met once a week for sessions of one hour and over. All the group sessions continued over a period of approximately fifteen months.

It will be clear that at many points I have been greatly helped by the work and writings of psychotherapists like Federn, Arieti, Sechehaye and others, but most of all by Harry Stack Sullivan. The general principles, the thought and the method of this work, however, belong very much to an existentialist climate; Heidegger, Buber and Tillich have occupied a prominent place in my study.

No claim is made for the therapeutic success of the work; this was not its purpose. I set out to 'be with' these patients, and they seemed to experience this. The forward-moving effect of this meeting was unmistakable. Something had happened to them. They knew that something had happened, and I knew it, and their families spoke at length about it.

The hospital where the main part of this work was done is situated in a Scottish country setting on the coastal plain, twelve miles north-west of the city of Aberdeen. It is one of the main mental hospitals, serving Aberdeen, the north-east of Scotland and the Shetland Islands. Historically and structurally, the hospital was once a custodial-type mental asylum. In recent years, however, some progressive changes have been made. The administration, the atmosphere, and the open-minded, forthright approach of the superintendent and staff have made a remarkable contribution to a more positive attitude both within and without the hospital.

Since my own presence assumed a peculiar significance in this work, it will be helpful to the reader to know something of my background.

My basic training was in the dual fields of psychology and theology. The idea behind this work had its origins some ten years ago when I was able to gain invaluable experience in the problems of treatment and rehabilitation of mental patients in a large mental hospital in Australia. In my contact with the patients there I became aware that the Church should be more articulate and specific in its approach to mental illness. I was also aware that many of the patients, although ill, were looking towards the world in quest of some meaning and hope. To those of us who have meaning and hope, this may not seem so important. But to those of us who have lived the experience of a life emptied of all meaning and hope, we know how important these can be. As a theologian, I saw that the Church could play a most important part here, if only it knew the way: and it falls upon me to do my part in attempting to find this way.

This book may be read in three sections. The first contains this introduction and some extracts from the group proceedings. The second section will present a general survey of what schizophrenia is like; what has happened with modern forms of treatment; and what contributions psychotherapy and group psychotherapy may make. Section three will deal more thoroughly with the existentialist contribution to psychotherapy. Discussion will surround the inadequacies of Heidegger's position and the possibilities to be found in the work of Buber and Tillich. After a brief discussion of schizophrenia from this point of view, the events of the groups will be reconsidered to see if some terminology can be derived which will help our understanding of this condition of schizophrenia.

Estrangement and Relationship

CHAPTER I

Meeting: I

The first group was made up of female patients drawn from the admission ward of the hospital, and diagnosed as suffering from schizophrenia in its acute form. This meant that the patient was experiencing her first episode of schizophrenia, though exceptions were made where subsequent episodes appeared to be situationally determined. The patients were under 35 years of age, except one who was 39 years of age. Care was taken to exclude those patients whose schizophrenic condition could have been complicated by or associated with brain damage, marked affective disorders or epilepsy. Leucotomized patients were also excluded. The work consisted of a series of groups.

The first series began with four patients. When these patients were ready for discharge from the hospital, the second series began with three patients. The same procedure was followed. The third series had three patients also, but one of them had previously been in the first group and had been re-admitted to the hospital. The fourth group had three patients. In all, therefore, twelve patients passed through this group. The group met four times a week for sessions of one hour. There was a total of 190 sessions.

It could be said that the improvement observed in these patients was due to the medication given concurrently with this form of group-therapy. Certainly the medication played an important part in breaking down the symptom formation, in reducing anxiety, and in making the patient more accessible, but beyond this it is difficult to draw any further conclusions.

But it must also be said that those who were conversant with the group situation were unanimous in their judgement that this form of group therapy opened the patient to possibilities which would otherwise have been unknown. In this interpersonal situation, it is difficult to demonstrate the objective results. Indeed, to attempt to do so would hinder and destroy the process of relation, which plays such a central part. It is significant that three different classes of people affirmed the positive aspects of this form of therapy – the professional workers in touch with these patients, the relatives of the patients, and the patients themselves. Often the measures adopted in this form of therapy had many similarities with the more traditional forms of psychotherapy, where the patient becomes aware of her inner and unconscious conflicts, and where skilled help is given to help her to adjust to her past history and to reorientate her towards her future.

In this present form of therapy, the re-orientation towards the future was the predominant emphasis; in this, much care was given to the process of relating to one another. Some of the extracts given later in this chapter will illustrate this movement, but before we can appropriately consider these, it is necessary to introduce the members of this first group.

KERRY

Kerry was 28 years old, married, and had four children. She herself had come from a family of seven but had never met her parents nor any of her brothers and sisters. She was adopted soon after birth, but when she was 5 years of age her mother-by-adoption remarried. Kerry was then passed over to the mother of her mother-by-adoption, who was known as 'Grannie'. Grannie proved to be strict and ruthless; she refused to let Kerry out to play and beat her viciously for trivial things.

Kerry married at 22. On her honeymoon, her husband accused her of having had premarital sex relations with some other man. This accusation was untrue but he persisted, and again and again, throughout their married life, the accusation was made. She found it difficult to cope with her domestic duties and at the same time keep the peace with a husband who always demanded higher standards than he himself could keep.

She was admitted to hospital in an extremely distressed condition. For three days she remained mute. After three E.C.T.s she spoke and revealed that she was confused and delusional and disturbed by auditory and visual hallucinations.

She was given a course of six E.C.T.s; Largactil was given and also a course of 70 comas of insulin. She entered the group shortly after she had begun insulin.

STELLA

Stella was 32 years of age, married, with three sons. After an unhappy schooling, she worked in a factory for four years. During the war, she joined the Red Cross, where she met her husband. Her marriage was punctuated by long periods of unhappiness. In addition to her three sons, she had had five miscarriages, one of which was self-induced.

On admission to hospital, she would sit and stare into space. She was withdrawn, sullen, and suspicious. She could hear voices; there were also delusions of persecution. She had contemplated suicide. She rejected insulin treatment and was then given an intensive course of E.C.T. and, later, Largactil.

EMILY

Emily was an unmarried woman of 23 years. She was large and awkward in appearance and spoke with a broad accent. She was the third of four children from a working-class family. At primary school she showed promise, but left at 14 to begin a record of a long succession of jobs as a salesgirl. She was dismissed from each job without any full explanation and was never accepted by her fellow saleswomen. She became extremely suspicious.

Her family showed no awareness of her illness, despite the fact that its outward manifestations seemed to have their origins in an incident which occurred six years earlier, when she was wrongfully accused of taking money from the cloakrooms at her place of employment.

On admission to hospital Emily was acutely distressed and frightened. One minute she would be in fits of laughter, and the next she would scream with anger. Her thoughts showed no coherence and she would ramble from one point to the next.

She had delusions of persecution and was hallucinating. There was a marked degree of preoccupation with matters of religion.

She was placed on Largactil and then deep insulin.

KATE

Although Kate was admitted to hospital suffering from 'a schizophrenic illness of some chronicity' it became clear that it was an episode of schizophrenia. She was 29 years of age, married, with four children, aged seven, five, three, and two.

She was admitted to hospital muddled and delusional. She walked into the ward, flopped down on the floor, and hugged her legs into her body. Later, she was able to say she was depressed and had intense guilt feelings over two events in her earlier life: as a child a man had made advances towards her and, later, her mother had made her feel responsible for the death of her brother.

Kate was the youngest of a family of five. After a time at high school she left and worked in an office. She married at 21. When I met her she admitted delusions and mild hallucinations. She told me how she had only one friend who had gone off to another country. Her father had forbidden her to have boy friends, and she felt that her husband would not like her 'to take up with' any of the neighbours.

Extracts from the group in which Kerry, Stella, Emily, and Kate were members:

Session 2: All the members of the group confessed they were tense and anxious. Stella was worried about saying 'the right thing', about being able to 'answer all the questions', and that 'there were no long silences'. The group tension was clear when Stella asked me if I were anxious too. I asked, 'Will it help you if you feel that everybody is anxious?' Stella and Kerry said it would.

Kate showed signs of aggression towards me and asked what right I had to wear a Fraser tartan tie when in fact that was not my name. This was interpreted as her attempt to discover who and what I was.

Session 3 began with a discussion by Stella as to why Emily should have sat in Kerry's chair. It was noted that on the previous day, Kerry had done a good deal of the talking. Perhaps Emily was 'trying to be like Kerry today, so she sat in her chair'. But Emily rejected this.

Emily did not make any spontaneous discussion and refused to be drawn into the group.

Session 4: The other members of the group were noticeably helping Emily to grasp the subject of the group discussion and there were many assurances of their concern for Emily. Kate however did not join these attempts to support Emily. I directed her to this and suggested a number of reasons, among them that she was repelled by Emily. Emily jumped to her feet and said, 'I goes to church on Sundays and hates nobody.'

The group pointed out to Emily the apparent lack of logic in her statement. Emily continued that she did not go to church when at home, but even if she did hate anybody she would not show it. Later, she said if she hated anybody she would not make any bones about it, she would tell them 'straight out'. Kerry tried persistently to direct Emily to her many contradictions, but Emily went on as if nothing had been said, 'If mum was angry . . . if I had not washed the dishes, she would do it and say nothing.'

Out of a group tension Emily became extremely annoyed. I asked the group what could be the basis for this hostility. Kerry interrupted and said, 'Hostility! My education is nae vera good.' (Meaning she wanted a definition of the word.)

In *Session 5* the group discussed Emily's confusion of identity between herself and her friend and her friend's boss. The group also ventilated Emily's homosexual tendencies and there were suggestions that these could be related to her delusions of persecution.

Session 7: No one arrived on time. When they did arrive, the session began in a long silence. It was broken by Stella, who commented on the weather. Again there was a long silence. I broke this silence with the suggestion that they had formed a unity and that at present this unity was against me. (Shown by their late arrival and by their resistance to break the silences.) It then became evident that there was a collective fear of me.

Why? 'Because of the consequences. . . .' the consequences that I might make a judgement on them. (Thus there was difficulty in evaluating the interpersonal climate.)

We explored the relationship between themselves and myself. Kate, however, insisted that she need not come to these group sessions again. I interpreted that she too wanted clarification of the relationship. She agreed and said, 'We are all withdrawing from you. We are afraid of the consequences.'

Kate then revealed that one of her problems was the fact that she was in a mental hospital. This could only have a negative effect on her already flimsy neighbour relationships. She said she had really resolved her problems. 'I'm going to bury myself in my husband and my family. I'm going to go out with them, do everything for them, do everything with them, and I'll just ignore what the neighbours think.'

Session 8: I arrived late. Stella said she had seen me speaking with the nurse, thought that I was speaking about them, and 'just left it at that'.

Kerry interrupted and said that if it were a matter of people going to work, they should be on time. On the other hand, if it were a matter of making a friend, a few minutes did not matter. I asked which applied in this case; she replied that she did not know. When she first saw me, she thought of me as a friend; now she did not think so. She thought I had discussed her private affairs . . . that I had used her affairs for another purpose . . . that in fact I regarded her as being quite unimportant . . . and anyway she could never get better again.

She wanted to know again the state of our relationship. She asked me many direct questions as though wanting to form an exclusive relationship with me. I switched this to the group and she was then able to accept the fact that if she were going to be 'happy' again, it was a matter of full participation with each other.

Session 9: I entered the room to find the group members huddled round the table in the centre of the room. Kerry laughed and said, 'Well, we said we were going to talk about the future.' Stella began to tremble. She complained of a draught, then shifted her seat. The trembling increased. There was a long silence as the group waited, apparently expecting her to give an explanation.

'I used to do this a lot when I was first married . . .'

During this session Emily was frequently distracted. She continually looked out of the window, squinted her eyes, folded her legs and unfolded them, often yawned loudly. At one stage she admitted to Kerry that she had not been listening.

Session 10: Kate had received her discharge, though she was far from well. Emily began the session by saying in panic tones, 'There's one missing . . . there used to be four of us.'

Stella discussed the problems of her family and why she should feel she had to smack them as much as she did.

Kerry also spoke of her adoption, her parentage, and the social stigma under which she had lived.

In *Session 13* Stella began to speak of her relationships with her husband. Her trembling was again most noticeable. She told us it was the accepted thing for her and her husband to quarrel in the early hours of the morning and to engage in physical combat. Recently she and her husband had, for the first time, talked things over.

There was an open expression of concern when I said I was going to see their relatives. I explained that I wanted to get to know them as fully as I could, and this meant getting to know their kinsfolk too.

Session 14 began with discussion about their relatives visiting me. Kerry did not participate. She had placed a chair between us and when I asked if this meant she was 'distancing herself from me', she said she wanted to go home. I commented that the others had asked about the visit of their relatives but she had not. 'I asked my husband!' she said.

Session 15 was also concerned with family issues. The question was raised of how Stella should show her children that she loved them. It was highly amusing as Emily put her viewpoint. She said that the children, no matter what they asked, should get it from one parent or the other and if it were money then either the mother or the father 'should come good with it'. 'Of course,' she added, 'if it is a large sum, you might have to wait till the week-end for it.' We all laughed.

Kerry told us her husband had found them a new home in one of the new housing areas. She discussed this at length, making references to the different social climate of the new area. She then stopped and said, 'Will this be taken down against me?' and looked inquiringly at the sheaf of papers on my table. I invited her to inspect them so she examined the papers carefully. One paper contained a list of book references. She looked down the list until she came to 'The Chronic Mental Patient'. Then read this out and said, 'That's us.'

In order to explain the type of notes I took I said to Kerry that it was important for future reference to note the general trends and also to give a few examples of what went on in this group, adding, 'So if I were to die, someone else could take over, and he could see where we were, whether his interpretation agreed with mine, and then he could proceed.'

KERRY: 'And what if I die?' I said, 'Then I shall write that down.' Kerry laughed and turning to the others she said, 'Just like that!'

Session 17: Kerry propounded at length that she was 'fed up with these sessions' and 'fed up with this place'. She should be home. To make her point clear she stood up and advanced towards me, shaking her fist. 'I can strike you, but you can't strike me; I'm a mental patient,' she said. The others laughed.

Session 21 was marked first by the group flight and later by cohesion and attraction. Initially the group proceeded, excluding the therapist. When this had continued for some time, I interpreted that they felt they no longer needed me. This was rejected. I interpreted that for some reason they were afraid of me. Emily agreed and said she was afraid of what her mother had been telling me. This seemed to break the flight tension and they all came in and discussed their anxieties about the group meeting of the relatives. Kerry said, 'Did you tell them how you were getting on with the three girls . . . I mean these three girls?'

Session 22 revealed many tensions between the members of the group. For example, Stella expressed exasperation at Kerry asking questions all the time. On the other hand Kerry retorted with a joke about Stella, referring to an earlier incident in Stella's hospital record when she ran away. 'So Stella vanished,' – giggles – 'a real adventure story, and now she has to take her tablets with her!'

In *Session 24* Stella and Kerry discussed the sex-play in which they were involved when girls at school. Emily, who did not share these experiences, simply said, 'No! It was my head they were after.' She then described in great detail how, on two occasions, boys had tripped her up and her forehead was 'split open'.

Session 25: Stella asked if they could continue for she felt that, through a ventilation of her sexual life and sexual fears, 'a tremendous load is being lifted from my mind.'

Kerry told the group of one of her 'dreaded' experiences: 'I thought I was a windmill. I thought I was not human any more, but was just something somebody used. I came out of my sleep and I shouted at the nurses, but it made no difference. It was as if I was that windmill instead of being a human person. I used to live in the country. I know what these things look like. I was just a windmill.' (See Sessions 38–9.)

In *Session 29* Stella was having trouble with some side-effects from her medication. Her right foot would not stop tapping. Emily said spontaneously, 'You should cross them like mine.' Emily then went on to say, 'If I put 'em apart like this I wonder if they will move.' She placed her feet apart. 'No they don't move.'

Kerry, with considerable display of weeping and emotion, told of her fears for her marriage and how she fretted that her children did not seem to love her. She had had a 'terrible struggle' in her own life and knew that nobody loved her. Now, as far as she was concerned, she was being deprived of the love of her children and they were being deprived of her love. She sobbed again.

It was then that I saw that the individual must move into the group. I told her that she should 'get alongside' Stella, as many of their problems were the same. 'They are exactly the same,' Stella said.

Session 31: The group discussed the levels of relatedness one to the other. Kerry again revealed her anxiety over her childhood masturbation and how she was afraid there was a disease here which might be transmitted to the children. In her childhood she had been shocked by the complete absence of warmth or love. She had to live in the anguish of unimportance. The enforced non-outward expression (not allowed to go out and play, not allowed to have dolls) led her to an inward expression: self-love. When Kerry told us again that she was not allowed out to play, Emily twice interrupted with a laugh, saying: 'Perhaps it was raining.'

In the next session Stella urged me to proceed the way it had been on the previous day. I was hesitant, as I sensed too much dependence: I ventilated my hesitancy.

Kerry intimated that there was something she had to say but did not know how to. Stella gave her support by telling of an earlier tendency towards infidelity which she once experienced.

Emily followed what was now a well-known pattern. She took one of Kerry's phrases and identified this with one of her experiences. Kerry had said she had something to say but did not know how. Emily said she had something to say that would 'never pass' her lips and she then went on to tell the story of how, when she was 20, a girl had told her that her boss had piles. She wondered if her silence about this had contributed to her getting the sack so frequently. Stella told her, 'It is stupid to think like that.'

There was the further request to proceed as in the previous session and Stella said, 'We are just like children . . . learning all over again . . . or even for the first time.'

I mentioned that it was my intention to have newcomers in the group. Immediately Stella said, 'I don't like that a bit.' Kerry and Emily voiced protests and Stella and Kerry offered to stay away. (Note the solidarity.) In Session 37, they all agreed to have the newcomers.

Session 38: Kerry was retarded in her speech, there were indications of slight amnesia and she said she was muddled. Was this because her husband, noting her improvements, had resumed his demands for high standards? Was it that she was feeling the impact of the burdens of the home? She was also showing a clear desire to stay with Stella and Emily, so perhaps she felt that here was some 'belonging'! 'I was beginning to think I didna belong anywhere.' Stella: 'You must be feeling as if you are not the Kerry you used to be . . . you feel as if you are somebody else.'

Kerry reminded us of her 'windmill experience'. Her mind was acting in such a way as to make her 'feel as if I am a windmill'. 'It is just as if I can see and hear, but everything is strange, and I think of that windmill, and I think I am that windmill. It sounds silly, doesn't it?' Stella sympathized and said, 'Is it that everything is going round and round in your head?' Kerry agreed but emphasized that it was more than this: 'It is just as if *I AM* that windmill!'

In the following session Kerry again elaborated upon her fears. Recalling her childhood memories again and again, she said, 'I feel as if I am the windmill, yet I am standing back looking at it . . . there is water going around it, but the water is not touching it . . . the water is going around but not touching me. I'm scared I'll turn into that wheel!'

Session 40 was a difficult session and interaction was at a minimum. Stella began to 'chatter' about its being cold, that they had been shifted to another ward, that they were getting home for the week-end and that the new members of the group had not arrived.

Kerry and Stella said, Well, we *are* here just to be helped,' Emily chipped in and said spontaneously, 'I'm just here to keep them two company.'

The second series in this female group concerned Mona, Sophie, and Chris.

MONA

According to her husband, Mona was once 'happy-go-lucky', but when she was admitted to hospital, she was delusional and suspicious and incapable of giving any coherent account about herself. She was 39 years old, had come from a family of three, and she herself had three children. Two years before admission she had undergone an abortion which was now her predominant preoccupation. She was suffering from severe guilt feelings and she suspiciously regarded everyone as knowing all about her. She made nightly and heavy sexual demands on her husband; her children were neglected as were also her domestic duties.

At one time she was able to mix easily, but as a result of her illness she had quarrelled with her neighbours and would walk up and down the streets shouting and waving her hands.

When she was 7 her mother died suddenly. This was a great shock to a girl already lacking in resources. She went into sales-work, until she had to marry at the age of 24.

During her illness, Mona's husband was sympathetic and always endeavoured to act responsibly. She was given a course of E.C.T. and placed on Largactil. When she first came to see me she slumped into the chair and presented a forsaken and slovenly picture.

SOPHIE

Sophie was 34 years of age and married. She left school at 14 and worked in a soft-drink business until she was 15, when, for two years of the war, she was a telephonist at a local hospital.

She became engaged to a boy-friend of her adolescence, but contracted V.D. from him. She attended the V.D. clinic for four years and was cured. Her fiancé was posted overseas, and while he was away she consorted with another man, became pregnant, but underwent an abortion. When her fiancé returned, she married him without telling him of this incident. He joined the Foreign Service and this took them to Frankfurt, away from Sophie's home town and her own people. The marriage was far from happy. She became pregnant, but the child died shortly after birth.

When admitted to hospital she had paranoid delusions about her husband. She denied hallucinations, but she was very guarded and suspicious in the interview. It was reported that over the past two years she had complained of excessive tiredness and she had become more and more withdrawn. She was given E.C.T. and Largactil.

CHRIS

This woman was 26 years of age when admitted to hospital.

Her illness emerged after the birth of her last child, and the consensus of opinion was that she had puerperal schizophrenia.

She complained of intense headaches, was withdrawn and apathetic, and had paranoid delusions about her neighbours. She was given E.C.T. and placed on Largactil, but showed no response. Deep insulin was begun, but her reaction showed this was unsuitable. A few weeks later she was discharged.

In *Session 41* these three patients were introduced to the group. Mona was exalted in activity and speech, showed signs of confusion and was often delusional. She chipped in on the conversation and changed its direction and content at whim. She took command of the group and told them that she had been in hospital 'long enough'. I turned this over to Stella, who told Mona that she had been in hospital for five months, that her children were in a home, and that she was now longing to get home, but realized she had to wait. 'I don't want to undo the good work,' Stella said.

Mona shouted, 'It's a *shame*! If Stella has had her treatment and if she's talkin' all right she should be able to get home.' I elaborated to Mona that my aim was to see them all quite well, that when they left the hospital I did not want to see them again. She jumped to her feet and shouted: 'You will *not*! *As sure as that*,' and she snapped her fingers. '*You will never see me here with this young lady again*!'

The group members looked at each other wondering what she meant by 'this young lady'. When I suggested she was referring to Sophie, she said, 'I am *not*! I'm speakin' about my neighbour.' Asked again, she said she really meant her husband.

The group interchange was very rapid. Mona kept jumping up, demanding as she pointed at me, 'We know *nothing about HIM yet*! What about *you*? We know nothing about *you*!'

Sophie asked to return to the ward because her back was aching 'terribly'. (She had recently had a lumbar puncture.) Mona turned to her, as if in surprise, grabbed her, and started rubbing her back mercilessly. '*This is what it needs*!' she shouted, and rubbed all the more vigorously. The group laughed.

In the next session I encouraged Stella and Kerry to participate in the problems, of the others. This they did, giving them the benefit of their group knowledge and making appropriate interpretations of Mona's and Sophie's behaviour. At the end of this session I walked back to the ward with Emily, Kerry, and Stella. It was obvious that they wanted to retrieve the old relationship with me; and in their own way they asked me how I thought they were 'getting on'. Emily, in similar intimacy, confided that she was a 'bittie disappointed' that she was not getting home for the coming week-end. Since the others were, she was afraid that the nurse might think she was 'jealous'.

In *Session 43* Chris created discussion and concern by her statement that the reason why 'people' were coming into hospital was that 'so many people had gone overseas'. She went on to say:

(*a*) her neighbours had left to go overseas, and her other neighbours had either just come or just gone or were away working;

(*b*) another man – a research worker – had been very kind to her, but he too had gone overseas.;

(*c*) her baby had broken out in a rash;

(*d*) she suddenly felt dazed and everything seemed to go slower.

Session 45: During this session I was called to the telephone. I returned to the room to find them all laughing heartily. I discovered this had been set off by Mona saying to them all, '*He's* a funny mannie, that!'

Mona asked how long they would be in hospital. She was downcast when she heard that the others had been in five and a half months, but then she recapitulated and said, 'Well, at least we know where we are now.'

Stella and Kerry spoke of their forthcoming week's pass. They arranged to meet each other one evening apart from that on which they were to report to see me. Kerry, however, told Stella there might be difficulties for her in view of her husband's present attitude. She was obviously delighted when Stella suggested, 'Well, instead of you coming to see me, I'll come and see you.' I commented that it was good to see they had made friends as they had. (I said this not so much in conversation but as clear interpretation.) Kerry replied, 'It *certainly* is!'

In *Session 46* the group tension centred on Mona again. She said to me, 'You must think we are a funny lot – the unlearned often seem funny to them that are learned.'

I sought to ventilate this inferiority which was creeping into the relationship and suggested that it was hiding something else which she was afraid would reflect on this relationship. She flatly rejected this, and refused any further self-disclosure.

Stella and Kerry participated by telling the group how they had 'opened up'. Stella, for example, told them about her miscarriages, and how she had had difficulty in expressing herself about these.

After some discussion Mona revealed that each of her pregnancies had been unplanned and that her first child had been conceived outside the marriage relation. Stella and Kerry supported her here and pointed out that she would 'automatically love' the child for it was her 'own flesh and blood', which pleased Mona.

In *Session 47* Sophie told the group that she would not accept the principle of self-disclosure; in addition to not wanting to speak about her past, she was too ashamed of it. Kerry told her the first part of her statement was unacceptable – as for the second part, she need not be anxious since they were all in this together. Sophie accepted this, and proceeded to tell of her disloyalty to her fiancé (who later became her husband) and how she had become pregnant by another man. She had a miscarriage and later married her fiancé. She wept excessively.

The group then turned to Mona. She was cantankerous and kept saying, 'Dinna *bother* me!' She said, 'I jis' hate comin' through here. . . . I'd rather go to O.T., where I could do somethin' wi' my hands.'

STELLA: 'But you've got to get your mind straight first.'

MONA: 'There's nothin' wrang wi' my mind.'

Emily caused a commotion by chipping in, 'I'm nae interested . . . they're all married . . . I'm a virgin.'

STELLA: 'You told us you knew nothing about sex.'

EMILY: 'Nor I do.'

MONA (referring to the state the group session had come to): 'There'll be no Christmas pudding at this rate!'

In *Session 50* Sophie prepared the group for her further disclosure by saying she was about to tell something which hitherto she had been unable to tell. She then told how, in her premarital relations, she had contracted venereal disease, had been treated over a long period and cured.

Chris struggled to give Sophie support by saying, 'It all seemed to arise from loneliness.' Mona was silent and sullen, but thought Sophie had done 'the right thing' in telling. It became clear that this issue of V.D. had played a large part in the marital unhappiness. Chris thought this was due to the fact that they had had no children. 'They always had to sit and just look at each other.'

In *Session 51* Mona, after receiving support and the assurance of acceptance from the group, began her further disclosure. 'All right, I'll tell you straight out,' she said. Her fourth child had not been born because she had undergone an illegal bortion. Mona wept at length. It was clear that no one had any overtones of reprimand. Sophie and Chris gave their support.

In *Session 53* Kerry told of her week-end at home and how her husband had tried to counter her excessive tiredness with his determination to have sexual intercourse. She said she broke down and wept. Her husband, who had become 'furious' with her, became 'all considerate'. They had then 'sat and talked things over . . . for the first time, ever'.

In *Session 55* Chris revealed her extreme loneliness and described the misery this sometimes brought her. Here we discovered that there was not only an 'existential loneliness', i.e. the accepted experience of being alone and isolated, but a loneliness which had about it the character of a severe loss.

In *Session 56* the group tried to lead Kerry into seeing how she was under great stress, and that she should be prepared for the emergence of her former psychotic symptoms:

(*a*) She was under stress, wondering what her husband, mother-in-law, cousins, Stella, the therapist, and the relatives at the relatives' group would think of her if she were not discharged with Stella.

(*b*) She was under stress that Stella would be discharged before her.

(*c*) She was under stress that Stella's departure would leave her (Kerry) on her own.

(*d*) She was under stress because there were signs of the old symptoms emerging.

Session 59 seemed to proceed along the established pattern. There were a few more silences than usual, some of them more extensive. Then, without warning, Mona broke one silence by bursting into tears. I said nothing. It was clear that Sophie was disturbed by the behaviour. Mona at length said, 'I'm jis fed up!' 'Who would have expected a mental hospital to be like this? Locked doors, and people askin' questions ye canna understand . . . and that ye canna answer.'

In *Session 61* the silence was uncomfortable. The group members spoke voluntarily with each other, but most of the conversation was apparently futile in content:

'Do you go to O.T.?'

'Have you a family too?'

'Do you know Ivy?'

In some silences Sophie would look anxiously from Mona to me. She would lean forward on her knees, then back. Now and again she would break the silence by saying, 'Well, well . . .' she often gazed into the far corner of the floor and at one stage appeared quite oblivious to a question from Chris. Then, after some time had elapsed, she snapped out of it and answered the question.

Session 63: I was feeling very aggressive, particularly towards Mona and Sophie. Sophie's denial and compliance, her lack of depth, her refusal to ask the existential question, her failure to behave even as a schizophrenic 'should' behave, were all aggravating.

The group heard played a recording of the Christmas greetings sent by the relatives' group. This gave them all a good boost; when it was over they called for a repeat playing. They then sat and talked about it. At the end of the session, the members seemed satisfied with the proceedings.

In *Session 64* Mona saw Sophie distancing herself from us and said, 'She's makin' an awfu' mess of the groupie from what it was yesterday.'

Session 65: I directed the group to Mona who said she would talk about anything at all except her sexual relations with her husband. 'Anything at all – but when it comes to this!' She began talking about anything and everything and at times would chip in on herself and talk about something very different. This went on for so long that at length I said, 'It has to be *your* way or mine. If it is *your* way, you return to the ward, and I will not see you again. If it is *my* way, I will get you well.' She immediately began to tell me about her husband.

When she was leaving I became aware of the deterioration in her appearance and dress and told her directly that she must tidy herself up, get herself washed, put on make-up and a clean cardigan, and brush her skirt. She sat down again and burst into a flood of tears. I did not remit but told her to return to the ward, which she did and continued to weep.

Next session Mona walked into my room with a broad smile. 'Am I tidier today?' she asked. The difference was amazing. She then asked me what it was about her that had prompted me to speak to her on the previous day.

Session 69 was didactic. By diagram I attempted to help them in their attitude towards themselves and others. Here the theory of ego boundaries was expounded. Mona broke down and wept. I interpreted that this concerned her perception of the relationship with me: she felt inferior, felt a threat, and because she was unable to follow me at times the relationship was jeopardized and, in turn, her discharge from hospital. She accepted this but wept on. I explained that I was aware of her capabilities and was fully ready to accept her. She began to recompose herself, and to re-apply herself to the task.

In *Session 70* they told me how they had tried to generalize what I had said in the previous session about their ward relationships. They used diagrams to illustrate this. In subsequent sessions, Mona and Sophie told me of the various activities they were now doing together, e.g. going to the dentist together; going to the hairdresser together; discussing possible hair styles, and so on.

In *Session 74* Mona and Sophie faced their 'scatteredness' and spoke of the possibilities of 'fullness'. Here their religious apprehension was relevant and was discussed openly and frankly and continued in the subsequent session. This meant a fresh appraisal of their guilt and shame over the past, i.e. it involved a frank perception of their own condition; an apprehension of forgiveness; the acceptance of acceptance, first within the group and then with God. They explored how this was meaningless unless they knew what it was to 'live together', i.e. to be 'related'.

It soon emerged that Sophie was experiencing a conflict over being a Roman Catholic and returning to Confession. This was ventilated and she arrived at her necessary course of action, namely, for her husband and herself to go to Confession.

Session 76 marked the introduction of two new members – Desma and Heather.

DESMA

Desma, a young woman of 20 years of age, had been admitted to hospital in a distressed and withdrawn condition. Her main preoccupation was the size of her bust which, she said, was too small for a woman of her build. Despite her despairing attempts to encourage growth, the opposite seemed to occur and she dreaded that her falsity would be discovered. The fact that she was soon to be married only exacerbated her condition; she had even contemplated suicide.

She was the youngest of a family of three and had come from a good home. After leaving school, where her record was good, she became a physiotherapist and was commended as industrious and competent. Socially she had been congenial and gay, but after her engagement to Paul she became markedly less sociable. She broke off her regular church attendance; all her spare time was spent in Paul's company. He, however, had received an appointment in Sarawak and had proceeded to his post on the understanding that Desma would follow later and they would marry out there.

After Paul had left, Desma developed her illness. Her father volunteered every assistance, but her mother, who had a serious heart condition, suffered a further setback in her health after Desma's admission.

Desma was placed on Largactil and this was later supplemented by E.C.T.

HEATHER

Heather was an unassuming woman of 24 years, married, with three children. The first child was born out of wedlock, the father being the man who became her husband. Heather was the youngest of a family of five. Her father was often away from home, and when he returned he was constantly drunk.

She left school at 15 to work in an office. When she was admitted to hospital she had already made two attempts at suicide. She was experiencing hallucinations and had sexual fantasies. She was also distressed by her guilt over her premarital relations both with her husband and with other boys. Her work had become too much for her and she was excessively anxious. Her brother, of whom she was particularly fond, was drowned in an accident in London, and she had become preoccupied with this.

She was given E.C.T. and placed on Elimit. Her husband, also 24 years old, was a taxi-cab driver. Although he professed his love for his wife, he showed little self-control or understanding.

In the group Heather was overwhelmed by the fact that she was in the same group as Desma, whom she perceived to be much higher on the social scale. This was fully ventilated. Desma could not control a compulsion to run away from hospital, and it was out of this that Heather was able to accept the possibility of a group bond.

Session 79: Heather disclosed herself on issues over which she had been socially sensitive: her father was a drunkard; they once lived (seven of a family) in a slum area; her first child was 10 weeks old when she was married; she had had premarital relations with three different men, the first time when she was 16 years old.

Desma said she was 'shocked at this revelation' but very soon she was telling of her own intimacies with her fiancé.

In *Session 81* Heather told of her auditory hallucinations, which kept saying:

'You don't care for anybody else.'

'You just care for yourself.'

'You don't love anybody, you just pretend to love.'

The subsequent few sessions concentrated on orienting the members away from themselves to the group. A point of religious significance came up in *Session 82*, when Desma explained that when she became engaged to Paul she gave up her religion. She said she had 'thrown over' what her parents had brought her up to accept and was rebelling against her parents – 'but not my mother!' She said she had been extremely angry with her father who would never buy them a 'proper' home. 'But now he's going to, when Mum and I get better; so he could have done it all the time!'

In *Session 83* it emerged that there had been a considerable carry-over from the relatives' group, so it became necessary to discuss the significance of the theory of ego boundaries. It was of interest to find that the relatives had virtually quoted me word for word.

In *Session 88* Desma began to tell us of her childhood. During the war, she had lived with her grandmother in a small fishing village on the south-west coast of England. (This was between the ages of 5 and 10 years.)

'My father was a sort of stranger when he came back. I sort of resented him – my grandfather was easy with me, but my father was strict and wanted to be the boss – he always wanted to be in charge. He was trying to take the place of my grandfather.' She described ways by which she showed her resentment.

In *Session 91* Desma told us how her feeling for Paul was now 'indifference'. She intended to delay her visit to Borneo so that she could go back to work and spend some time with her parents. Questioned by Heather, she said she would go to Borneo in August, i.e. one month later than previously planned.

In *Session 93* Desma had just been brought back from Banchory where she had fled after she had eluded one of the nurses. The group discussed the significance of being in hospital: how before they were admitted they thought only 'queer' people came here; now they no longer thought that way.

After *Session 95* Kerry was readmitted. She was greatly distressed, self-punitive, and distracted, and kept crying out that she was sorry and that she had done 'something terrible – spreading disease – cancer!' She joined *Session 96*. At first, on hearing Kerry's history, Heather jumped up and said, 'That doesn't mean that *we'll* have to come back, does it?' By *Session 98*, Kerry had been accepted into the group, and was beginning to play a leading role.

In *Session 100* there was a long silence. Kerry rose and said, 'Do you mind if I leave the room – I could be reading a book back in the ward.' It became clear that Kerry was becoming the 'balance of power' in a three-cornered relationship, with Desma and Heather contending for her regard. I observed this, but did not interpret.

In *Session 102* Heather spoke again of her guilt and how it was impossible to experience any peace of mind. She said, 'God is punishing me, making me like this. How can he forgive too?' I attempted to assure her that his forgiveness overrode any retribution. She said, 'It would be good if that would happen.' We discussed the Biblical passage where the adulterous woman was thrust before Jesus for his judgement. Heather followed all that was said, and when the discussion had ended, she asked, 'Will I have to come through here again?' I questioned this. She said, 'I thought that was the finish.'

Session 105: Desma began to talk of her resentment towards her father. She said she was aware that church-going was a standard of her father's which she had accepted until Paul came along. Her consorting with Paul signified part of her rebellion against her father. Her absence from the church was a rebellion against her father, and thus the Father of the Church.

In *Session 109* Kerry appealed to the others to help her to find a way to persuade her husband of her fidelity. They were not very helpful, but Kerry continued to turn from one to the other, trying to involve them, e.g. to Desma she said, 'If your father said you were not to go dancing . . .' Kerry recalled how, prior to her first admission to hospital, she had been outside wandering about in the early hours of the morning. She said, 'I have often thought' – pause – 'you know I have often thought that I might have been imagining things.' She asked me directly and it was necessary to explain the difference between imagination and delusions. There was an animated group discussion on this point. We also discussed the various threats which could shatter or fluidify the ego boundaries. Kerry then went on week-end pass, returning after the week-end in a much deteriorated condition. Her husband had again accused her of infidelity and had beaten her physically. There were large bruises on her left temple, her right arm, and stomach, and there was a red mark around her neck where he had tried to strangle her.

On the way back to hospital her husband was deeply penitent. 'I ken I'm in for it,' he said. 'I never thought I'd sink so low as to hit a woman.' Kerry said, 'I hope my husband comes to the next relatives' meeting. He needs help.' She thought, however, that it would be extremely difficult, for he was very stubborn.

In *Session 113* (i.e. a few sessions later) Kerry said, 'I am on my own now.' The group gave her more than support; it assured her that this was not the case. The matter with her husband distressed her, she said, not so much for her own sake, but for the children. 'They need a mother . . . their own mother . . . and I want them.'

Desma told Kerry she could 'rely' on them. Kerry turned to her and said, 'Thank you, Desma, I know you are trying to help.'

Heather then turned to me and said I was belittling her illness by not giving her enough serious attention. I accepted this partially, pointing out that becoming involved in the problems of others was the first effective step in getting her to live outside (as well as inside) her own world.

Sessions 115 ff were marked by the group solidarity. A personal issue would quickly become a matter for the group.

Session 119: Kerry's husband had then been to see me. Kerry told how, when she was returning after her recent week-end, she almost missed the bus. Her husband helped her aboard and cried after her, 'For heaven's sake hurry up and get home.' She said,

'I thought he didn't want me hame . . . I hope he willna batter me a second time.'

In *Session 121* the group gave lively discussion to Desma's underlying guilt and resolved that her absence from church was due to her deception over her bust, her intimacies with Paul, and her feelings for her father.

Session 122 was devoted largely to discussion on their paintings. Desma had painted a car, her father and herself in the front seat; Heather and Kerry in the back seat.

Suggestions ran along these lines:

(*a*) She wants us to be together.

(*b*) The three people in the painting are key people for Desma at the moment.

(*c*) Kerry observed the large space between the front and back seats. Heather said this could mean that Desma fancied she was well ahead of them.

(*d*) Was it Desma's father or me in the front seat with Desma?

Kerry's painting was of some windswept drooping trees on an otherwise open landscape. The hilltops in the distance contained the only bright colours. She said, 'I'm thinking of the future – something in the future I mean to achieve. The hills are supposed to be in the distance – well, after that trouble we had at the week-end, it is going to take a wee while before I can get home again, and a while before me and my husband get on together. These trees drooping – I feel just – sort of down in the dumps – sorta sitting silent at times, thinking – maybe the trees are like me.'

HEATHER: 'I think Kerry has been like those trees – she often lies on the couch and sleeps.'

Heather's painting was of herself and Kerry walking down a path together. This triggered off some vigorous and heated words, for she had left Desma out. Kerry said of Desma, 'Aye, I sometimes think that – sometimes I've thought that she thought me a wee bittie stupid – well, I don't know the meaning of umpteen words.'

The matter was well ventilated.

Session 126 was devoted to a discussion on what was involved in belonging to this group. This, they felt, was necessary, for soon they would be moving out of this into other groups outside. Heather said she liked this group because 'we did not have to worry about what we said – nobody judged us.' Kerry joined in here, saying, 'We can speak our innermost thoughts about things that we would not tell other people – and we know that it would not go any further. We seem to have faith in each other – sort of trusting each other – and we feel that you can help us.' As dis-distinct from being 'linked' together, they spoke of 'bonds' which bound them together.

Session 127 marked the introduction of three newcomers to the group – Margaret, Marie, and Barbara.

MARGARET

Margaret was a short, slim, blonde-haired girl of 22 years, who was admitted to the hospital in an extremely distressed condition. At first she was too confused to tell what was happening to her. Later she kept repeating that she was in hospital because of her sins. She was hallucinating and when spoken to she would ask for silence while she waited and listened to the voices before replying. Her delusions made her feel that people had control over her.

During childhood she had been most unhappy. Her father, she said, was irresponsible and constantly drunk. Her mother was a determined business woman. Margaret was the fourth in a family of five. Because of the constant rowing and brawling, she ran away twice, but was brought back to face severe punishment. At length she left, never to return. She became friendly with some young men, around whom much of her delusional material revolved.

She was given a course of E.C.T. and placed on Largactil.

MARIE

Marie was 25 years old when she gave up her ordinary employment to become a prostitute, but, unable to go through with it, she attempted suicide. She was admitted to hospital hallucinating, withdrawn, and delusional. She felt she was two people; one of her was being ruled by an outside influence.

She was the eldest of a family of three. Her father was a

drunkard part of the time, and a distillery worker the other part. Her mother was in poor health and, possibly, suffered from a mental disorder. It was a very unhappy home. Marie left school at 16 to go to work, where she smoked and drank, and was eventually dismissed. Having nowhere to stay, she spent the night in buses.

Later she took a sales position in Manchester, where she met a man who had left his wife and child and was living with another woman. He invited Marie to live with him, which she did for three months, when he decided to go back to his *wife*. Marie returned to Aberdeen, but began to feel that a doctor there had 'strange power' over her. She left her job to become a prostitute.

When admitted to hospital, she was given E.C.T. and Largactil, but left the hospital against professional advice.

BARBARA

Barbara had to get married. She and her husband went to live with her parents but this was unsatisfactory. They then went to live with his parents but this, too, failed. They rented a house of their own and here Barbara's illness began to emerge. She neglected herself, her home, and her two children. She soaked her husband's pyjamas in urine and stored soiled diapers in the chest of drawers. Ashes from the fireplace had been deposited in her handbag. Her husband left her, so she went to live with her parents. They found she would have strange fits of rage and outbursts of physical violence and on one occasion they feared suicide.

She had three elder sisters and two brothers. At 17 she left school, having failed her university entrance examinations. After that she went from job to job.

Barbara was admitted to hospital in an agitated condition. She was delusional and showed a marked flight of ideas. She was given 50 comas of insulin. On the second admission two and a half years later and in much the same condition as on the first she was given E.C.T. and Elimit.

Session 129: Marie was negative and hostile and rejected any suggestion of participation in the group affairs. Margaret was aggressive while Barbara just sat and grinned.

Desma, Kerry, and Heather continued to work through the dynamics of the relationship and more particularly their relationship with me (*Session 130*).

Session 131 (with Margaret, Marie, and Barbara) began with a long silence. Barbara laughed. 'It seems funny,' she said, 'that four people should come in here to say nothing.' Margaret did not laugh, but snapped, 'I think it's madness!' Barbara laughed again. Margaret repeated that it was madness.

Marie began to speak, but said it was very difficult 'especially when you don't know people very well – you don't know if they like you or not.' Margaret began to laugh and went on laughing. At length she collected herself and said: 'It's so *silly* . . . that we should come here to see if other people like us or not.' She laughed again, looking at Barbara as if to induce her to join her. Marie said, 'Well, it's all right for Margaret. She's got plenty of confidence. She can live her life without caring a thing for anybody else. I'm not a person like that. I want to get close to people. Margaret doesn't want that. She's got confidence to live on her own.' Margaret then began to gabble. 'That's the way *she* sees me. But you want us to talk about everything, but I don't want to be a "nosey-parker" like that.' At the end of the session, Margaret clamoured to know 'how long' this course of treatment would take. I began to explain to her the nature and depth of her illness and her anxiety seemed to be relieved.

Session 132: They all arrived twelve minutes late. Margaret said she had forgotten; Barbara said she had been waiting for me to come through and get them as I had with 'Desma and the others'.

During this session Margaret sat and stared at me. It was difficult to assess if this was masking a desire for a close relationship, or if it was another way of placing a distance between us.

In the next session, for which they arrived ten minutes early, there were many long silences. Barbara accepted everything that was said, and always grinned readily. Margaret began to disclose herself and the nature of her condition. She described 'horrifying nightmares', 'like spiritualism', 'like death', 'something to do with the spirits' – a horrible feeling would come over her and it was as if something were drawing something out of her – right over her head. She was 'going queer'. The sight of a red pencil would make her feel her nose was going to bleed, and she would rub it vigorously.

She then told of one occasion where she had had sexual intercourse with one of her boy-friends. They had been to a drinking party and later returned to Margaret's boarding house. The landlady was away, so the boy stayed the night. No precautions had been taken against conception, and this had thrown her into 'frantic worry'. After intercourse she haemorrhaged and this made her panic more. (As she told the story she puffed heavily and gripped on to herself – this had been profoundly disturbing to her.) They decided to become engaged, just in case she was pregnant, but the boy-friend was not at all concerned. He went down south and was not seen again. Her next boy-friend was curious and had questioned her about this, and the fact that she had given him so much information worried her greatly.

Barbara had been very quiet. When she returned to the ward the sister in charge asked her how she was getting along with me, to which she replied, 'Oh, he's very quiet . . . I haven't managed to get much out of him yet.'

In the next session Marie prefaced her disclosure by saying, 'It is too long and too confused,' and then went ahead to tell of her life with the man in Manchester.

Session 136: Margaret had received a message that her mother could not visit her. She chain-smoked during the whole session. The mother issue led to a further disclosure in which she told how she was brought up in the midst of poverty, drunkenness, orgies, and the like.

MARIE: 'I'm feeling inferior.'

MARGARET: 'Is it personal? There's no need to feel inferior!'

At length Marie said she admired anyone who had had a hard upbringing. This triggered off a tirade of aggression from Margaret, who vigorously defended the integrity of her mother. Marie tried to help Margaret to understand her meaning. At least Margaret knew where she was. On the other hand, in Marie's family the mother was never strict; she placed no prohibitions on them, then leathered them when they least deserved it. We discussed fully Margaret's need of a mother although she had long since rejected hers. Was she turning to a 'fantasy-mother' in the hour of crisis? Margaret then attacked Barbara over the nature of her mother-relationship, refusing to accept the idea of a good mother now. 'Your mother can hurt you where it hurts most; she knows that. She does not have to hit. She knows what words to use.'

In *Session 138* Marie disclosed to the group further matters about her mother and the mother-relationship. There had been many fierce quarrels between them but she had come to the stage where she would never let her mother see her crying. Her father drank excessively and when intoxicated 'he was *bad*'. He would fight; furniture would be broken; an innocent tourist was in hospital for weeks after one of his drunken assaults. Marie would often try to thwart her father's intention to drink by slipping unnoticed into the shed and pouring his store of proof whisky down the drain.

In *Session 141* the group almost collapsed as a result of Barbara's divulging information to people outside the group. Margaret launched into an attack upon her. Barbara immediately stood up to stub her cigarette, remained standing, and so blocked Margaret's line of communication with me. Margaret and Marie were firm – to form ties with anyone outside the group was equivalent to rejecting the group and its rules. Barbara agreed that she had broken the rules but had not betrayed any confidence.

MARIE: 'Well! I think we should put her out!'

MARGARET: 'I think so too.'

MARIE: 'Two is better anyway. Three is a crowd!'

All this visibly shook Barbara. It became necessary for me to break in on this rigid situation. I asked Margaret if there were conditions which, if enforced, would make Barbara acceptable to the group.

BARBARA: 'Well, I'll leave these two to it.' I moved in and said this only reflected her common attitude of submission.

Margaret said Barbara could remain on certain conditions: first, she should show herself to be trustworthy; secondly, she should watch carefully what friends she made outside the group; thirdly, she should keep the group rules. Marie agreed with this, and Barbara accepted. I then gave Barbara some necessary support, and directed the others as to how they themselves must respond to this new situation.

During *Session 142* Margaret described one of her dreams. She was sitting on some grass watching a dancer. Behind the dancer she could see her mother, who kept calling out to her by name. Margaret said she looked, but would not go. 'She wanted to know if I loved her – she kept calling out, "Margaret, Margaret, come" – but I did not go and then somebody in white – a nurse – came and led me away. And then it was too late. I could not go after her. Anyway, I went after the dancer. It was terrible!' When she reached the conclusion of her description Margaret was leaning over, flushed in the face, perspiring, and panting heavily.

She then went on to describe how she had been 'told' she must 'do penance' and walk the streets in her bare feet. The Virgin Mary had appeared to her. Margaret 'got down on the floor and began to pray and pray. I was wide awake!' She said she was not a Roman Catholic, but she started 'yelling out "Hail Mary's"' and then she heard a voice crying to her: '*look – look closer*'. Margaret cried back, 'I can't read it – I can't read it.' The voice cried louder: 'Look closer!' She looked, and there were the words of prayers, written in gold, and she said, '*I* prayed them.'

Marie and Barbara had entered a relationship with two male patients which provoked much tension. Margaret criticized their actions, but Marie told her that she would not tolerate her interference. 'I resent people telling me what I am going to do – I've got a mind of my own!'

MARGARET: 'But it's sick!'

MARIE: 'So is yours; so is Barbara's.'

MARGARET: 'But I know mine is sick.'

MARIE: 'Well, I'm not taking advice from you or anybody else.'

In *Session 146* the group turned to consider Marie and her relationship with her mother. This precipitated a ten-minute silence, which was broken by Margaret, saying, 'Ten minutes have gone!' In the silence Marie maintained a fixed gaze on the upper corner of the room. Barbara nodded and smiled inanely. Margaret chewed her gum, sometimes loudly. At length Margaret told Marie to 'get talking'. After another long silence Marie said with emotion: 'Do you really want to know about it? Do you? Well, I'll tell you. Every time the radio was turned on – she laughed! Every time she went to the pictures – she laughed! Now, would you like that – would you?' 'She was a very possessive woman; she took the children to the pictures three times a week to keep us away from our father. Whenever we spoke to him there was a scene!' The mother persistently abused the neighbours and imagined the local grocer was in love with her.

Marie went on to say how she 'hated' this atmosphere, 'I would like my children to love and respect their parents.' Here I pointed out that a few weeks ago she had told us she would have been pleased to have had a child by the man with whom she was living. Could this child have been proud of its parents? She said, 'But we would have been married later!' We explored this further with regard to her own unacknowledged guilt. 'I admit I was not happy with the way I was living.' She then admitted that though her parents had brought her up in an atmosphere she despised, she was going about the same thing in a different way.

I: 'You not only hate your mother. You hate yourself.'

MARIE: 'Could be.'

I: 'You hate yourself for ever associating with your parents. You hate yourself for all the thoughts you have had about them. And you hate yourself for what you have done now.'

Marie asked for a match for her cigarette. I told her that at this moment she was feeling the need of something – something to hang on to. She had a need; she felt she would not get through these things unaided. But I wanted her to do just this – go through with it without the aid of a cigarette. She accepted.

She said, 'It's my mother's fault. I hate her for it. I hate her, because it's her fault I'm like I am.' Was she here responding to me as to her mother-image? A long silence.

In the next session, Marie entered and smiled, then began to say that people were not really interested in her, and it was foolish to let them play with her feelings. She refused any interpretations; she had now made up her mind to leave hospital. Margaret heaved a sigh and said, 'Oh hell! Here we go again!'

I directed them to the group and how they had been behaving as 'individuals'. Margaret: 'But I *am* concerned about Marie – I want to see her get well, but I get fed up when she won't co-operate.' This immediately precipitated a heated exchange between Margaret and Marie.

Session 152 began with twenty minutes of silence. Marie sat and stared, looking like a sphinx. Margaret sighed. Barbara sighed. Marie sighed. Marie asked for a light. Silence again until Margaret broke it by asking me, 'Are you not feeling well?' Without waiting for any comment from me, she quickly asked if I had seen her brother.

Marie said she had nothing to say, and what was more, she was determined that the things that happen 'in this little room are not going to upset me'. I told her she was afraid, afraid of what might happen, so in order to defend her 'self' she behaved like a sphinx. Did she feel that she could not turn others into stone, so she turned herself? Is this self-fulfilment for her – no contact, no relatedness?

It was in *Session 154* that Barbara began to disclose herself. She told how she had failed her university entrance examinations; how her mother had interfered in her marriage; how she and her husband had fought physically with each other; how her relations with a male patient had complicated matters. 'It's all confused,' she said.

Session 155: Margaret wept three times as she told how 'horrible' her past was. 'The trouble is there is no answer to my problem.' 'I've got no home to go to. *My* past is so different from the other two – these fights used to go on – every day there would be fights, every night there would be fights. Sometimes my mother would get me up in the early hours of the morning and preach to me.'

She said, 'Our family will never be reconciled again. My brother's bitter and my sister goes from pub to pub with sailors.' She had lost contact with the other members of the family.

In the next session, Margaret proceeded with her disclosures.

Her father was a drunkard. Sometimes he would be away for as long as twenty-eight months without sending money home. He would often be involved in severe debt. When at home, he would fight with his wife and would make pathetic accusations regarding the morality of his wife and family. Meantime, he would become drunk again and 'carry on with other women'. Margaret admitted the possibility that her sister was not a full sister, but she doubted it and anyway it was an 'unpleasant thought'. On the one hand she said she always thought her mother 'could do no wrong' but, on the other hand, there were times when she 'hated' her. When her mother went to have her youngest child, Margaret, though only 9 years old, said then: 'I hope to God they both die!' A new child would only mean 'more fights' – 'more rows' – 'more slavery for me'.

On one occasion she stole a pound and ran away from home. When she returned there was a 'terrible row'. Her mother 'thrashed' her at midnight, she woke her at three o'clock in the morning to thrash her, and then, when it was time to get up, thrashed her again. Often her mother would tell her to 'go out and enjoy yourself', but she had no clothes to wear. On other occasions her mother would threaten that if she went dancing she would come down and pull her out. And so the story went on.

In *Session 158* Margaret spoke of her last boy-friend. About a fortnight after she began seeing him, she had severe headaches. After seeing the doctor the headaches actually became worse. Subsequently, every time she saw red, in particular a red pencil, she experienced the sensation of nose-bleeding (but not in actuality). She felt that the girls at work were all looking at her and that they knew what was happening to her. At nights she would be 'lonely and very, very tired'. She would go to her boarding house, have a sandwich, smoke a cigarette and go to bed.

In *Session 160* the group returned to this matter which had worried Margaret so much. They discussed the possible relationship between the headaches and nose-bleeding sensations, and the 'affair' she had had with her 'fiancé'. The affair had been traumatic to her. They openly discussed the pain of penetration, the erection of the penis, and the haemorrhaging. Was there a symbolic relation between these issues and those of headache, nose-bleeding, and red pencils? These latter issues occurred after she had begun to see another boy-friend, i.e. the one who succeeded the fiancé. Thus it is feasible that associations with him could precipitate such reactions. Margaret discussed these matters, to and fro, and then said, 'Well, sounds very feasible – so – my illness stems from that! That's a relief!'

(It is significant that Margaret had been complaining of these headaches and sensations right up until this session. After this session she had no such further complaints.)

In *Session 163* Marie made a further disclosure regarding her illness. While she was working at a research laboratory, she felt that a doctor had control over her mind. She also felt that people were watching her and that they actually knew what she was going to do. After sexual promiscuities of various kinds, she decided to become a prostitute but, when put in the position of doing so, she found she could not go through with it. She then left her work, took a room in a hotel, and managed to demolish four bottles of codeine. 'I wasn't afraid to die – I wanted to finish it,' she said. It was then that she was taken to hospital.

Margaret immediately shared Marie's experience – she too felt that people had control over her, and she had tried to cut her wrists. She went on to say she saw 'a great pit, and out of it there were belching flames and smoke. I was scared.' She said she knew she was to go 'in there' and, if she did not go in, her family would. 'Judas and Jesus were both there.' She had to do penance by walking the streets in her bare feet.

Margaret then spoke about dying. 'If you just die and that's all there is to it, well, that would be O.K., but this heaven and hell business – and you don't know if there's a God – it all makes me very frightened.' 'When I thought of dying and going to hell I was scared that you never got out of that place, so I thought it would be better to stick it out here!' (Laughter.)

Session 164: Marie presented her dream in which she saw herself inside a room. A black cat was swinging from rafter to rafter, until it missed one, and fell to the ground, dead. Then it came to life, and turned out to be Rodney (her former man friend). He then began kissing her on the face. She kept telling him he was dead, but he would not believe her. She then generalized this to her deep and tormenting fear that certain people were marked to become vampires. She disclosed that she had been trying to obtain a St Christopher's Cross for protection against vampires, saying it was not so much that she was afraid of being attacked by vampires, but that she was afraid of becoming a vampire herself and killing her people.

Before *Session 167* was due to begin, Margaret and Marie had taken a trip into town. Marie had refused to return. When Margaret and Barbara came to the group room they pulled their chairs close to me.

In *Session 170* Margaret recounted again one of her 'horrifying' experiences. As she told us the story, she again frequently rubbed her nose, as if she thought it might be bleeding. She told us once more about the pit and about the prayers, and the Virgin Mary standing before her, dressed in white. 'She was pure, I was not. She was a virgin; I was a virgin once, now I'm a virgin no longer.' Relief came by helping her to see herself in this 'experience'. She was tense, then became relaxed; there was no longer any need for fear, for it was now all under her control.

I was soon to leave for three weeks' holiday. Dr Tod, a lady doctor, was to take this group during my absence. She sat in on two sessions before I left. The attitude of the group members was seen in Margaret's hostility: 'Well, tomorrow Dr Tod takes over for three weeks! She'll be good – we might get on better with her – I like *her* – she's a woman – I'll go over all this with her.'

During this time with Dr Tod, attention was given to Barbara's continued negativism. So great was the gain here that Barbara became able to discuss her problems not only at length, but with noticeable coherence. The change of therapist played an important part; Dr Tod, however, experienced an exasperation similar to mine.

On my return – *Session 180* – both Margaret and Barbara seemed to be well and pestered for their discharge. Margaret complained about the staff. There had been compulsory queueing for meals on all days except when the Commissioner was coming. On these latter occasions, they were told to sit at the tables and the nurses waited on them.

MARGARET: 'It's all false! They're not sincere! That's why I want to get out of this hospital!'

Barbara, in *Session 181*, recapitulated what she saw as the significant events in her illness:

'It was just that my husband and I were going to make it up, and then we changed our minds – it wouldn't work out. We used to quarrel an awful lot, then I just went back and stayed with my people. And that's where I am now – I was always very depressed; I used to hear voices; I used to hear my husband's voice telling me to come back, and when I used to tell my mother I was hearing the voice, she would say I was hearing things; but I did hear his voice . . . I've got over it now. I've decided that I wouldn't be happy with my husband, and I'll divorce him in May; and my people agree with me. I can always get a job. . . .'

Margaret then gave a more discerning summary of Barbara's illness. She pointed to: (*a*) her failure in her university entrance examinations; (*b*) her failure in marriage; (*c*) her failure in her work and in her home; (*d*) her failure in meeting and mixing with people. She was never confirmed as a person; never made 'to feel like somebody, always like nobody'.

In *Session 182* Barbara was once again encouraged to see herself and her past in perspective. She persisted for some time, but then said: 'This treatment has not helped me a bit!' Margaret: 'Oh, I don't know! I was quite surprised to see how everything linked up and how my subconscious had such an impact.' Barbara then agreed!

In *Session 183* Barbara again persisted in her negativism. 'I have nothing to say – I can't remember – Do I have to come here? – Why can't I go home?' In sheer exasperation I told her she was behaving like a bloody moron! So, with this tension between Barbara and myself, and a mounting tension between Margaret and Barbara, group work was becoming very difficult.

Margaret disclosed her attitude to her religious background.

She told of the strict instruction which her grandmother had given her. (Her grandmother belonged to a religious sect.)

'Religion gets you all muddled,' Margaret said. 'They carry the flag and beat that drum – they preach and they pray – and the next thing, they are in court for something they should not do.' She continued at length, then added, 'You have no evidence that Jesus Christ was actually a person, have you? I've never gone to a minister when I've been in trouble. As far as religion is concerned, it's best left alone.'

In *Session 185* she again took up this issue, but added, 'Religion is best left alone.' Nevertheless, she talked on and, as if feeling this was what was required, suddenly exclaimed, 'This is not a Bible Class!' She then said, 'Religion is like an ugly fester in my mind, that burst.' She again talked on, without any comment from me, but interspersed what she said with protests that she did not want to talk about it. She explained her earlier experiences in a religious organization and how she used to imagine that one day she would be a missionary. 'In fact, I used to think that if I was a Roman Catholic, I'd have become a nun. . . .'

She said that when she came into hospital first she was 'very frightened' about religious matters. The next session she came in and said, 'We're finished with religion, aren't we? There's nothing more to say – I'm not frightened – that's what you think I am.' I told her she was obviously troubled about these things and we must get them straightened out. She said, 'Well, let's get them straightened out today.'

She then described how 'scared' she was that she was 'going to hell' for what she had done. The concept and experience of forgiveness were discussed; she felt it was too much like stealing. 'You find you're O.K., so you steal again.'

In *Session 187* Margaret discussed the significance of her premarital relations in the light of her religious fears, but concluded the discussion by saying: 'When I get out of here, I'm going to have a good time. I'm going to enjoy myself – go dancing – have a drink – it will be "Operation Pleasure".'

Session 189 was devoted to those issues concerning their future. Following Margaret's reactions it became clear that there was still a desire (if not a need) to live on her own, and a desire to assert her self-sufficiency. She was unwilling to consider any out-groups.

In *Session 190*, some pressure was brought to bear on Margaret's assumptive world. As soon as she sat down I said, 'Why do you keep wearing that cross?' (a pendant). She was shocked by this confrontation, but then told me she 'always' wore it, even when it could not be seen. It cost £5. 'I don't like cheap things. I like a cross – I just like it, that's all – I *did* believe in the church at one time, you know.' (She asked for a light.) 'I bought that when I was quite religious – when I was a "goody-goody". I don't know what my unconscious mind is saying to me about this.'

She told me that I reminded her of her mother who used to say, 'You can't pull the wool over my eyes. My mother was wasted. She should have been a psychotherapist. She would have wound them all up and made them tell the truth. She'd have fairly taken their breath away.'

She then took up the cross and (despite its value to her) said to me, 'Do you want it?' I interpreted that this was a symbolic undressing in front of me, and compared it to her statements in a previous session where she told me the requirements for a suitable sex-partner. Here in this cross there was also a conflict with her morality and that for which the cross stood.

I said, 'At the moment this cross helps you. It stops you from throwing away all you've got. You'd better keep wearing it.'

She heaved a sigh – 'That's fine. I thought you were going to persuade me to stop wearing it.' Silence.

I: 'You are craving for what that cross stands for?'

M: 'I believe it. I believe Jesus was crucified.'

I: 'There is some connection between your strong attachment to this cross and the fact that Jesus was crucified?'

M: 'I don't know.'

I: 'Does it have a meaning – that you fear there is nobody in your life?'

M: 'You are the only person I have met who has been genuinely interested in me.'

I: 'And even I am not to be had?'

She then exploded. People do not try to understand one another. It was just a matter of 'morbid curiosity'. There was no 'genuine sympathy'.

I: 'And in face of this, you want assurance that there is love in the world?'

M: 'I used to really feel that God loved me. When my grandmother died I lost contact. I was trying to hang on to my childhood.'

I: 'You wanted assurance that, in spite of it all, there is love in the world.'

M: 'I suppose so. But I was confused. Why – instead of all this business about heaven and hell – why don't they preach that He loves you . . . it's other human beings that confuse others, not God. They want you to be scared into going to church.'

I: 'And you are scared. But it is the assurance you want; so you keep wearing this cross as a symbol of your assurance?'

M. 'It must be right. It must be right.'

Long silence.

M: 'I was just thinking. . . .' Silence.

I: 'You were thinking. . . .'

M: 'I was thinking about God. If I really was brought face to face with God, what would he say?'

I: 'What do you think he would say?' Silence.

M: 'Nobody can say . . . I think I will be judged fairly. I would tell him I really believed in him. He'd understand – all my days haven't been bad. . . .'

I: 'This cross around your neck. . . .'

M: 'It means he will forgive me. Everybody is so smug. The churches lack something. This cross – I get something from it that no minister can give. I could easily have bought something else, but I wanted a cross, so I bought this one.'

I: 'Well, you keep wearing it.'

(In following through this religious issue, I have omitted reference to Barbara or any of the themes which were of concern to her. This was done for two reasons: (*a*) it gives continuity to the issue before Margaret; (*b*) there was no coherent theme or issue before Barbara, who continued in her negative and confused way right to the point of her discharge, e.g. she said, 'I want a supervisor's job. I want responsibility.' Asked why she felt she 'wanted' responsibility, she replied: 'I don't know why I want it, I just want it.')

At the conclusion of *Session 190*, both Margaret and Barbara were given a week's pass. They returned, eager to obtain their discharge. When it appeared doubtful whether they would get it or not, Margaret became very annoyed and said, 'This place is like a prison camp. The only difference is they don't have sentries on the gate!'

They were discharged.

FOLLOW-UP GROUP

All patients who passed through Group I were asked to report weekly for the follow-up group.

It took the form of a private interview followed by a group session, lasting altogether about one hour.

There were forty-two of these sessions. Records of these sessions are not presented here.

The follow-up group attempted to serve the following purposes:

(a) to retain the group contacts made in hospital;

(b) to give mutual support as the patient once again faced the world;

(c) to give a sense of belonging and solidarity, when all else may appear insecure;

(d) to help the patient in all the issues of her social readjustment;

(e) to detect any deterioration in the condition of the patient.

The records show discussions on problems covering: husbands and boy-friends, family and finance, religious beliefs and employment, and other general problems of adjustment to their world. The sustained link with the therapist was an important feature of this group.

CHAPTER II

Meeting: II

The second group consisted of six male patients, diagnosed by two consultant psychiatrists as chronic schizophrenics. These patients were all under 40 years of age, and all had been in hospital for more than six years. They were designated incurable. This group met for one-hour sessions, four times a week, for 189 sessions. As the project neared its conclusion, the number of sessions a week was reduced. The group consisted of Arthur, Norman, Walter, Edward, Davis, Gordon, and Fred. After four sessions Gordon refused to attend. No pressure was put on him to come, and he dropped out altogether.

ARTHUR

Arthur was a married man with three children. He had a long history of difficult relationships; his wife had been advised to leave him, and she had done so. Six years after admission, he still had outbursts from time to time. Ordinarily, he would present as a pleasant, gentlemanly person, but reports and the later personal experience of the author testified to his ready aggression. When he was admitted to hospital he was in a very agitated condition. He was delusional and hallucinated, and was preoccupied with philosophical and religious ideas.

He was given two courses of insulin (48 and 27 comas) supplemented by five courses of E.C.T. (6 shocks in each course). There was no change in his condition.

When I first met this patient, he was 32 years of age and had been in hospital for seven years. He showed a severe thought disorder, his articulation was very poor, and he was delusional and aggressive.

NORMAN

Norman was a short, stout, neatly dressed man of 36 years of age. He was married, although the marriage had never been successful. He had always lived with his adoptive parents, but had never been told of his adoption. At 14 years of age he left school, and for three years worked as an engineer-apprentice. He then joined the Navy, and served for six years. At the time of his discharge he was showing signs of disturbance, but help was not sought until three years later. When he was admitted to hospital, his behaviour was erratic, his power of concentration was disturbed, and there was a gross confusion and disintegration of thought.

He was given 30 E.C.T.s. At first he became composed, but soon deteriorated. Over a long period he was given E.C.T. from time to time, amounting to about 60 E.C.T.s in all. He began occupational therapy and here he showed himself to be conscientious and thorough. Over the past three years he had been taking a week-end pass.

When I first met Norman he had been in hospital for eleven years. He was friendly towards me, but at times he adopted a very superior attitude and was in great haste. He was very confused in his thinking and was unable to sustain a conversation on any specific topic.

WALTER

Walter was an unmarried man of 30 years of age. He came from a family of four boys and three girls. His parents lived in an upper tenement dwelling in the heart of the city. His contact with his family was negligible.

Walter's physical appearance and his dress presented a picture of marked deterioration and dilapidation. When he was admitted to hospital – eleven years before my first interview with him took place – he was in 'a typical catatonic stupor'. He was roused from this by E.C.T., but later developed hallucinations and catatonic excitement. At one time he left hospital against advice, but soon returned, hallucinated and delusional, emphatically claiming that the king was his father.

Over the years he became withdrawn; there was an increasing poverty of thought and loss of spontaneity. There were marked tendencies towards self-mutilation, but this was usually restricted to his hands.

EDWARD

Edward was an unmarried man of 25 years of age. His hospital record in Scotland began in 1951, but there had been previous hospital care in South Africa.

He had decided to migrate to Australia, but had become mentally disturbed during the voyage. His mother and father had died suddenly. This seemed to render a shattering blow. His thinking showed a gross confusion with ramblings, disintegration, and perseveration. He was hallucinating and delusional. (His predominant delusion was that he believed he was God.) After insulin and E.C.T. had been given without effect, his condition was controlled (to some extent) with Largactil. Yet, despite this, he often behaved in an uninhibited manner, his language was often obscene, and he was frequently preoccupied with masturbation.

DAVIS

Davis had been in hospital for more than seventeen years. He was an unmarried man of 37 years. He was discharged from the Air Force in 1943, and admitted to hospital in a disturbed condition. He was suspicious, impulsive, grimacing, and giggling, and acted as if hallucinations and delusions were present.

He was given a course of modified insulin supplemented with E.C.T., and over the years E.C.T. was given from time to time. There had been an increasing poverty in his thought and spontaneity. He was able to carry out light routine duties in the pharmacy.

GORDON

Gordon was aged 24. He was admitted to hospital in 1951. He had lost all interest in his work; he had been day-dreaming, and there was a general retardation and scattering of his thought. He was given 70 comas of insulin and later a course of E.C.T., but without response. He preferred to keep to himself and was often found brooding.

FRED

Fred was 28 years of age. He was admitted to hospital when he was 16. He had shown a good scholastic potential in his early schooling, but this dropped off sharply at the age of 14. He then left school and began work in a sales department of a city store. After passing through a number of jobs in a short period of time, he broke down. When admitted to hospital he would talk and laugh to himself; he would grimace fiercely and grasp his head tightly. After a course of E.C.T. his condition became more florid. Again, after 70 comas of insulin, there was no change. Largactil had controlled the condition to some extent. He remained withdrawn, however, and often grimaced and clenched himself.

He was the youngest of a family of four boys and two girls. The other members of the family had a university background, as had his mother.

Session 1: The first session was intended to be introductory and explanatory. It exhibited the plain manifestations of the hesitancy and isolation of some schizophrenics, and the aggression and separation of others.

I suggested that they should introduce themselves to each other. This gave rise to a swift and heated interchange between Gordon and Norman. Norman accused Gordon of being a liar. This was quickly reciprocated; Gordon then launched into a vicious attack on each one in turn, and refused to be interrupted. Walter stared straight ahead. Despite Gordon's outburst, Walter, undisturbed by it all, blew his nose into his hands and then rubbed his hands together. For a time he continued to pick his nose. On two occasions he turned round and looked out of the window. Edward grinned without reason, but did not speak.

Session 2 continued this exploration and encounter, patient with patient, patient with therapist.

At one stage I left the room. As I walked down the corridor I became conscious of someone following. It was Walter. As soon as I turned round he raced back into the group room.

The point was raised that three members of the group would be absent on the following day. Edward then burst into very loud laughter. I asked him directly but sympathetically what this meant. Very seriously he said that Arthur had said, 'We will be the only three dumplings here,' i.e. referring to an earlier discussion. Gordon objected; he had heard nothing. He cross-examined Edward, and asked each member of the group if he had heard anything. Gordon then asked Edward to explain carefully what he had heard, whether it came by 'noise', 'by the tongue', or 'by the lips' or 'how'? Edward said, 'It definitely came; but it was very soft.'

Session 3 began with Walter and Arthur. Walter volunteered the information that it was a 'poor sort of a day'. 'Monotonous,' he added, 'but we'll have to wait for the others.' Edward entered and said immediately, 'Only three today.'

The group interchange was extremely slow, so I directed them to each other. I asked Walter what he thought of the other two. Walter looked from one to the other and then said of Edward, 'Could have more forehead.' I then asked Walter actually to touch Edward's forehead. He walked over, stood erect – as if adopting an excellent professional attitude – placed his hand on Edward's forehead and said: 'I don't think he needs an operation.' When asked, he did likewise to Arthur, and said: 'He's a swimmer.' Arthur agreed. I then asked Walter what his (his own) name was. He replied 'Doctor Walter'. Edward laughed and disagreed with this.

Walter told the group how he came from Nevada, where he had a ranch of 6,000 cattle, 3 horses, but 'no men working there as I am not sure if I have got it'. At a later stage in the session I asked Walter about this ranch. He laughed, bent his head over, shook it, looked up with a grin, and said, 'No, it's not right.'

Arthur spoke of his home and told us where it was. Walter chipped in and said, 'Up among the toffs.' Was Arthur a toff? 'Yes,' said Walter, 'He's a toff, the swank!' Edward agreed. Why was he a toff? Walter said, 'His trousers.' I asked Arthur to stand so that the other two could name features which made him a toff: (a) his blue trousers; (b) his shoes 'to match' (they were brown); (c) 'his neat tie'; (d) 'his hair brushed back'. I stood beside Arthur and directed their attention to the same features in myself. Am I then a toff? I suggested that Walter and Edward might also like to become toffs. Walter said, 'I havena a proper tie – it's a hospital tie.' His tie was twisted and loose, so I loosened mine. Walter became interested and said, 'I'll straighten mine.' Walter and Edward then stood up to be numbered among the toffs. I pointed out that we had agreed that we were all toffs. Walter added: 'Meeting of the toffs.' Edward laughed.

Walter then said, 'They are spoon-feeding us.' I asked who were 'they'. Walter replied: 'Our mothers.' He continued to speak on, but I could not understand.

In the following session, Norman asked if 'anything happened yesterday'. I directed this to Walter who said, 'Environment'. I asked Davis to describe what he had done on his day away. He spoke for twenty minutes, but said very little indeed. He perspired freely and moved his arms about awkwardly. The remainder of the session consisted of Gordon airing his grievance about coming to this group.

Session 5, Gordon refused to attend. Davis noticed his absence, but the others were silent. Davis talked on in a monologue about Gordon.

Norman turned to Arthur and asked his name. (In fact Norman and Arthur had lived in the same villa at the hospital for many years.) Without question Arthur told him his name. Norman then said, 'Well, Connor (calling him by his surname), I suppose you don't have much to say.'

Edward yawned and stretched and, when spoken to, showed he had not been listening. Walter was silent and picked his nose. (Earlier in the day he had seen me in the grounds, and although at a distance, he called out, 'Meeting today?')

In *Session 6* group bonds were absent and the discussion seemed futile. There were many long silences, all of which were broken by Davis who would talk on at length. Davis began to hum a tune. I encouraged this. After some time the group as a whole (excepting Walter) began humming 'Tipperary'. Norman kept interrupting with the words: 'So long as it is not too idiotic for you.'

In the following session Arthur, Norman, and Davis spoke on, regardless of one another. At times the three of them would be speaking at once. I singled Arthur out. He rambled on in a way which seemed to me incoherent. Five times I directed his talk, but he continued to ramble. Norman interrupted: 'Arthur, you're just like a newspaper.' Silence. I asked Norman to clarify this statement. He explained: 'Well, so often a newspaper has nothing to say but it manages to be full.' At another stage Norman told Arthur, 'You're talking about the past; I'm interested in the future – football in Aberdeen.'

Edward then chipped in to remind me, 'You were talking about the cow.' In fact, nothing had been said about 'the cow', so I asked further. He replied: 'Some cows give milk, some don't' (laughed loudly).

Walter recalled that the group was going to sing together again. I asked him to give the lead. He began to breathe heavily and looked around at the others with a grin. I suggested he should stand up and sing. He stood up with chest out, but still continued to heave with his breathing. 'I need a light before I can sing,' he said. He tried to sing, but after much heaving with his breath, he sat down. His breathing returned to normal. I again encouraged him. Walter stood up again, and called out: 'A fag, must have a fag.' Davis gave him one; he inhaled deeply and blew out long streams of smoke. He again tried to sing, but failed. He sat down and said, 'Na, I canna sing t'day.' Norman said, 'I'll help you,' and gave Walter the words of Tipperary. But Walter could not go through with it. Davis began singing, 'Keep right on to the end of the road,' and Edward joined in. Meanwhile Walter finished his cigarette.

Session 8: Norman produced an evening paper and began to read to the others. He came to the horoscopes and said, 'Oh here's something. When are your birthdays? Mine is the 1st May.' He read out his own horoscope, then those of the others,

Walter smiled widely when we noticed he had had a haircut. Each member of the group then stood up in turn while the other members made comments about him. When Davis stood up Walter looked at him and laughed heartily. 'He's like a horse!' he said.

In *Session 9*, an idea of sub-grouping came to me. There were many long silences and no involvement. I asked Norman to move nearer to Edward. Edward flatly refused to move near Norman. Norman moved but could not settle to the idea of sitting face to face with Edward. After a lot of shifting about. Norman decided 'the only thing for it really' was 'to make it like a motorbus', so he sat thus:

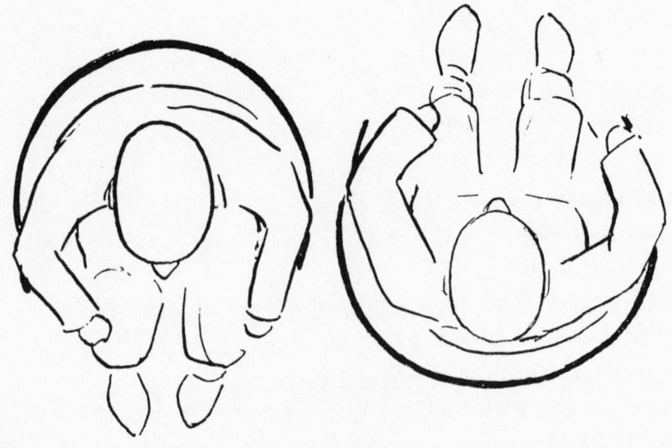

Edward would not co-operate.

I placed Arthur with Walter and Davis. Davis monopolized all the conversation. I had to tell him that instead of talking in an incessant monologue, he should wait for the others to speak back. This he did. He then encouraged them to speak and later it was difficult to interrupt them.

The seating positions of Edward and Norman lent themselves to some sociodrama. I suggested we should all get aboard this 'motorbus' that Norman had contrived. Walter rejected the offer to be the driver, but Davis quickly volunteered. He sat in the 'driver's seat' and made appropriate noises and actions. Norman acceded to the request to be conductor, but looking towards me, said, 'So long as it's under your jurisdiction.' Edward was persuaded to turn around and face the way the bus was going. Davis and Norman had come to an agreement over the route; there was talk as to whether the bus belonged to the Corporation or to a private company. At length it was decided that it belonged to one of the local private companies, and that it was travelling from Bucksburn to Culter (a distance of eight to nine miles). Norman went round to each one, asked where he was going and collected the fare. When the bus began to 'move', Walter laughed heartily.

The next 'bus' was going to Peterhead (a distance of thirty-five miles). This time Norman took over the driver's seat. Arthur was easily persuaded to be the conductor and enthusiastically collected the fares. I observed that after Walter 'alighted' he became withdrawn. I suggested that the road rules had been broken and a policeman might be necessary. Walter was on his feet immediately saying to Norman: 'Can I see your licence? Where do you come from? London? England? Where?' Norman soberly replied, 'Aberdeen'. Norman questioned Walter's authority, and looking towards me said he wondered if Walter was still acting under my 'jurisdiction'. At this Walter went and sat down. Norman said, 'We are not trying to make a fool of you, Walter.' Norman then turned to continue the journey. He looked back over his shoulder and said to Arthur, 'Well, Connor, collect the fares!' He then addressed me and said, 'I hope this is not too idiotic for you.'

I suggested that Walter should interview the conductor. Edward called out, 'Take his name and address.' Walter turned to Edward, 'I haven't got a pencil.' Norman supplied a pencil and a tin on which to rest his paper, but told him not to look in the tin. Walter looked in the tin. Walter then took Arthur's number and the bus number, both of which were given by Norman. Walter then returned to his seat. Norman and Arthur speculated as to their procedure now, e.g. Norman said, 'Well, Connor, where do we go from here? I don't know whether this bus has been confiscated or not!'

The group re-assembled. I asked them if they liked coming to these sessions. Walter immediately answered, 'Yes, very much.'

In *Session 11* Walter appeared very agitated. He whispered to himself and laughed heartily without apparent reason. Three times he mentioned irrelevantly 'yellow fish'. He interrupted the discussion at one stage and asked me directly: 'Have you got a yellow fish on you?' He said he was 'fatigued' and asked me: 'Could you get me a slice of bread please?' I took this seriously and asked if this was in fact his desire. He replied: 'No, I just said it to see what you would say.' He then asked if I could get him a passage on the 'Queen Mary' so that he could sail the 'trans-atlantic' where he might 'sport' and 'play tennis' and 'get my health back.'

Arthur asked Walter if his mother had come to visit him, and if she was going to attend the relatives' group. Walter did not answer. I prompted Edward to ask him. Walter did not answer. After a long silence Walter said: 'I'm a bittie deaf.' Arthur raised his voice, but Walter did not answer.

In *Session 14* the group acted the story of 'The Ten Commandments'. This was related to the film of that name then showing in one of the Aberdeen cinemas. Arthur volunteered to be the Pharaoh but refused to use the first person in this role. After some persuasion he did so, with the comment: 'I know I'm *not* the Pharaoh, but I will pretend I am.' Walter had to be persuaded to act his part of Moses. He would go back to his seat and say, 'I can't act it.' He refused to return to the 'scene'. On prompting, Davis, Norman, and Edward all called him back and he came.

In *Session 15* Fred, who to this point had not participated in the group activities, seemed to become the focus of our attention. Walter kept looking towards Fred with marked discomfort. Walter, however, refused to discuss the issue. He would not stand up, and he would not lead the others in any activity as he had done before. He sat and stared – first at me and then at Fred. Fred took no interest. He would frequently clasp his hands tightly, and at the same time grimace as if in pain. In the next session Norman asked Fred to give us his account of the story of 'The Ten Commandments'. Fred's telling of the story was mechanical in the extreme.

At times he would bend over, his head almost between his legs, clasp his head with his hands and say, 'What comes next?'

Walter asked, 'How did they put Moses to death? Did they bleed him from the side?' I asked the group who Walter was speaking about. Arthur and Fred said it was Caesar. But Walter said, 'No, it was Christ; they bled him from the side . . . the Pharisees, or was it the Jews?'

Davis produced his newspaper. Walter took it and began to read. Looking at me over the top of it he said: 'Which trait do you belong to? Do you belong to the Jews or the Pharisees? . . . Are you a traitor? I tried to allay any fears he might have regarding the issue which seemed to have arisen between himself and Fred.

In *Session 17* each member stood up in turn for comments from the other members of the group. Walter rose before it was his turn, turned his back towards the group and rubbed his hand up the back of his head to direct our attention to his haircut. 'Not a bad trim, eh?' he said. Edward was deeply withdrawn in this session, and this state continued into session 18. He stared rigidly in front of him, his head in his hands, his elbows on his knees. At times I could hear him grinding his teeth.

In *Session 18* Walter said he would like to talk about music. He said he was proficient on the saxophone. I handed him a chair. He protested that this was not a saxophone but a chair. He then turned the chair upside down put his head on a partial incline and (with saxophone-noises) rendered 'Love's old sweet song'. He stood up and bowed, and the group applauded.

I wanted to introduce the idea of art therapy to the group. Edward had already been attending art therapy, so I brought one of his paintings to the group and asked him to show it to the other members. His painting consisted of four or five straight lines drawn across the page.

ARTHUR: 'Oh, there's nothing there. If you are going to paint, you've got to draw in some pattern and shape.'

FRED: 'It's very good; better than I could do.'

WALTER: 'What is it? What is it? It's heaven. It's surely a misrepresentation of the world.'

NORMAN: 'Shift it back, Edward, for my eyes. That's it.' (Pause.) 'Take it away!'

As he showed his painting, Edward had to be told to move from one person to the next.

Session 20: As soon as Norman arrived, he asked what had happened in the relatives' group.

In *Session 21* Edward showed a notable change. He was ready and waiting to begin; he met me with a great smile and was keen to talk with the others. Despite his apparent withdrawal on the previous days, we discovered that he had, in fact, heard and noted everything that was said. At one stage he laughed heartily without apparent reason.

Throughout the session Walter stared at me persistently. I winked at him. He said, 'I wondered if you were a film star, the way you winked.' Norman chipped in: 'Well, the dress is appropriate, anyway.' Walter continued to stare at me. I commented on this. He replied, 'As a matter of fact, I prefer to look at Norman.' Norman said, 'Don't bother. I'm just about to have tea, and I don't want to be put off.'

Session 23 was the first session after their first visit to the art therapist. Walter entered the group room, and began laughing. He said it was all because Norman had 'threatened to shove the water jar down my throat'. Norman immediately flared up, contradicted Walter's statement, and with each added remark from Walter, Norman would become more and more heated.

They all presented their individual paintings to the group in turn. I encouraged them to speak about each other's paintings and to ask questions. When it was Walter's turn to show his painting, he said, 'Could I have a jug of beer and a piece of cake, please? A jug of beer and some sugar.'

In *Session 24* I entered the room to find the group seated, but my chair had gone. I portrayed this dramatically and suggested that this was their rejection of me. Norman, Walter, and Davis protested. Twice Arthur heatedly accused Norman of taking my chair. Norman drew the analogy: 'It's just like a big family. Everybody is seated, then one of your sisters comes in and says, "Where's my chair?" '

Norman asked me about the relatives' group. I told them in full what happened. I told Arthur, for example, that his mother had mentioned the matter of his house. He jumped in: 'Yes, my private affairs!' He went on in a tirade to say how he refused to speak of his private affairs as it would lead to the same as it had done in the past, namely, they would become topics of gossip in the hospital.

In *Session 26* Arthur repeated what he had said two sessions earlier, that Walter refused to converse with him outside the group room. Walter immediately explained that this was 'a matter of the second sequence'. I said: 'But you'll get him in the third sequence', and he agreed.

It was notable that, in *Session 27*, Walter showed signs of awareness of the other members making up the group. He noticed the absence of Davis and said: 'We're waiting on Doddie, are we?'

During this session the group operated without any help from me; apparently they wanted to do without me and, on their own account, broke into sub-groups. Later I asked them to come back into the large group, but Edward and Davis continued in their sub-group.

In *Session 28* I suggested we should discuss the more personal matters of their lives. Arthur became confused and disturbed, and spoke uncontrollably about contacting the police, consulting his relatives, about somebody getting hurt, and so on. On one occasion Norman began to disclose matters about himself. He said, 'Now you fellows, this is a private conversation between me and Mr Macnab.' He then began to chain-smoke (a most unusual form of behaviour for him) but said very little.

Session 29 was noted for its long silences. At length Walter said, 'It's a blackout for the meeting if we can't think of anything to say.' The next day, Edward entered and said spontaneously, 'I want to talk about getting home.' Davis said he was pleased to hear Edward say this. Arthur said: 'But we can't help Edward unless we know something about his home.' Norman: 'It's a matter of environment; we must know that.' Arthur: 'That's a bit of nonsense. Environment refers to the past. We are interested in helping him for his future.'

Fred interrupted and asked, 'What is a lunatic?' Norman said that such a term was 'out of date these days', and he refused to discuss it. I asked if he was afraid of it. He said he was not, but he thought the group 'atmosphere' was 'not ready for it'. Fred said that lunatic was synonymous with mental patient, and although he did not fancy the word, he thought it would have to be applied to himself. Arthur: 'There you go . . . waving your brush about!' I asked, 'What brush?' He said: 'The brush that smears everybody a lunatic.' The discussion continued, sometimes with Arthur, Norman, and Davis all talking at once, and all very excited. Norman said that Fred had 'thrown a squib into the group'. It was 'just a flare-up'. At length, Norman gave a dictionary definition of the word 'lunatic'. I asked why he was giving it now, and he replied, 'The level of the group is ready for it.'

Again, in *Session 34*, the relatives' group was discussed. The discussion was initiated by Norman. I asked him if he was concerned in case his relatives should tell me something he would not like. He answered, 'Yes and no.' What would he not like me to hear? He replied, 'Oh, such as my mother ripping her stocking on the way up the stairs.'

It became necessary for Fred to change his chair. He took another one and squeezed it in between Walter and Davis. The effect was that Walter, Davis, and Edward were all packed tightly together. Arthur said (gesticulating): 'There they all are . . . like stooges . . . waiting for Norman and me to talk.' He qualified his statement slightly by saying Davis had in fact 'improved slightly'. Norman thought this session was of no profit. He picked up Fred's vacated chair, walked around the room with it and placed it in a far corner. 'That represents "no profit",' he said, 'that's just what this meeting has been – no profit.'

Walter kept yawning. He was tired after his morning out picking potatoes. I suggested he could have a sleep. 'I'd be fear't of what you might do to me,' he said. 'You might take a knife out of your pocket and kill me.' I told him I would not do this, and in any case, the other members of the group would look after him. So he got down on the floor, stretched out, and began to 'sleep'. After a few minutes he was up again and, half laughing, looked round at the others as if to see what they thought of this. He got down again. 'This is the last time,' he said. After a few minutes I said to him: 'Are you asleep?' He replied: 'Aye.' He then arose and said: 'I feel better now.'

In *Session 35* Edward began to tell of his experiences on his trip out to Australia, and how for a period of time he was in hospital in Cape Town. On being brought back to Aberdeen, he was told that his mother was dying. 'I came out here after that,' he said. ('Out here' refers to the mental hospital.) He said his brother also told him that his father was dead. Edward said, 'I could not believe that, sir; I could not believe that.'

Fred spoke of his father as 'very strict'. 'He is at me all the time to get out of this asylum as soon as I can.'

I asked them to write letters to me. All, except Walter, responded. I held out my hand for his letter. He grasped my hand and, beaming widely, said: 'Oh, happy New Year to you; pleased to meet you.'

Edward continued to speak of his parents. He was not certain whether his father was dead or not. He would only know he was dead if he saw him in heaven. Arthur asked about this term 'heaven'. 'Are you using it as a figure of speech? Of course you are!' Edward replied: 'No, I am not! I believe it and I mean what I say.' Arthur: 'But you don't *really* believe it?' Edward became belligerent, shook his fist at Arthur, and shouted: 'Yes I *do* believe it. And you'd better watch yourself.' I asked about his attitude, and he said, 'Well, Arthur was speakin' in an insane manner. He was taking an advantage . . . and if needs be, I'll fight for my rights.' Arthur replied: 'You've overstepped the mark now! It's ridiculous . . . it's obvious that I have been misunderstood . . . it just goes to show, we should watch what we say from now on.'

I asked Edward what he thought Arthur had said. Edward replied: 'He said I was going to be burnt up.' The whole group told Edward this was not so. Edward said he had not heard it 'outwardly, but inwardly . . . that's what I thought he meant.' The group continued to persuade Edward that he had misunderstood Arthur. Edward then said he was prepared to be friends.

Norman said: 'Well, that's worth a clap. A good debate over without a fight!'

It was hospital routine to have a nurse waiting at the end of each session to conduct the men back to their respective wards. On this occasion no nurse was present. I asked the group to remain while I went for one. Walter immediately jumped to his feet, came walking to the door, and said to me: 'I think we will manage on our own.' 'You are a good man,' I said, and let them go. I learned later that they had gone to their wards (villas), each one of them dropping off in turn.

In *Session 37* Edward chafed his mouth continuously. He said he did it 'to keep my breath in'. At frequent intervals he burst into such loud and long laughter that no one else could be heard. I quietly told him I was concerned about him, just as I was concerned about every one of the group. I told him I wanted him to share the group with the others, and that if he continued with this loud laughter, everything would centre on him and the group would be lost. Edward replied bluntly: 'Yes sir,' and forthwith stopped. His attitude also changed, and he appeared to take an interest in the group.

Walter and Edward frequently came without having written their letters and would often write them during the session. In *Session 39* Walter began writing to the accompaniment of much puffing and blowing, looking up at me now and then and smiling. Once he pointed to me with the end of his pencil and said, 'What's the matter with you?'

Arthur brought pressure upon Walter to do more talking in the group. I suggested that perhaps if Walter sat in Arthur's chair he might speak better. Walter said 'Will we try?' They did so, and Walter forthwith began talking about this and that. Soon he had nothing further to talk about, and was once again subjected to the pressures of Arthur. 'Come on, Walter! Perhaps we should talk about you!' Walter leant on the table with his right elbow; one leg was crossed over the other; he was partially slumped down in his chair. (This was one of my own habitual postures.)

Walter then turned and looked at me with a sudden glance. He got up on the table. '*I'll* give them a speech,' he said. 'What will I talk about?' He began doing exercises. I suggested he should get the others to join in. He pointed to Davis and Edward and said, 'Will you two get up and follow me?' But the whole group got up and followed.

Norman was talkative. I suggested that he wanted to get up there too, Immediately he responded, and as he climbed on to the table it almost capsized. Walter narrowly saved himself from being tipped over backwards and Davis rushed to his aid. I persuaded Walter and Norman to think of the other fellow as they climbed on and off the table.

Then they began to sing songs, led by Norman, who launched them into the National Anthem. When Walter resumed his seat later he said: 'That was good, that, I enjoyed it.'

A number of silences followed, punctuated by Walter asking: 'What does "dissipate" mean?' 'What does "fuck" mean?', etc. 'What does "fracture" mean?' I asked Walter if he had had a fracture. Fred jumped in quickly and said 'I have', then a silence. Walter was looking at Fred, then turned to me and said: '*That's* terrible.' Questioned, he said: 'That Fred should have a fracture, and we were talking about it like that.' He turned to Fred and said: 'I'm sorry.' Fred replied: 'It's very kind of you . . . to say you are sorry.' Walter then asked me if I had had a fracture. I replied that I had not, 'but what if I had?' Walter: 'If you had, we could say we were sorry.'

In *Session 40* the group had just come from the hospital film show. Walter began laughing and, turning to me, said, 'If you had seen those pictures! You'd a screamed.' Edward joined in, 'That monkey! He looked just like me.' I questioned this, and Edward replied, 'In a way he looked like *you*, sir.' Davis said, 'When he laughed he opened his mouth and showed his teeth and looked just like a human being.' Edward chipped in: 'And he had a gap in his teeth.' (Note: Edward and I both have a small space between the two upper incisor teeth.)

In *Session 42* Norman made his customary weekly inquiry regarding the relatives' group meeting. Arthur broke in with an intensive and highly-charged statement about his wife. He said his wife had been troubled with members of the hospital staff as well as psychiatrists going to see her. If this pestering continued his wife would probably leave him, and more than likely have a nervous breakdown. (In fact his wife had already left him and Arthur had not seen her for many months.)

Arthur attacked Davis for his 'immature attachment to his mother'. He told Davis he was deluding himself if he thought his mother loved him because one side of her clearly did not. Davis refused to accept this. Arthur then turned to Fred and Walter, and accused them of lack of participation in the group, 'yet you will go and tell your mothers all about it'. Arthur recalled that he had often heard Walter say at the meal table that he would 'tell his mum'.

Norman commented that Edward now had someone attending the relatives' group on his behalf. He was referring to Edward's girl-friend. Edward looked up and smiled.

Arthur entered *Session 43* very aggressively. 'I would like to take up the discussion from yesterday . . . after the first child was born, my wife was advised to see a psychiatrist. They told her I had sent the psychiatrist to her. Now I had nothing to do with that. I informed the police and my solicitor that I knew nothing about it – it was news to me – the result was that relations between me and my wife have become somewhat strained.' He said to me: 'The policeman and the solicitor mentioned your name as having something to do with her case . . . it had nothing to do with me and I certainly did not discuss it.' (This was an impossibility, for I had not met Arthur or his people at that stage.)

He then became involved with Norman who had told him he was 'just digging up old soil'. 'You are talking tripe.' Arthur became heated: 'Certainly it is *not* tripe. I'm speaking the truth. Anybody would think I was mad. You sit and argue like a child.' A heated argument followed. At length Norman said: 'I know your personality, and if that's the way, I'll withdraw it and apologize.' Arthur accepted the apology but insisted on making 'a few points clear'. The session had already gone over time and I attempted to bring it to a close. Arthur said: 'How can a session like this end? How does it leave us? I don't know whether I should go on talking openly to you and to them if it's all *tripe*!'

It became a problem to see how the session would close. Anything I said, or anything Norman said, Arthur would challenge. At one stage he stamped his foot at Norman. I then said to Arthur: 'The only way we can resolve this at the moment is like this. In the next session you can challenge Norman. You can say, "Now I spoke openly about my affairs. It's up to you to do the same. You told me I was talking tripe. Now let me see what *you* can do!" ' Arthur nodded and accepted. The session closed.

Next session (*44*), Norman arrived very late, but rejected Arthur's suggestion that this was related to what was said in the previous session.

I walked into *Session 45* carrying my satchel. Walter pointed at me and said: 'You look like an American carrying that bag. Is there anything in it?' He then finished writing his letter to me and, passing it to me, said: 'That should satisfy you, you bloody cunt!' Norman and Arthur immediately censured Walter for using this word.

Edward jubilantly announced that it was his birthday, since it was the 14th. Norman said, 'Here, here, Edward. It is the 18th today.' 'No,' said Edward, 'it is the 14th.' I asked how he knew. He replied, 'Because is it my birthday.' I had to show him my diary to convince him it was the 18th, and with feeling he said, 'I'm sorry sir.' Nevertheless the group sang 'Happy Birthday', and Edward responded well.

Session 46: Norman and Davis asked about the relatives' group. I mentioned that Walter's mother had said she would like him to go home for his brother's wedding. Walter at first said he would like to go, but then refused. Davis offered to sit beside him in the bus and put him off at the right stop. They all stated that this would be 'good for him'. Walter refused. Norman said: 'You're upsetting the chain of events; your mother has arranged it, and the wheels are in motion; we're trying to get you to say "yes" and you won't. In fact, it would not matter if you get back intoxicated; you haven't been out for six years.'

In *Session 47* Walter began talking about his ship. I asked, 'What about giving me a ride in your ship.' He replied:

'You've had it.' Questioned, he said: 'I gave you it through my mind.'

The session then turned into sociodrama as each member took his role for the ship's crew, and the ship began to 'sail' (with all the appropriate noises). At one stage Arthur said, 'The ship has stopped!' Davis replied: 'Oh my God!' and started shaking the table vigorously.

In *Session 48* Walter appeared to be in a deep day-dream. I asked him what was going on in his head. Walter: 'I don't know. Could you tell me Edward?' Edward: 'What?' Walter: 'What's been going on in your head?' I asked Walter again. He replied: 'I think that what's been going on in my head is a lot of bunk – the war has disturbed our minds.' I asked him how this had happened, and he answered, 'You're asking a difficult question!'

In *Session 50* Walter read his letter, which had very little sequence. Arthur took it and said, 'What's all this scribble? Were you confused or something?' Walter replied: 'Aye, it was utter confusion,' and then he asked a number of questions, difficult to understand, such as, 'Could you tell me, please, how to go about making reparations of a bus?' 'How fast does a seaplane go?'

The group was about to close when Walter said something to Norman, who became heated and said, 'Look here, Walter, you watch your language!' Walter: 'Go and pull yourself!' Norman, more angered, said: 'Look here, Walter, if you don't watch yourself *and* your language you'll hear about it. Now we just heard that Edward's father said something to him about his penis, but that's different; they were friends. We're not friends really. We're only here out of circumstance – and what is more, we are in respectable company. So watch yourself.' Walter was silent. I asked if he had any comment. He looked at Norman and said: 'That's very good . . . but I'm not a conversationalist.'

In *Session 52* Edward broke into a tirade of aggression which concluded: 'I want out of Kingseat, not otherwise. You're tryin' to help – in a humble sort of way, you're tryin' to help. But we want to get out, and none of this palaverin' about.' I asked if I was palavering about. Edward said, 'In a way, yes!' Norman:

'Well, I for one don't think so,' at which Edward laughed heartily. Norman went on, 'It's no laughing matter.' Edward ıeplied, 'It is a laughing matter. If I'm happy I laugh.' He turned to me: 'I'm very sorry for sayin' you were palaverin' about, you're doing a very fine job.' I asked Walter his opinion of what had been said. He answered, 'A lot of commercial tripe – can't derive any goodness from it.'

Session 55: I asked the group to read their letters. Walter and Arthur began simultaneously so that it was impossible to discern what was being said. They behaved in this way until Arthur said: 'Hold on, Walter! I'm first.' Walter continued regardless, so Arthur went on again, ignoring Walter.

Edward, very seriously, told us how some of the patients were going to burn him alive. Walter burst into raucous laughter, and Arthur said to Edward: 'I think they were exaggerating a little.' Walter said, 'Am I going to be burnt alive? What do you think of that, Edward?'

In *Session 57* Walter walked into the room. With his back towards me he said, 'Hello, Arthur.' I asked about this. He said he was talking to Arthur, but at that stage he was pointing to Edward.

Fred presented the painting which he had done in art therapy. It was out of proportion. I asked about this and he replied, 'I have no sense of perspective.'

In *Session 58* the group turned to consider why Walter's mother was not attending the relatives' group meeting. Walter did not speak, but blew his nose loudly into his hands. He then rubbed the mucus, which was coloured and in large quantities, between his hands. He picked his nose vigorously, drawing out residue of extraordinary dimensions and this, also, he rubbed in his hands.

In *Session 59* their letters were directed to each other, rather than to me. Arthur said to Edward, 'Edward, I'm directing this to you.' Edward addressed his to Walter. He read it but Walter was busy writing his letter and did not appear to be listening. At length he said, 'It's quite good, Edward, but you should be more polite.'

The group portrayed for me some of the events of their Christmas social. When I asked Walter to sing one of the songs, he said, 'I haven't the personality.' Norman laughed and said, 'Nor have I . . . I'm over 21, and you don't have a personality after that.' At the end of this session I announced that there would be a break in the group sessions over Christmas.

In the next session, Arthur complained bitterly that the occupational therapy department had interfered with his work. 'As far as I am concerned,' he said, 'this is characteristic of the whole staff . . . and it was the abrupt way in which she told me to pull it out!' (Compare with my concluding remarks in the previous session.) Later in the session Norman brought up the issue of the Christmas break. Walter chipped in, 'How long for? Two weeks? Do we come on Thursday?'

Session 61: Edward had painted a picture of God, a figure in white, and alongside it he had painted the sun. He explained, 'His beliefs are in the sun, and the hot streams shining on him each day, and he is getting better.' When questioned, he said, 'God is getting better.'

Session 64 was held in the Deputy Superintendent's Office so that the tape-recorder could be used to hear the Christmas greetings from the relatives' group. It took some time to settle into the new surroundings. Edward began to speak in a very confused manner about this past. Walter took his letter and set it on fire, using the electric radiator. Arthur was in an extreme rage and strongly opposed to the introduction of the tape-recorder.

However, the recording of the relatives' voices brought considerable interest. When Arthur's mother was speaking, Fred kept looking at Arthur, who said, 'I suppose "Arthur" is supposed to be me – it doesn't sound like my mother.' They were all eager for the recording to be played again. This time Arthur said, 'It's very good. It's a pity the other fellows' mothers were not there for them to get a message.'

When a voice on the recording said, 'Good wishes to you all,' Edward cocked his head at the recording and replied, 'Thank you, sir.'

Session 66 was noted for the fact that it was the first session after a fortnight's Christmas recess. The reception they gave me was quite remarkable. As I walked into the room they were all smiling and all spoke to me spontaneously. Norman said, 'It's good to see you again.' Walter: 'I'm feelin' grand, just grand.' Davis stood up, shook my hand, and wished me a 'Happy New Year'.

They began to speak of fishing and soon the room was converted into a fishing trawler. Walter was appointed captain, Edward the first mate, and I the second mate. Norman and Fred became the deckhands. The response was enthusiastic.

We had a long, animated discussion on the paintings they had done that morning. I asked each to look at his own paintings, and then, if they wished, they could ask to see someone else's. There was a pause as each one looked at his own. Then Norman asked Walter if he might see his. This started the enthusiastic discussion.

In *Session 67* I arrived to find Edward, Davis, and Norman waiting. Davis said to me, 'Edward and I have been having a smoke together.' Norman then explained how he had developed the routine of leaving occupational therapy, coming by the villas and picking up the other members of the group on his way to the sessions. 'Today,' he said 'the others are apparently late.' In this session there were many silences. When I asked about this Norman replied, 'It's like riding on a bus . . . two people side by side . . . then one opens a paper and sees the headline – "Rents go up" – and they are both united – they have something in common to talk about.'

Session 68: I arrived late and explained my reasons carefully. Walter began to sing, 'We meet at seven.'

In *Session 70*, those who had already gathered in the group room staged, at my request, a welcoming party for each member as he arrived. This was very successful. Walter was among the earlier welcoming party but insisted that he should be allowed to go out and be welcomed. Walter then began to read his letter, which he prefaced by saying, 'Oh, you'll be in hell with this today.' He shook his head. 'Have you got my glasses?' He held out his hands for his 'glasses'. He saw I was taking notes and asked, 'Have you got it down?'

The group turned to discuss the possibility of Norman taking a week's pass from hospital.

In the previous session, Edward had told the group a story. I suggested that the others, in turn, might do the same. This provoked an almost uncontrollable situation with Edward, Norman, Arthur, and Walter, talking and shouting at the same time, all contending to have the first turn.

In *Session 72* Edward entered the room and, as usual, handed me his letter; as usual, I asked him to hold on to it and read it to the group at a later stage. At this he burst into tears. He sat on his chair and he and the chair rocked with his sobbing. I asked him to come over and sit beside me telling him we would talk about his upset, but this made no difference. At length I said firmly, 'Come on, Edward! That is enough. Sit up and *stop* this!' He did so, immediately.

Later, when asked about his upset, Edward said, 'I was thinking about those times at home . . . when I went through that porthole . . . I remember going home into one room . . . and the blind was drawn. There was a flea on the window. I took it by the wings and burnt it alive.' I asked if he was in fact thinking of his mother's death. He replied, 'Oh, it's a terrible sin!', and burst into sobbing again. The group began to sympathize with Edward. He burst out laughing and said: 'I've burnt many fleas alive.'

In *Session 77* Walter failed to produce a letter. Arthur demanded a reason, for he had given Walter his pen so that he could write it. I asked Edward what he would do about Walter if he were me, and he replied, 'But I'm not you, sir!' Walter was very withdrawn. I suggested to Edward that he should try to help. At length Edward went over to Walter, patted him on the back and said, 'Speak, speak, speak, or forever hold your peace.' Walter said nothing. Edward then put his hand on Walter's shoulder, saying. 'You should have no worries. You're a patient. You should have no worries.' Walter burst into laughter, then began to thaw out and said, 'He said I should have no worries.'

I told him he should return Edward's kindness by thanking him. Walter went across to Edward, patted him on the back and said, 'Thank you very much, thank you for helping me.'

Session 78 marked the return of Norman after one week's leave. He gave an account of what happened and it was the best account I had heard from him, being rational and coherent. He told of all he did while away, of the reactions and welfare of his folks, of his trip to see me at Foresterhill (the Department of Mental Health). To the obvious interest of the others, he described the lighting and furniture in my room at Foresterhill, and then, as if they were all soon to be visiting me there, he said, 'Now when you go in, go in the front door and over to the right, to the lift which takes you to the third floor. . . .' He concluded his account by saying, 'It was a fine break . . . the folks and I are all ready for me to go again some time, in the not too distant future.'

In *Session 79* Edward showed some apprehension regarding his trip to see the psychologist. Walter had already been, so he volunteered to play the part of the psychologist and put Edward through his paces. He asked Edward to leave the room and then re-enter. As he re-entered, Walter said, 'So you are Edward Braceland Nicholson!' (Walter had heard Edward use his middle name from time to time.) Here is the account of what was said:

EDWARD: 'The group told me that I was to come to see you.'

WALTER: 'What is the opposite of "laconic"?'

EDWARD: 'Broad.' (Walter wrote this down and affirmed the answer.)

WALTER: 'What is the opposite of "school"?'

EDWARD: 'A human being – that's not the *opposite* of course.'

WALTER: 'What is the opposite of "school"?'

EDWARD: 'Side of a school.' Walter laughed and said 'Aye, three' (meaning he would move on to the third question).

WALTER: 'What is the word "Fahrenheit" used for?' Edward thought for a long time. Norman chipped in: 'It's all right Edward, it's something to do with tubes.'

EDWARD: 'I don't know.'

NORMAN: 'You get it by degrees.'

WALTER: 'Four then – what is the most holiest day of the year?' And so it went on.

Eventually Walter began writing at length. Then he said to Edward, 'Can you write down the missing letters there, please?' (Walter had written out the alphabet, omitting some here and there.) Edward applied himself studiously to the task. Walter watched his plight, but then sat back in his chair, gloating.

WALTER proceeded: 'What is the opposite of "whole"?'

EDWARD: 'You've got me beat.'

WALTER: 'I'll put in the right answer myself.' (He wrote 'in pieces'.)

WALTER: 'What is the opposite of "vitamined"?'

EDWARD admitted defeat. Walter wrote in 'malnutritioned'.

An interesting point was raised by Edward in *Session 83*. He asked me whether or not he was an Englishman. 'I could be an Englishman,' he said, 'because King Edward was an Englishman.' He then asked if his mother and father gave him his name 'or did King Edward?' Later I asked him, 'Now, Edward, are you a Scot or an Englishman?' Edward replied, 'No! I'm a voluntary patient at Kingseat.'

Session 84: I asked Walter what we would do today. He said, 'Tom cat'. This was enough to begin a form of sociodrama based on the film they had just seen. Walter at first remained unmoved but at length said he wanted to be the bugler. The scenes changed and they performed something which could have been a mock changing of the guard. At one stage Arthur asked Walter for some 'distinct orders!' I suggested that perhaps Arthur now wanted to be the leader instead of Walter who immediately said to him, 'Do you want to be King?' Arthur: 'No I don't want to be King!' Walter: 'Well get back into line!' Walter then turned to me: 'Will I march 'em down the corridors and back?' Before I could answer the door was open and they were away.

From time to time Walter would fail to bring his letter. The group devised various methods of treatment, e.g. on one occasion he was asked to stretch out on the floor, they then took him by the arms and legs, ran him the length of the corridor and back. (Imagine the concern of the conservative members of the staff as this scene was enacted before their eyes!)

In *Session 86* Walter entered the room waving his letter. The group applauded, and he began to read his letter. He looked up at me and said, 'I'm rather confidential today, if you don't mind. . . . You're on the hospital staff, aren't you? I'm in a confidential manner today. Any speech coming out of my throat is in direct contact with your hearing, and I want you to understand it as such. Regard it as confidential, you see?' Norman said, 'You're quite right, Walter.' Walter: 'No flies on me, eh?'

In *Session 87* I repeated a questionnaire which was given in Session 85. As soon as Walter recognized the repetition, he leaned over the table and said: 'Er – are we going to be gettin' this every day for a while?' I asked why he had asked this and he replied, 'Well, my eyes don't correspond with this at all.' He took a cigarette butt out of the ashtray, put it in his mouth and held it there until the questionnaire was concluded.

Edward refused to write because his memory would not let him. Walter said, 'Flooded, eh?' (Perhaps he meant 'blocked'.)

In *Session 89* they discussed their paintings as well as the group mural, which Arthur described as 'an utter wash-out'. He was much more interested in his own painting saying, 'We are your ball – you have played golf, of course. The group is illustrated by the ball. When we are at a loss, you have to explain and give an interpretation.' Norman chipped in, 'But none of us is bunkered. We just have a bit of work to do, that's all.' Walter said, 'I ask leave to lead the group in a discussion on English coal-mining.' (This subject had been selected some days previously.) I asked how many days ago it was since this had been decided. Fred said, 'Seven.' Arthur became concerned and said to me. 'Are you going on leave for seven days?'

Arthur raised a contentious issue pertaining to their behaviour in the wards, which was discussed with intense feelings. I asked them to settle the matter by 'judge and jury'. (Another form of sociodrama.)

In *Session 92* Edward wanted to speak about soldiers. Walter interrupted and said, 'Do you mind if I have a sleep while you talk about this?' He stretched out on the floor with his head in the corner and tried to sleep. The discussion moved to the paintings. Walter rose and said, 'Finished.'

Later Edward said, 'Excuse me sir, I hear a lot about these two persons – God and Jesus Christ. I have to figure it out: if these two people speak to me would I be able to give them the right answer? If I don't give the right answer – well! (He motioned with his hand indicating he would be lost.)

Norman said, 'Here, Edward, it is not the group's opinion to discuss anybody who is not present.' Arthur: 'Is Edward really serious? His questions are a bit stupid. We will get nowhere!'

I arrived late for *Session 99*. Walter gazed at me through half-closed eyes as I entered and sat down. I looked at him and he said, 'Nice day?' I said, 'You are angry with me?' He replied, 'Yes, why don't you come on time!' I explained myself and asked how I might have his forgiveness. Without hesitation he said, 'by promising to come on time!' I asked Edward if he would overlook it, to which he replied: 'Oh no, sir! You should be at the time that's set!'

In *Session 100* Edward was noticeably withdrawn. When I directed the attention of the group to this, Arthur made a speech to Edward 'on behalf of the group', assuring him of their united support and concern. The group applauded.

Session 102 had to be postponed half an hour. When the adjusted time approached, Arthur entered and said, 'I thought this change was most peculiar.' Davis arrived later than the rest. Walter opened the door for him, grabbed him by the jumper and shouted, 'Here he is! Here's the bastard!' (Was this displacing what he wished to do to me?)

The relatives' group was discussed in *Session 103*. I asked Davis about his mother, for she had absented herself from the group meetings without apology. 'Does she have your interests at heart'? I asked. Davis protested and perspired. He exhorted me to call on her and see. He produced a letter from her, but it was several weeks old. He then said, 'When she comes to see me at the week-end, I'll ask her point blank. I'll say exactly as you said . . . "if you have my interests at heart, you'll go to the meetings".'

As Good Friday approached I told them in *Session 104*, that the meetings would be suspended over Easter. Walter moved about on his chair and then said, 'I'm verra disappointed. I thought these meetings would go on for a long time yet.'

Edward and Walter spoke about the Crucifixion, and I asked them to demonstrate. Walter was to be crucified by Edward who said he would not like to crucify Walter, but he would 'surmise to crucify him . . . you're not Jesus Christ . . . you're Walter!'

The next day Edward recapitulated the story of Good Friday. 'Good Friday is the day Robinson Crusoe met the savage and he was good; and that's why there is a Good Friday.' Arthur said, 'Come on, Edward! That's not what we said yesterday. You were told yesterday that Good Friday was the day Christ died, and Sunday was the day he rose.'

The group had decided that their paintings for this session would relate to someone in the group, thus encouraging group orientation. Edward had drawn a design and when asked about this he said, 'I'm only a patient at Kingseat Mental Hospital.' I reminded him that it was he who had told Walter on the previous day what they were to paint. He said, 'I didn't tell him. They were only words that came out of my mouth.' He began to shuffle and looked as if he was going to weep. Fred said, 'He does not like being corrected.' Edward replied, 'That's exactly what it is! I'm only a voluntary patient at Kingseat Mental Hospital, and I can only obey the authorities – you're not Kingseat. You're Foresterhill!' (Foresterhill was the hospital at which the Department of Mental Health was located, my headquarters, as it were.)

In *Session 106* Walter gouged and bit his fingers, refusing to stop, even though blood was flowing freely. Later he was heard mumbling: 'We're not coming up to the Macnabs tomorrow, but we are coming up to the Macnabs on Tuesday, and we are coming up to the Macnabs on Thursday. . . .'

In *Session 107* Edward told the group that his brother had come to see him at long last! He entered the group room and said, 'I had a visitor at the week-end. I asked him why he had not been to the relatives' meetings, and he said "I'm too busy" . . . "I'm too busy" . . . "I'm too busy" . . . and he's broke his thumb.' Walter chipped in, 'Pity he hadna broken his neck.' Edward sat in silence, then said, 'I think Walter should apologize for that.' Walter did so and Norman said, 'You'd get yourself out of anything.'

In *Session 110* Edward entered carrying a large bag of sweets. He insisted that we should all have one. I asked Fred to thank Edward on behalf of the group. Fred stood and did so, adding, 'What made you give them to us, Edward?' Edward stood and said, 'Well, everybody's been kind to me, and I wanted to be kind to you.'

Davis spoke with Walter about their meeting while taking a walk around 'the mile'. Walter was excited about this and said, 'Aye, mind, I saw you on "the mile".'

The group arrived for *Session 111*, but I was still engaged with one of the women patients. When at length the group entered the room, Walter said, 'I was very vexed when I saw her here.' On questioning he began to fall off into psychosis again. Later he said: 'Y'ken y' was sayin' the other day – what would we do if these meetin's come to an end, y' ken? . . . I'd just go back and sit on my seat in the villa.'

The group urged Edward to accept his brother's invitation to have a week-end pass. Edward could not do this. First he claimed that the charge nurse had cautioned him, then he said Dr Fraser (misidentified as the superintendent) had forbidden him to leave hospital. I told him that Dr Fraser had now given permission and he stared at me in bewilderment. 'But I'm not goin' for a week-end,' he said. For a long time we stared at each other. Occasionally he smiled, but sustained his stare. At length he looked at Walter and, smiling, said, 'Ah, it's a great life . . . if you don't weaken.'

The group had painted a group mural of the hospital which was discussed in *Session 112*. In the middle of the mural Walter had painted 'The clown at the fair'. The group told me how Walter had painted the clown's face black, but later had been persuaded to change the colour. Arthur said to Walter, 'You were upset because they all scolded you.' Norman said, 'Walter was scattering the black powder around and making an awful mess. Walter replied, 'The woman [art therapist] came along and told me to change it. I was prognosticated about it but it turned out swell.' Norman snorted that he did not know the word 'prognosticated'. Walter said it meant 'dogmatic . . . dogmatic . . . 'ken?'

In the painting the chimney stack dominated the whole mural (and the horizon for miles around). They all agreed that here was the symbol of the hospital. Walter chipped in, 'They're a useless lot . . . they can't paint . . . Arthur – look at him – he can't paint a bit!' Arthur replied, 'Is that so, Walter? It's peculiar that one day you told me my painting was the best.' Walter said, 'All those paintings you've done! None of them has impressed me.' 'Is that so!' said Arthur.

In *Session 113* Davis hastened to ask if his parents had attended the relatives' meeting on the previous night. They had. 'Oh, that's fine,' Davis said, 'I'm awfully glad they've come. It shows interest. Everything's going to turn out fine – I was thinking I was being neglected a bit. But that's fine.'

The session was noted for heated exchanges and aggressive outbursts between Edward and Arthur, as to which of them should disclose his personal affairs in the group. Edward retained composure throughout, and at length said, 'If an outsider came in here and asked what the group was doing, what would we say? – What *could* we say? Well, what could we say, for instance, if I was an outsider and came into the group – but I'm not an outsider, I belong to the group' – he chuckled – 'if you see what I mean, and asked what the group was up to, what would you say?'

Norman said, 'We would say we were discussing my affairs.'

In *Session 114*, Edward spoke of his 'approaching death'. 'I have a weak heart; I'm going to die . . . not this year, but next. They've brought us here! But what did we do wrong? What mistakes did we make in our lives? What authority have they to hold us here? I've got to get home. I've got a lot of important things to do before I die . . . important people to see . . . girls – got to take them on some dates . . .'

Arthur refused to give his opinion. 'I have already given my opinion. My opinion becomes the group opinion.' Edward looked at me and asked, 'Are you dying, sir? 'I told him I was not and asked him what made him inquire. He said, 'I think you *are* dying, sir. It's your eyes, the way they hang.'

Fred said it was wrong of Edward to think that he was going to die, to which Edward replied, 'Oh, but if you've been through what I've been though – I've had a cut under my eye once; I've had a sore on my arm; and now I have a cut finger; and I've had my hair cut, I don't know how many times! There's nothing wrong with dying. We've all got to do it.' Walter: 'Dying is the first duty you perform when you are at death's door.'

In *Session 115* Walter gouged himself again. Arthur told the group that Walter's mother had been at the hospital and had gone to see the charge nurse. Walter: 'She wanted to get my money I earned at work.' Fred said, 'That's terrible.' Arthur said, 'Come on, Walter! I'm taking an interest; but only for the sake of the group. Now what did your mother want to see the nurse for? What was your mother about, Walter?' Walter stood up and scratched and gouged himself, refusing to speak. I exhorted the group to give him some support. 'At these times we should show him that we are his friends,' I said. Arthur chipped in, 'Well, *I've* already given that impression, haven't I, Walter?' Walter simply said, 'No.'

Edward leaned over to Walter and, with unusual chumminess, said, 'How y' doin', Walter? Are y' ready for your tea? We're all good friends in here, Walter.'

Prior to *Session 116*, the art therapist had mentioned to me the disproportionate size of the figures in the group mural. I raised this matter in the session. Walter said, 'The figures correspond to the er – er – the amount of paint you use.' Norman said bluntly, 'No, they're not out of proportion; they'll all stand out.' Edward chipped in, 'No man is as big as the lum (chimney stack). But if it's authority at Kingseat Hospital then he can make it as big as he likes. It's an authority man he has made – the clown as you call it.'

Session 118 presented some difficulties. Norman was late and I asked Walter where he was. Walter did not answer me, but turned to Arthur and said, 'Where is he, Davis?' Walter began to gouge himself again. I asked if something was upsetting him. He replied, 'Personal problems.' Questioned further he said, 'I haven't any.' (Is it because he has no personal problems that he is upset?) I asked Walter to take the chair and preside, but Arthur soon took over. Fred and he discussed how long they would boil an egg. Walter asked Edward how to draw a triangle. Norman broke out, 'Look, Walter! In my opinion that's wasting time. We want to discuss things to help us. And you should have your boots on today! And stop biting your fingers!' (Walter continued to bite.) 'Have we got to sit here and watch you do this? *Hey*!'

The discussion continued in a diverse manner, covering the construction of various objects, the nature of various soaps, syphilis, and 'the dose'. Norman got up, went over to Walter and buttoned up his shirt and coat – 'seeing it's Friday', he explained.

There were many long silences, one of which was broken by Arthur, saying, 'Why are we all sitting here like this?' Fred laughed and Arthur said, 'What are you laughing at, Fred?' 'Nothing,' Fred replied, 'It's obvious.'

Arthur arrived for *Session 120* half an hour late, puffing and very excited. Standing inside the door he said, 'I thought you two buggers would have the decency to tell me the time!' He explained that he was so engrossed in his occupational therapy that he had not noticed the time, and Norman and Fred had made no attempt to remind him. When he discovered the time he 'flung' his work away and 'made a dash for it'.

The group mural was again discussed. I asked Walter about his 'clown' and he said, 'It's too small.' I asked. 'Who in Kingseat Hospital is as big as the lum?' Walter: 'The King – the mannie that bides in the palace.' 'What's his name?' I asked. Walter replied, 'I dinna ken his name.' (The records show Walter once had delusions of regal grandeur about himself.)

The students of the university were conducting an appeal to help the spastic children and this was discussed in *Session 121.* Walter said, 'They need care and attention – taken out into the sun and invigorated by the sun.' Edward added, 'They're crippled, up to a point.' Arthur said, 'It's almost impossible to cure them.' I asked, 'What is the difference between you and the spastic child?' Edward answered, '*We're* really spastic to the feeling.'

Session 124 was very lively. At one stage I went over to Walter and, resting one hand on Edward's shoulder and the other hand on Walter, I asked Walter what he thought of Edward. He replied, 'He's a bit presumptuous . . . he hangs on to you.'

In *Sessions 126–128* I began to discuss their reactions to concluding the group sessions, weaning, substitutes, etc. Fred and Edward joined Arthur in rejecting the idea of a substitute. Edward said, 'It's your job. Your name is Macnab; and it's Macnab we want to see.' I observed Arthur's expression and said, 'You're looking very suspicious?' He replied, 'I was quite astounded to hear the rest of the group giving frank opinions, instead of just me.'

In *Session 130* I was very tired, so I asked the group to break into sub-groups. At first there was no interaction but, with a change of the sub-groups, it was difficult to conclude the group. I asked Edward to close the group. He stood up and, with a broad smile and a clap of the hands, he said, 'Will you all stop talking, we're going to close the group.' Norman undertoned, '. . . for the afternoon'. Edward said, 'Aye, it's a fine afternoon.'

An interesting discussion developed in *Session 131* over the approach of Whitsuntide. Edward said, 'Mary and Joseph bowed to Jesus on Whit Sunday.' Walter corrected this to say, 'Christ was hung on the Cross and he rose out of the grave on Whit Friday.' Arthur: 'Whit Sunday is descendant of primeval times recorded by the Druids as they changed to Christianity. They still hold to their religions. It's the remains of an ancient belief – pre-Roman.'

Norman then began to tell me that a relative of his was admitted to this hospital at the week-end. When I asked him to elaborate, he said, 'Oh, I'd better take my seat in for this.' He picked up his chair and brought it to the table near mine, and so excluded the other members of the group.

At the close of the session I asked if anyone remembered what was going to happen in the following week. Walter immediately replied, 'Er . . . that's a holiday. You said in a month's time it would be another holiday.' (No recent reference had been made to this impending vacation.)

Edward again closed the group.

The next session Edward arrived first. He was beaming. He quickly arranged the chairs, then sat listening for footsteps along the corridor, detecting which belonged to the group members, and opening the door for them.

Norman was late. I asked Walter to 'say a few words' to him. Walter: 'You are a dirty bastard, Norman. Why don't you come on fucking time?' Norman replied: 'Repeat the question please, in better language.'

In *Session 136* Arthur and Walter arrived fifteen minutes before time. I excused myself and went into the next room to do some writing. A short time later Walter knocked and came in. 'Have you got a match on ya?' he said. I had forgotten mine, so went to get some from a nurse. When I returned, Walter was standing in the middle of the room. 'Have you got one?' he asked. I suggested he might wish to stay in this room with me. 'Oh na,' he replied. 'I'd better go back and give Arthur a light.'

In discussing the art therapy the group gave its opinion on whether or not to continue with the murals. Walter, while agreeing with the group, said they should now return to the individual paintings and produce these as well. When I questioned him about this, he replied, 'Our minds have been contaminated, and I want to get back.'

Session 138 marked Davis's birthday. Norman arrived late but Edward reminded him of the occasion. Norman jumped from his chair and said, 'Here man. Congratulations.' They all sang 'Happy Birthday'. Davis thanked them and added that he hoped they would all have a happy birthday 'when it comes'.

The next mural was to centre on the Biblical narrative concerning the Gadarene maniac. After considerable preliminaries, in which he persistently asked for his 'specs' – he did not, in fact, wear spectacles – Walter read the story to the group.

Fred asked if the Gadarene maniac was a schizophrenic and I answered that he was. They then called their painting 'The Healing of a Schiz'.

It was of interest that when Walter read the part of the story which described Legion tearing himself and bruising himself with stones (cf. Walter's own behaviour), he looked up at me and said, 'He must have been mad – a madman.' Walter also knowledgeably explained to the group that the word 'swine' meant 'female pigs'!

Two of the group members were given week-end leave. In the next session (*139*), when I entered the room Edward told me that he and Walter and Arthur had been talking about 'the other two who aren't here but *should* be here'.

In *Session 140* I told the group that, in the near future (stipulating the exact date), the sessions would be reduced to three a week. Arthur said, 'I think Walter is bewildered!' Edward tapped his ear, 'I'm a bit deaf! What day will be cut out?' Davis said, 'What is the meaning of this? Are you going to be taking other groups?'

Edward chipped in and said, 'Who is Dr Stewart, anyway?' (Dr Stewart is the Physician Superintendent.) There was a long silence. Edward added, 'I don't know who he is. He's a fair size, about five feet, eight inches.' I asked Edward what was Dr Stewart's special job. Edward: 'Job? Caretaker!' Norman said, 'Caretaker! Good heavens!'

In *Session 143* Fred tried to see what I was writing. Noticing this, Edward said, 'Why do you look at his book?' Fred: 'Just out of curiosity.' Edward: 'Well, curiosity killed the cat, so you'd better remember.' Davis: 'What does that mean?' Edward: 'What? "Curiosity killed the cat"? Well it's just an expression that comes out of the mouth concerning a dumb animal; he can't speak back.'

Arrangements were made for the group to accompany the other patients on the annual bus drive. On their return they all gave their impressions and descriptions of the trip. As Edward was giving his account Norman chipped in to give his: 'I saw the letter boxes – they stand out in every village – in fact there is very little else to see.'

In *Session 146* I was called to a conference, so I asked the group to carry on without me. When I returned the members were alive with activity. Arthur had acted as chairman and gave me a full account of what had happened. I suggested that Arthur should be thanked for his efforts. Walter rose and said, 'On behalf of the discussion group I hereby give you thanks – for being the leader – for all the subjects – for bringing Mr Macnab's thoughts to us, and we thank you for being Arthur.' Norman said, 'This should be written down.'

In *Session 147* Arthur told me he had seen Walter's mother and had reminded her of the relatives' group meeting, but she had told him that she did not attend. Norman said, 'There are only fifty per cent supporting Mr Macnab, and fifty per cent are a wipe-off.' He suggested letters should be written to the absentee parents. I took up this suggestion with Walter, and began to search for a piece of paper for him to write his letter. Walter said, 'I can assure you, Mr Macnab, you are wasting your time.' Fred chuckled. Although Walter wrote the letter, he made no contribution to it, for it was dictated by the group. Arthur then said, 'Now read it out.' Walter: 'I haven't got my specs.' Arthur: 'Oh, give it to me!' and he read it out, then handed it back and asked Walter to read it. Walter did so, omitting such phrases as 'Dear Mother', and 'Your loving son, Walter.'

At length Arthur was persuaded to allow a tape-recording to be made of the group. This was done in *Session 147*, and duly transmitted to the relatives' group.

It was proposed that at some stage Professor Millar should visit the group. I raised this issue in *Session 149*, and asked where they thought this meeting should take place. Norman: 'I'm in favour of Foresterhill [the Professor's Department]. It's only courtesy.' Arthur: 'No, I think not. They won't be natural there. If he is going to see what we do in the group, then that would be unsuitable.'

At a later stage I intimated that there would be no further meetings on Monday. Norman said, 'We're advancing.' I asked Arthur to explain to the group what this meant. He made an excellent statement which I regret I was not able to record word for word. In effect, he said: We came here to progress in our communicating and talking with one another, so that we could strike up a sensible discussion with anybody. The stopping of the group session on Mondays means a step forwards, but 'you should remember you always have the group as you come into close conversation with each other . . .'

Edward, as usual, closed the group. His late arrival for this session had been discussed and, in closing, he said, 'Well, gentlemen, I have to close the group. I would just like to apologize for coming late, but I hope it won't happen again. So now I'll say "Good afternoon". We'll meet again tomorrow at half past three – that's Friday.'

In the next session Walter made two interesting remarks. First, he said to Fred, 'What did you think of the recording? We're to have it again on Tuesday. I s'pose Macnabs will be pleased with his self about that.' Second, 'What do you think of this Monday business, Fred? What do you think he'll be doing?' Fred replied, 'I don't know; I suppose he'll be having a good time.'

In *Session 153* I told the group that I would be taking my holidays. I was about to explain more fully but Walter leant forward in his chair and called out, 'How long? How long?' I replied, 'I'll be back on the 11th August.' Walter, turning to the others said, 'Not bad, eh? Not bad!' I asked Walter what he meant and his spontaneous reply was, 'Only three weeks.' Norman said, 'I thought it would be a month.' Walter replied correctly, 'Na, na, three weeks.'

Walter then sang to the group – first in 'Czech', then in 'Polish' – and there was animated applause. Every now and again he broke into his singing with little chuckles.

We then spoke of their condition of schizophrenia. Norman, showing signs of stress and reluctant to be numbered with anyone who was called a 'schiz', asked many questions. He said he preferred his old frame of reference – 'Hypomania'. Davis said,

'Schizophrenia? Is that what Fred and I have?' Walter said, 'Laryngitis I had – and a bleeding down the left side.'

After *Session 157* there was a break of three weeks for my vacation.

Session 160: When Fred arrived late Davis said to him, 'You'd better give an explanation.' Arthur added, 'Didn't you hear me call?' 'Throw the bastard out!' said Walter, 'Go on, *out*!' Fred left and Walter laughed. I then asked for someone to go and talk it over with Fred. Arthur went, followed by Walter. Later they all returned and Walter explained, 'He's coming on time after this.'

There was some group discussion about the attitude of the group to latecomers. Then Edward gave the group decision: 'If you don't come at half past three from now on we'll take it that you don't want to come, and the door won't be opened, so you'll have to turn back to home.'

In spite of this it was Edward who arrived late for the next session, breathless and obviously distressed. The nurse had detained him. The group unanimously agreed to allow Edward to stay in the group.

Professor Millar's impending visit was discussed. Edward was voted chairman to welcome the professor when he arrived.

The group then discussed their opinions of themselves. Arthur had much to say about 'endeavour', 'satisfaction', and such terms, but Edward forthrightly said that he was kept going by the thought that he was not only Edward Braceland Nicholson but he was also God. The group discussed this at length.

Norman not only spoke of himself, but was anxious to speak of other people: 'Now, as far as other people are concerned – well – if it's a summer's day, it's hot, and if it's a winter's day, it's cold. As far as I'm conerned, that's the general public!'

In *Session 162* Walter spontaneously turned to Fred and said, 'What would you do to preserve yourself in the face of the oncoming general elections of America?' Fred appeared bewildered. Walter himself provided an answer. 'You'd hold yourself throughout all humanity. You'd behave yourself at the state meetings.' (Note later reference to the behaviour in the group meetings.)

Davis asked Walter, 'What would you do?' Walter: 'I'd go back to olden times. I'd take birth in the discussions.' I said, 'Well give birth now!' Walter replied, 'Well, I don't like Davis, for one thing. Arthur is sulky and I don't like sulkiness.' Arthur: 'Sulkiness! You mean I show I'm not pleased with you, Walter? But I'm always pleased with you, Walter.'

Norman turned to Fred and said, 'Edward thinks he's God. Have you got it?' Fred: 'That's absurd.' Davis said, 'No, he thinks he's a god. That means he thinks a lot of himself.' Arthur: 'Probably Edward thinks he is misunderstood.' Arthur went on to refer to Edward's lateness in the previous session and to the fact that the group excused him. 'This,' said Arthur, 'clashes with any idea that he is God.' 'He said he was God, but he made a mistake and *we* had to excuse him. These things clash.'

FRED: 'I think Edward is stupid when he calls himself God.'

EDWARD: I'm an individual!'

FRED: 'It's stupid to think you are the Supreme Being.'

EDWARD: 'Maybe it sounds absurd, but it's quite right. It's only commonsense by birth.'

ARTHUR: 'One loses faith in you altogether. We all know what a jolly good fellow you are, but we have all been scolded.'

NORMAN: 'The problem has my sympathy. It's a bit of a puzzle. One moment he says he's God, the next he doesn't.'

Professor Millar then arrived and spoke to the group. Each of the group spoke to him in turn, telling him about individual members of the group and about the group as a whole. The professor showed them some card tricks which evoked intense interest. He then asked them to think about paying him a visit in Aberdeen.

In *Session 163* I left a pack of cards on the table. Walter entered, took up the cards, and followed the exact movements of Professor Millar. The tricks however did not work. He put the cards down on the table and took his seat, but scarcely participated further.

There was strong controversy over paying a return visit to the professor. Davis thought it 'only manners'. Arthur thought that the group was assuming a false importance in its own eyes.

There were some paintings on the table. Edward kept staring at one of them and said, 'I thought it was a lifeboat.' Norman replied, 'It *is*, Edward. It's the group coming back from holidays.' Edward: 'They are in a ship.' I said: 'They?' Edward replied, 'Aye – the group.' He gesticulated circularly: 'We're the group.'

In *Session 165* Norman produced a painting of Edward 'in his dual role – Edward as Edward, and Edward as God'. Norman explained, 'First we have Edward seated, as he thinks he is – plain-suited as he is; and second we have him purple-suited, as he is God. Then we have these traffic robot signals. Edward changes from one to the other – he changes like robot signals, as illustrated at the cross roads. One lot is at "stop", the other at "go". Edward changes as quickly as that when you are listening to his comments. For most of us we can never pass robot signals. We must stop at robot signals – that is law. But in comparison to Edward being God he just carries on like the robot signals, sort of automatic.'

The group, except Walter, voted to go on a walk. 'I'm against it, but I'll just go through,' he said. The walk was a great success. Group coherence was maintained on the journey, not only by breaking into small groups and then going back into the big group, but also by throwing a tennis ball to each other. Whenever one member got behind or the ball was lost, etc., the others were readily taught to wait.

Edward remained chairman of the group, and with unprecedented animation he had the group decide:

(a) to make a recording of one of the group sessions;

(b) to visit Professor Millar in Aberdeen.

Many questions were asked and Edward answered them. To the question: 'How are we going to get to Aberdeen to see Professor Millar?' Edward replied, 'Professor Millar will come out in his car for us.'

I asked Edward to inquire how Norman's father was. Norman gave an awkward laugh and said his father had died the day before and that his funeral would be taking place within two hours' time. He said his mother and sister were upset, but not too much for they were expecting it. Arthur, with obvious feeling, said, 'I'm very sorry to hear that, Norman.' Walter said simply, 'With deepest sympathy.' Davis chuckled (with unusual awkwardness) and said it was something which came to us all. Edward chuckled also, but then became silent. He looked down at the ground, rubbed his trousers with his hand: 'I don't know how to put it,' he said, 'but we are all sorry to hear that your father has died, Norman.' Norman: 'They just let him drift out.'

In *Session 166* I told the group that in the near future the sessions would be coming to an end. I explained the situation carefully and in detail, trying to help them to keep their anxiety in perspective. Even though I emphasized that we would be continuing for another eight weeks, my statement was treated as if the group was concluding there and then. Each member in turn made a farewell speech, expressing his appreciation and concluding with remarks such as 'God bless you', 'Goodbye, and behave yourself', 'My only hope is that there will be someone to supersede you'. Walter said, 'We won't have to look at each other again with grim faces. . . .'

Fred began to grow a beard, to which Norman immediately drew our attention. Arthur said, 'I wouldn't care very much if it was becoming to him.' Norman added, 'Never mind, it'll make you look older and more sensible.' 'No,' said Davis, 'it's not quite the job – I dinna want to hurt your feelings or anything. . . .' Fred told the group that he thought he was 'extremely good looking', and with the beard he was 'a little better than extremely good'.

Edward announced that all the nurses in Kingseat 'have less than three years to live'. Norman chipped in, 'This is you playing at being God again, Edward. The staff does a turn of three years in each hospital ward, is that what you mean?' Edward replied, 'They'll die in three years. Since I have been here, that's been the term, isn't it? And I have two years to live myself.' Walter: 'It sounds like a jumble of nonsense to me. It doesn't make sense or reason, none of it.' Davis agreed, 'Three years to live! God knows it sounds like nonsense to me.'

Before *Session 170*, the table had been shifted to a new position. Edward said, 'I think the table should be back where it was.' The group voted. Edward did not count the votes; he noted that a majority of hands were in favour of his opinion, so said, 'It goes back,' Norman said, 'Well, Mr Chairman, you got your own way.'

Session 171 was held in Professor Millar's rooms in Aberdeen. It was recorded and will be found in the Appendix (p. 253).

In the next session, the group discussed the events of their trip to see Professor Millar. The most interesting remarks were those pertaining to the professor himself. Walter began by saying, 'I didn't like his moustache; it should have been more fully grown. He should have had a bigger car though, shouldn't he? Do you think he should have given us a better tea than that?' Edward said, 'I *did* object to him asking me where I was going after I leave Kingseat Mental Hospital. It put too much of a strain on me. Anyway he was being too personal. I could see no other place that I *could* go to.' Norman said he liked the professor's 'amicable manner'.

Walter began to discuss 'intrinsic and instrumental values'. From a man of his intelligence and education, this was astonishing. I asked what he meant by these terms. He said intrinsic values were something in themselves – 'enjoyment that you get from a glass of beer', and instrumental values, 'well, that was the glass of beer itself'.

In *Session 176* Edward said he was tired, so he sat down on the floor. I suggested that I could come and sit closer to him. He laughed and I asked why. 'Because you were going to come closer to me.' Discussion then followed about Edward's sexual fantasies, both towards me and towards a woman he had seen in the hospital on the previous day. Of his sexual feelings towards me, he concluded: 'It's a warm and guilty feeling, sir.'

Walter appeared disturbed. I asked what he was afraid of and he replied, 'I'm afraid of the sea.'

ARTHUR: 'I'm surprised at that. Why? Help me to understand you?'

WALTER: 'Are you afraid of the sea?'

ARTHUR: 'No.'

WALTER: 'You are – you are.'

ARTHUR: 'No – only in a storm; but not normally. . . .'
WALTER: 'You're frightened to tell anyone else.'
ARTHUR: 'Why are you afraid?'
WALTER: 'Why are *you* afraid?'
ARTHUR: 'My fear is not of the sea, but of what the sea can do . . . What's your particular fear of the sea?'
WALTER: 'But in your heart you are afraid of the sea.'
ARTHUR: 'No, not me.'
WALTER: 'Yes, you are. Yes you are.'

I then interrupted and said to Walter, 'I thought this all began with you saying that the sea was *your* greatest fear.' Walter replied, 'Did I say that? Oh, I didn't know what I was saying.'

This session had already begun when Norman and Fred arrived. The group voted that they should not be allowed to stay, but should remain in the next room and write out their reasons and apology. At length they were recalled. Norman was anxious to have his say, but Edward would not listen, demanding that they should 'stand in the centre of the group'. Edward: 'We think, gentlemen, that what's expected of you is for you to read out what you've written, and that's all – that's all we want of you. You can have a seat first. You speak first, Norman.' Norman asked to be called 'Mr Hawkins'. Norman passed his letter to Edward. Edward studied it, then said, 'I can't read this!' Norman: 'I'll not have that!' Edward replied, 'You read it out. We let you back. Get reading, gentlemen.'

On hearing what they had written, Edward said, 'I think their stories are very good and they should be forgiven.' The group agreed and Edward admonished them for their lateness, adding, 'So you are forgiven – on behalf of the group.'

In *Session 177* Davis announced that he had not been to art therapy that morning as he thought the art therapist was still on leave. 'Mr Chairman, am I forgiven? I want to be in the clear. I thought the art therapist was ill, but I was wrong.' Edward said, 'Is Davis forgiven? I'm asking the group . . . the group agrees. You're forgiven.'

Norman realistically spoke of getting a job in Aberdeen, but he said the designation of schizophrenia was 'a pinhole in the employment officer's sheet' and this would hold him up in getting a job. It would be more pleasing to him if he could revert to the old designation – 'hypomania'.

Walter gouged a large chunk of flesh off his fingers and then whispered, 'I deserve a smack.'

Davis asked Norman, 'What about that letter you gave to Mr Macnab?' Norman replied, 'That was personal.' Davis went on, 'Well, if it's too personal – but you should tell us—'. Norman said, 'You're getting aggressive.'

Fred said he was 'still in the same old rut', but added he wanted 'to get out of this asylum'. 'Asylum, did you say?' Davis asked. When Fred said 'Yes', Davis simply said, 'That's what I thought you said.' Later Davis added, ' "Mental hospital" is a nicer word – "asylum" is where you're locked up.' Edward chipped in, 'This is just one step better than an asylum.'

In *Session 179* Edward announced that he had 'a sickness of the body', viz. 'an irritation of the penis'. This made him masturbate. He said he had lost a lot of blood this way (semen = blood). 'Patients come here – it's punishment in a way for what they've done in life. Foresterhill is the next step.' (Foresterhill is the main general hospital in Aberdeen.) He gave lurid descriptions of how he would be put to death there. 'I've always been with my parents,' he said. 'Now they are dead. I believe I should die with them. If I can't see my parents, I can't go and work 'cause I haven't the strength to face up to what's left.' I asked the group to support Edward. Norman said, 'Well, you're a fine sight, Edward; one arm down and one arm up; jacket too tight. You'd better relax a bit.' Edward replied: 'I'm relaxed.'

Session 181: Edward entered, looked around, and said: 'I see that everyone's shaved bar me.' They discussed this. Norman then told how he, Walter, Arthur, and Fred had gone to watch television in an adjoining villa. (Previously I had encouraged them to take a more active interest in the forthcoming elections.) Norman said, 'We saw everything else but politics.' Edward turned to Fred and said, 'What is really "Conservative" and "Labour" anyway?' Fred replied, 'Conservative is for the rich man, and the other is the worker.'

In *Session 182* we again went for a walk. A group meeting was held around a stump on which Edward, as chairman, sat. Fred wanted to stretch out and take no interest. Arthur took him to task over this and asked him bluntly if he had contempt for the other members of the group. He then asked him if he had been too forceful with him. Fred replied simply, 'No.' Arthur said, 'Well, I'm relieved to hear that.' Fred described how he wanted to be 'important'; he wanted to see his name 'written in letters six feet high. I don't like feeling small; I like to feel I'm somebody of note.' He turned to me and said, 'I know just as much as you do. I think I could step into your shoes. I could treat mental patients just as well as you do.'

Edward confessed he was worried: 'I've swallowed a stone. I'm in pain because of these stones in my stomach. It's disgusting. The stone should be taken right away. I'm making a kind of nuisance of myself. I go about smoking and things like that – every time I blow smoke, I'm blowing my breath on to them. It's an operation I want.' The group discussed the matter at length.

Walter, in *Session 184*, refused to participate. 'Real solid!' said Norman, having tried again and again to speak with him. Davis asked him if he had something to say to me which he would not like the others to hear. Then Walter asked if he could come close to me. He did so, and said, 'Do we come here on Saturday by appointment?' This seemed to indicate that he was preoccupied about the group sessions terminating, so I opened this matter up for discussion.

It was of interest – in view of the imminent termination of the group – that at art therapy they entitled the next group mural 'Disintegration'.

The next day Davis recounted to me the great difficulty they had experienced in art therapy in achieving a united effort on such a topic as 'Disintegration'. Arthur referred to the disintegration of the group and the trends of 'individualism' as each one tried to usurp the mural to put his own ideas down on the paper. Arthur said: 'When the group disintegrates it will be a great blow for us, but since we are all together, the blow will be softened for some time. When something arises in the villa, we can go and discuss it with one of the members of the group.'

In *Session 187* Edward told the group that when they take him to Foresterhill he will 'be needled to death'. 'I'm tired of living ... I've got a stone in my stomach and I feel all dry.' Arthur began to talk to him about this and asked if it had anything to do with the termination of the group, but Edward was not listening and seemed preoccupied. Arthur shouted, 'Edward!' Edward said, 'I feel like going home.' I told Edward I was confused. 'Do you think I don't love you any more?' He replied, 'Oh, I don't think you don't love us any more, but I've swallowed a stone, and I think *you're* that stone! I just say I should get home as quick as possible, where I'm safe.'

At the end of this session, members of the staff met, and the doctor in charge of Norman's ward decided that he could be discharged. We all agreed, however, that it would be better for him to find a job first. The District Employment Officer was advised.

Before *Session 188*, I saw Edward on his own and he openly said that my going away was 'connected with the stone'. I tried to convey to him that my warmth and regard would remain with him even though I was going away.

I then saw Walter on his own. When I asked him the date, he replied, '20th. Only two days to go, isn't it?' – referring to my departure. He blew his nose vigorously. 'You're upset?' I asked. Walter fingered the ledge of the door and said, 'There'll be no Macnabs to come to.' 'Are you sad about this?' I asked. 'No, no,' he replied, 'I'm happy. I've got my work to go to.' (Compare with the Walter at the beginning of this group therapy. At that time he was virtually vegetating, always passive and withdrawn, preferring to remain seated on his chair in the ward for most of the day.)

When the group met for *Session 188* Edward was absent. The next day I discovered that after he had left me he had left the hospital. He was found late that night. He had removed his shoes and had travelled a long distance. His feet were excessively blistered. On his return he said, 'I was tryin' to get home, but I just went round and round. ...'

Session 189 marked the end of the group. They all made their speeches in turn regarding its termination.

ARTHUR: 'I enjoyed the discussions very much and thought there was an understanding between each other. . . .'

FRED: 'I too, am very sorry to hear the group is stopping.'

EDWARD: 'I just feel like running away again. I just feel it's uncomfortable here and I should get out of here pretty quickly.' (When he left the room, he did so with much haste.)

WALTER: 'Er – I don't know what to say. What do you think I should say? I like the way you talk very much' – scratched himself – 'and I hope you'll be happy.'

DAVIS: 'I can only say "thank you" for what you have done for me and the boys here; I'm just sorry to see it close, but I hope we gained by it.'

NORMAN: 'Well, gentlemen, thank you for your kind attention in the past.' He named each in turn, including myself, and said 'thank you'.

There was a silence; presently Walter whistled.

I then spoke to them all as a group and told them how much I had enjoyed being with them. I then spoke to each one in turn and told them my thoughts would often be with them. Walter looked upset and began to sing.

There was a silence.

Norman jumped to his feet and said, 'Oh, to hang with this! Let's give a hand for Mr Macnab.' He named them all, then they stood up and clapped. I left the room. As I walked in one direction down the corridor, I heard the sound of their footsteps as they moved out and down the corridor in the opposite direction. I stopped and turned and watched them pass out of sight.

CHAPTER III

Schizophrenia: A General Survey

Schizophrenia is an illness in which the person seems to abandon the world as we know it and turns to an unreal and distorted world of his own. His thinking and emotions show far-reaching disturbances, experience itself takes on different meanings, so normal communications and social relationships are either extremely difficult or impossible. The broadening gulf between the person and his society becomes pronounced and tragic. The magnitude of the suffering and the issues involved can be so all-embracing that contributions from different disciplines are to be welcomed. In this study as a whole we are concerned with the disciplines of theology and psychiatry, but this chapter deals particularly with the contribution of psychiatry. It is necessary to survey the phenomena of schizophrenia and the issues relating to them so that the nature and immensity of the problems may be appreciated.

THE TERM 'SCHIZOPHRENIA'

Traditionally, and even today, schizophrenia is a term with many unhappy connotations. There is an air of mystery, hopelessness, and superstition surrounding it, even among the most educated sections of our society.

The illness generally known as schizophrenia was originally called 'dementia praecox'. This name, which originated with Morel (1856), reflected the character of the illness as occurring in early life, and developing to its terminal stage of deterioration.

Later, Kraepelin, who presented the first detailed and systematic study of dementia praecox, clarified and refined the term. Eugen Bleuler (1908) continued the study but introduced the term 'schizophrenia' to replace that of dementia praecox. He discarded the term dementia praecox, for he observed that the disease did not always occur in early or adolescent life, nor was it always associated with dementia.

He saw that the illness was not a single entity, as the name 'dementia praecox' might imply, but was comprised of a group of heterogeneous conditions, the common factor of which was a fragmentation or 'splitting' of the mental processes. Hence his choice of the term 'schizophrenia', or 'the group of schizophrenias'.

THE GENERAL FORM OF THE ILLNESS

While it is thought that there are forms of schizophrenia to be found in the community but not referred for medical treatment, the almost inevitable progression of symptoms means that a large and fairly constant number of established schizophrenics are to be found in the hospitals. The hospital populations show two main forms of schizophrenia:

(a) the episodic form, where the patient is rehabilitated to society within a few months. In its early episodes this form may be called 'acute' schizophrenia. Although showing the symptoms of the illness, permanent deterioration need not follow.

(b) the chronic form which, in spite of treatment, presents the picture of permanent deterioration.

THE NATURAL HISTORY OF THE ILLNESS

The natural history of schizophrenia – that is the course which it usually follows if no effective treatment is provided – is as follows:

There are the brief episodes from which the person may recover spontaneously. Sometimes these episodes are coloured by depressions, hysteria, neurotic manifestations or other secondary illnesses, so that the schizophrenic episode is itself atypical. Similar episodes may occur with remission from time to time, but each attack may bring with it more serious and long-standing intractable symptoms in the patient, e.g. the tendency to day-dream, to wander, to speak to himself; there is a definite falling-off in abilities and interests, an appearance of bizarre symptoms and erratic behaviour, and the setting of an increased distance between the patient and his family or those about him.

The progress of the illness may be so gradual that often relatives do not detect the changes occurring from day to day, or even from month to month. There follows the appearance of more psychotic symptoms which create major problems for relatives, employers, and friends of the patient. There may be episodes of excitement, stupor, hallucinations; there may be spells of incoherent speech and bizarre behaviour such as shouting in the streets, walking out without clothes, physical and sexual assaults and major scenes of violence. This is the active phase.

After a variable period of months or even years there is a gradual supervention of apathy, dilapidation of the personality, incoherence of speech, and withdrawal into an inner world from which it is difficult (at times impossible) to bring the patient back to reality. This is the stage of so-called dementia.

It is now clear, however, that there is no impairment of intellectual factors, and under favourable conditions there have been remissions.

With the advent of modern methods of treatment the number of patients reaching this ultimate stage of the natural history of schizophrenia has been greatly reduced. These methods, however, are only partially successful, and even now there are many patients who reach a state approaching the end-point described above. It can also be noted that older patients, admitted to hospital years ago before modern treatments were introduced, have already reached the advanced stage of the illness, and these form a large section of the chronic schizophrenic population.

Normally it would be necessary to give a more systematic account of the condition, but for this the reader is referred to the classical description given by Eugen Bleuler. It is true that since Bleuler subsequent accounts have thrown new light on this mysterious condition and have helped to bring greater precision to our thinking about its various manifestations and meaning. But the overall picture of the schizophrenic condition as it appears to the observer has not been modified to any marked extent.

THE CAUSES OF SCHIZOPHRENIA

The cause of schizophrenia is unknown.[1] What Eugen Bleuler said in 1911 still obtains:

> 'Schizophrenia appears to be independent of external conditions and circumstances. It is seen among the poor as well as among the rich, in all walks of life, and in the most varied conditions whether orderly or disorderly, fortunate or unfortunate. City and country harbour them [schizophrenics] equally' (Bleuler, 1950 edn., p. 342).

There have been many suggestions as to its cause. Some have stressed the role of psychological factors, others the role of physical factors, either of which may contribute to the schizophrenic breakdown or to its actual cause. A wide variety of named causes include prenatal and postnatal traumata, constitutional factors, disturbances in the body metabolism, genetic changes, experiential factors in early childhood, inimical social and environmental factors, and so on.

The following discussion will be concerned with:

(a) heredity factors
(b) constitutional factors
(c) endocrine factors
(d) metabolic factors
(e) the central nervous system
(f) the autonomic nervous system
(g) precipitating factors

[1] *v.* Henderson & Gillespie (1946, pp. 289, 296); Mayer-Gross *et al.* (1954, p. 218); Redlich, in Brody & Redlich (1952, p. 18); Alexander & Moore (1958, pp. 114, 581).

(h) developmental factors
(j) family factors

(a) *Heredity Factors*

The purpose here will be to give a brief summary of the accepted findings regarding the heredity factor in schizophrenia. It would be inappropriate for a study of this nature to attempt to discourse at length on the variety of work which has been done in this field. (For this the reader is referred to the expert accounts in the literature.[1])

There is general agreement that heredity plays some part in the illness, but what part it plays, and to what extent, is as yet an open question.[2]

Reference to some of the studies carried out will give an indication of the trend towards accepting the heredity factor as part of the disease process:

(i) Schulz (1932) made a revision of an earlier study done by Rudin, with 660 families. He found the frequency of schizophrenia among the children of schizophrenics was 7 per cent compared with the already established figure for the average person of 0·8 per cent (*v.* Mayer-Gross *et al.*, op. cit., p. 219).

(ii) Kallmann (1938) studied 1,000 patients in a mental hospital and found the frequency of schizophrenia among the children of schizophrenics was 10–22 per cent (ibid.). In 1946, he carried out a study of schizophrenia among twins and found a high concordance (86 per cent) among identical twins and a much lower concordance among fraternal twins. Many have placed considerable emphasis on these studies, but I believe that more careful scrutiny of Kallmann's work will raise serious doubts about the validity and reliability of his findings.

(iii) M. Bleuler (1941) studied grandparents, grand-uncles, and grand-aunts and, comparing these with the average population, found a 'considerable frequency reaction' among the former. This was supplemented by studies by others of marriage partners of schizophrenics and of marriage partners of relatives of schizo-

[1] *v.* Bleuler, M. (1955, pp. 10–22); Overholser & Werkman, in Bellak (1958, p. 102f.).
[2] *v.* Bleuler, E. (1908, p. 337); Bleuler, M. (1955, p. 15); Redlich, in Brody & Redlich (1952, p. 20).

phrenics, and these showed a slight increase for schizophrenic reaction as compared with the average population (Bleuler, M., 1955, p. 12).

(iv) The work of Kleist (*circa* 1943) and Leonhard (*circa* 1943) designated a large number of subdivisions of schizophrenia. Through family studies they attempted to show that these subdivisions reflected independent (and mixed) hereditary diseases. This contributed to the view that schizophrenia, whilst having hereditary components, was not in itself a unitary trait of heredity (ibid., p. 14f.).

Thus, although present knowledge does not clearly designate the heredity factor, there is some evidence to attest to its presence. The consensus of opinion goes beyond the fact that there is a genetic effect in schizophrenia, and suggests that this effect is likely to be mediated through one or more recessive genes which may produce a certain vulnerability, rather than the disease process itself. If a person has the gene it need not have an inevitable effect; other factors may be necessary, such as separation from parents in childhood, an illness or trauma in early life, and so on. If this were so it would be a further indication of the indivisible relationship deemed to obtain between heredity and environmental factors.

(b) *Constitutional Factors*

There is a widespread agreement that prior to some schizophrenics actually developing the illness they will have shown signs or appearances that they *were going* to develop it. This preliminary appearance is sometimes referred to as a 'schizoid constitution'. People having such a constitution need not become schizophrenic, but this does not preclude their description in these terms.

The person having a schizoid constitution may be asocial, quiet, reticent, serious, or eccentric; he may be timid, shy, delicate, over-sensitive, nervous, excitable, fond of nature and books; he may be well-behaved, consistent, dull, stupid, docile, good-hearted. These descriptions, however, are so comprehensive that not only is their value diminished, but they will arouse resentment in those to whom the descriptions may apply.

It is often difficult to know the prior condition of the schizophrenic, and in any case some care must be exercised in identifying the symptoms of the psychosis with features noticeable in the patient before the psychosis developed. It is to be noted also that while many schizophrenics exhibit abnormalities or eccentricities before the actual breakdown, many do not.

(c) *Endocrine Factors*

The endocrine functioning concerns the thyroid, adrenal, and pituitary glands, and the gonads. At one stage considerable emphasis and interest surrounded the influence of these glands in the schizophrenic illness. Endocrine origins were suggested by the fact that the illness rarely occurred before puberty, and that it was frequently associated with adolescence, childbirth, or menopause (Mayer-Gross *et al.*, 1954, p. 223). It is now generally agreed that there is no certain evidence for a causal factor in endocrine functioning but there are indications of causative effects, for example, M. Bleuler (1955, p. 37) describes how a schizophrenic-like condition has been caused or influenced by thyrotoxicosis.

The absence of evidence of a causal factor may be due to the techniques of endocrinology or it may be that the endocrine changes are concomitant effects or after-effects of the psychosis. A notable change in the endocrine function is often observed in schizophrenia but, as Arieti (1955, p. 402f) points out, it is difficult to know if this is due to a decrease or change in the hormone production or to a change in response to them. The schizophrenic in his withdrawal from the world thereby reduces the stimulation which would normally come to the endocrine system, and this could bring a corresponding reduction in its functioning. Alternatively, the decrease in endocrine function may be due to a change in functioning of the autonomic nervous system which controls the endocrine system.

(d) *Metabolic Factors*

Kraepelin called schizophrenia a metabolic disease. The patients often appear to be in poor physical health and to exhibit somatic changes in different degrees. In the various studies made on the metabolic functions (sugar metabolism, liver function, responsiveness of the vegetative nervous system, circulation, enzymes, and so on), greater variations were noted than would have been found in the normal person. This does not necessarily indicate a somatic cause of the illness. Some suggest that the reverse could be the case, namely, that the psychosis produces the somatic abnormalities, or that these somatic abnormalities are concomitant effects of the emotional changes (Bleuler, M., 1955, p. 27). Thus, for example, when the schizophrenic shows a deficient intake in oxygen the question is raised – does the reduction in psychological activity cause the low intake of oxygen or are they concomitant effects arising from some previous cause? (Bleuler, M., 1955, p. 25; *v.q.* Arieti, 1955, p. 404.)

Selye (1946, 1950) proposed the General Adaptation Syndrome (G.A.S.) theory in which he showed the part that 'stress' could play in metabolic changes. The reaction to some stress is initiated by the pituitary gland which gives an increased secretion of adrenocorticotropic hormone and vasopressin with a corresponding reduction in its other secretions. This results in a decrease in adrenal cortex hormones which, in turn, affects the metabolism of carbohydrate, albumin, minerals, the blood circulation, kidney functions, and other systems. M. Bleuler concluded that although the search for somatic causes of schizophrenia has virtually failed, the evidence suggests that the somatic changes are manifestations of emotional tension.

(There have been some recent studies concerned with the production of a 'model psychosis' by induction of mescaline and lysergic acid. These lend some support to the view that an abnormal metabolic product arising spontaneously may be responsible for many of the symptoms of schizophrenia, particularly those of the catatonic variety.)

(e) *The Central Nervous System*

The central nervous system must play some part in the illness, for there can be no thinking without it.

Whether or not the pathology occurring in the central nervous system is causative of the schizophrenic illness, or again, whether or not it is a concomitant or resultant effect, has not been finally determined.

There are indications, however, that changes in the central nervous system are related to the symptoms of schizophrenia. It has been found for example by Heath (1954) in his E.E.G. studies with implanted electrodes, that abnormal bursts of activity from deeper structures, e.g. the amygdaloid nucleus, occurred at the time of a burst of hallucinosis. It has also been found that in wartime a person could develop schizophrenia after brain damage, although this did not necessarily mean that the brain damage was the cause.

When it was observed that certain schizophrenic symptoms were similar to the effects of brain damage, attempts were made to discover a relation between the schizophrenic symptom and a particular area of the brain. The studies of Arieti (1955, p. 414ff) would fall into this category. He suggested that the cerebral cortex played a significant part. (He did not, however, exclude an extra-cortical pathology such as from the diencephalon which exercises an influence over the emotions and metabolism generally.) He argued that, as a result of attempts to avoid stress and anxiety, a pathology of the central nervous system may develop and this may involve three cortical areas:

(i) The archipallium and mesopallium, including the rhinencephalon, the hippocampus, the cingulate gyrus, and possibly the posterior orbital gyri.

(ii) the prefrontal area.

(iii) the central undefined area in the temporal, occipital, and parietal lobes, which area Arieti calls 'T O P'.

Considering the area 'T O P' first, this area is of late development in phylogenetic history, and is concerned with the higher forms of thinking and socialization. In schizophrenia an attempt is made to avoid these higher forms, so abstract thought falls away to concrete thought, symbolic thought to paleo-symbolism, conceptualizations to sensorial perceptions. By relinquishing the area 'T O P', maladjustments may become evident in other areas of the central nervous system, and atrophy may also occur.

The prefrontal area is concerned with planned thinking and anticipation of future events, and thus is involved in considerable consequential anxiety which again the schizophrenic sets out to avoid. Thus the prefrontal area functions are relinquished as in the TOP areas, and likewise there is an emergent predominance of lower centre functions.

The archipallium area, concerned with the emotions, also appears to be affected, and its altered functioning may lead us to believe it to be the cause of the condition. Arieti allows this as a possibility, but suggests it is implausible if schizophrenia is seen as involving the relinquishing of the higher centres. The higher centres pertain to a late phylogenetic development, but since the archipallium pertains to an early phylogenetic development, its disturbed function cannot play such a central part.

(f) *The Autonomic Nervous System*

Since every somatic function is related in some way to the autonomic nervous system (as also with the central nervous system) the autonomic nervous system is necessarily involved in the schizophrenic illness.

The autonomic nervous system falls into a state of inactivity and dysfunction; there is a poverty in emotional experience and emotional expression; there is a reduction in reception of stimuli from the external world; and there are defective homeostatic reactions. In the normal condition a change in metabolism or body conditions is followed by a reaction to maintain an equilibrium, but in schizophrenia there is no effort to maintain or retain the equilibrium.

As previously stated, it is difficult to determine the causative factor: Does the reduction of stimuli from the external world produce the dysfunction of the autonomic nervous system, or vice versa?

It is also a matter for consideration that the central and autonomic nervous systems, in having the function of mediating intellectual and emotional psychological processes, may reflect, in their abnormal functioning, a primary malfunctioning in the psychological processes. As yet it is too early to make any clear designation of a primary pathological condition within the nervous systems themselves.

(g) *Precipitating Factors*

There is a wide variety of possible precipitating factors in schizophrenia. There are those of physical stress arising from physical illness, fatigue, overwork, or from traumas to the head or body; there are the psychological stresses arising from conflicts in loyalties, in religion or in sexual relations, and there are the experiences such as rejection, pregnancy, and parturition; there are situational stresses such as financial, domestic, and employment difficulties.

Schizophrenia can be associated with any of these factors, but it is frequently suggested that even in the absence of these factors, the disease may still develop. The possibility of a precipitating factor is denied by some on the grounds that a true dementia could have no such factor, while there are others who claim that the presence or absence of a precipitating factor will determine whether the schizophrenia will be 'process' or 'reactive'.

There is little doubt that the patient usually associates his illness with some 'precipitating' event, and although this event may be regarded as insignificant by the observer, for the patient it is highly significant. It may not have a causative value, but it frequently colours and determines the manifestation of the illness. It may be asked why an event should become a precipitating event for one person and not for another. This can be answered in terms of the experience and predisposition of the one over and against the other. It is common knowledge that a particular event has a different significance for different people. It is the meaning of the event for the person that matters more than its commonly accepted or 'dictionary' meaning, e.g. a man in his late fifties who complained of slight urinary symptoms in the course of routine examination underwent cystoscopic examination that led to pain and some blood in the urine. He immediately became profoundly depressed and suicidal. It was learned later that thirty years before this and prior to his marriage he had contracted venereal disease which was successfully treated. The symptoms of pain and blood in the urine at the time of routine examination convinced him that he still had venereal disease and that he must have infected his wife and son. The symptoms themselves were benign and cleared up rapidly, but their significance for this patient was so highly specific in activating an earlier period of stress that he became devastated by them.

(h) *Developmental Factors*

The psycho-analytic schools and certain learning-theorists consider that schizophrenia is due to some failure in the early psychic development. In order to present this viewpoint it is necessary to consider the general background theory of child development. In the interests of clarity, the Freudian viewpoint will be presented, although it is realized that there are many important and significant deviants from this view.

At birth, the child has no clearly defined ego, so objects in the external world are undifferentiated from the self. The early state of the child is therefore one of primary narcissism wherein the energy of the instinctual drive of the eros, i.e. libido, is directed inwards towards the self.

The capacity to distinguish self from not-self develops slowly. The libido, which had been vested in the love-objects of primary narcissism, is withdrawn into the ego (secondary narcissism) and is then directed outwards towards defined external objects.

Libido always has an origin, an aim, and an object. Its origins are associated with the erotogenic zones of the developmental phases of the child. The libido arises in the first phase of development in the *oral* zone; its aim is to swallow or incorporate its object (milk, the mother's breast, or other objects with which the child may show an oral preoccupation).

In the second phase of development the libido has its origin in the *anal* zone; here the child shows a preoccupation with anal material or with issues relating to it. The aim of the libido becomes a matter of controlling or retaining the object (excreta).

The third phase of development is the phallic and genital phase where the aim of the libido is to obtain pleasure through the object (genitals) by masturbatory activity. From this phase there develops the oedipal phase wherein the child shows an intensive attachment to the parent of the opposite sex, and shows fear and destructive tendencies toward the parent of the same sex.

In the child's development towards maturity, there may be an over-investment of energy during one of these phases, with an ensuing reluctance to abandon the objects of this phase in favour of the objects of the next. This over-investment may arise out of a predisposition in the constitution of the child or out of an experience of the child during that phase and can become so accentuated that it is called a fixation. There is also the phenomenon of regression to an earlier phase of development, i.e. at a certain phase the child may be subjected to certain stress or frustration such that the libido will be withdrawn from the objects of this phase and redirected to the objects of an earlier phase (in which it can be presumed certain deep satisfactions have been found) and a form of adaptation takes place.

It is now possible to apply this theory to schizophrenia. In this condition the person adopts a form of behaviour which has similarities to that of the objectless condition of an infant in the early oral phase of development (Freud, 1949, pp. 32, 128f). The libido is withdrawn from external objects and redirected inwards towards the ego; there is a return of primary identification where the ego loses its differentiation from external objects; there is an oral preoccupation, a complete dependence, a lack of control of natural functions (feeding and elimination); there is a preoccupation with inner reality, and even the manners and posture may have similarities with the infant, e.g. the foetal position and the *Schnauzkrampf* of the lips.

For this present study it is relevant to note that whereas Freud saw the condition of schizophrenia arising out of the abandonment of object relationships, Federn (1953) postulated that there was a previous development, namely in the creation of a false world of reality in consequence of the withdrawal of the libido from the ego-boundary. For Federn, the ego was an experience and its boundary extended out from the ego and acted as a sense organ, determining what was ego and what was not-ego. The ego-boundary itself was invested with a libidinal charge, which in schizophrenia became defective or withdrawn and, in consequence, there ensued an invasion of false reality, a regression to former states and a loss of the capacity for abstract thinking.

In recent times an increasing number of studies employing a 'genetic' approach have been made in schizophrenia, and these leave little doubt that this approach has brought invaluable insight and hope to this condition.

(j) *Family Factors*

Recent work in schizophrenia has given more attention to the family situation and particularly to the influence of the mother. These studies, in common with psycho-analytic studies, point to the importance of the family influence in the early years of the child's life, and although conclusive findings are not available at this stage, certain clear indications emerge.

The mother often plays a significant role in the life of the schizophrenic, and many studies concentrate their investigation on her in an attempt to ascertain whether or not her attitude and behaviour towards the patient as a child have contributed to his later development of schizophrenia.

It appears, however, that the maleficent factor may not occur in the overt behaviour or overt teaching, but in the atmosphere of the family. The understanding and warmth and the non-verbal solidarity of the family can evoke a sense of security and self-confidence in the child, but absence of these may lead him to considerable anxiety. There are also suggestions that schizophrenia may develop where the child has been reared in an atmosphere in which the parent has masked and concealed the facts of reality from him. Consequently, no open, genuine, and mutual relationships develop between the parent and the child. On the contrary, the parent-child relationship may be a peculiar one in which the mother, for example, may attempt to 'use' the child in a parasitic way to satisfy her own inner personality needs. She may thus bind the child to her and by inducing his shame may deprive him of his individuality or preclude him from developing into maturity. Indeed she may shame him into a devotion to her. It may not be surprising that some have called her a 'schizophrenogenic mother', but this term implies a causative relation which has not yet been established.

A situation may develop between parent and child known as the 'double-bind' situation (Bateson *et al.*, 1956; Weakland & Jackson, 1958). Here the child is caught up in hopelessly conflicting multiple injunctions (verbal and non-verbal) on which he feels he cannot comment and from which he cannot escape. Some suggest that it is not so much a matter of the mother holding or 'trapping' the child in this situation but that the child comes to feel he cannot escape for fear of what may happen to the mother. He sacrifices himself in her interests; and out of this sacrifice, it is suggested, schizophrenia may develop.

It is thought that the mother reacts to her child in this way because of her fear of the relationship; she fears her own feelings. These fears have developed out of her own mother's fears, and out of the low self-esteem arising from later repressions. This gives the impression of an enclosed determinism from which we might rightfully react, for it is common knowledge that certain groups of parents may show similar features, yet a child of only one set of parents may develop schizophrenia. There is also the situation in which only one child in a family will develop schizophrenia. Attention has been given to such problems by those involved in these studies. They suggest that a child can and does manoeuvre itself out of the schizophrenic impasse; or a mother may single out one child from her family and see in him the fulfilment of her unfulfilled aspirations (Hill, 1955, p. 121ff.; Lidz *et al.*, 1957).

The father has also been a figure for consideration and, as with the mother, there are many clear indications that the child needs a good parent. The child who grows up with a maladjusted father or a bad father-image is clearly at a serious disadvantage compared with those who have a good father or those who have no father.

The father, however, can also be involved with his own problems which become reflected in the family and influence his father-role. He may be disappointed in his wife and expect his daughters to conform where the mother failed. He may be hostile to his son, rival him, belittle his efforts and sabotage his self-confidence. He may remain aloof, conveying the impression that his children cannot approach his achievements; on the other hand, he may become a nonentity, unable to accept responsibility for his family.

There are many difficulties associated with the investigations of these family factors, not least that parents conceal the facts and pretend that the family situation has always been harmonious and all that could be desired. It must be noted, however, that though available evidence suggests that family factors may play a significant role in the development of schizophrenia, these may have become known to us simply and only because a member of that family became ill. Such factors may not have a direct implication for schizophrenia, but may be widely prevalent. Yet in so far as they do obtain, they indicate that the atmosphere and warmth of families are too often inadequate and unsatisfactory for the future development and happiness of the child.

Although these investigations must continue, there are already clear indications that positive steps should be taken to inculcate an awareness of the family situation and, where necessary, help should be given to adjust it. This seems to extend beyond the help which may be found in mothers' meetings, young women's clubs, marriage guidance, etc., to a more intensive counselling and therapy through both individual and group media. Clearly the theologian could be involved in this task, but so often he is either unaware of the need, or untrained to meet it.

Having discussed the issues of the family situation, the patient must still be the centre of our concern. It is important to know what he thinks and feels about his family situation though his account may not be a true representation of the facts. On the one hand it may reflect his inner diffusion and fragmentation, but on the other hand we must attempt to ascertain if this is his *experience*, and if so, attempt to understand it.

THE ONSET OF SCHIZOPHRENIA

In its onset, the illness is associated with adolescence and early adulthood, although there are wide variations to include childhood and aged schizophrenics. Generally, however, the statistics show the highest proportion of breakdowns occur in early adulthood. Kraepelin estimated that 60 per cent of his patients developed schizophrenia before the twenty-fifth year; E. Bleuler put his estimate at 44 per cent. Mayer-Gross, Slater, and Roth estimate that 75 per cent of their schizophrenics fell ill between the fifteenth and twenty-fifth years.

There are difficulties, however, in accurately determining the age of onset. The outward symptoms may not become noticeable until the patient has reached later life, or he may not seek attention until the illness is in its late stage of development where it is difficult to determine when the illness began. In regard to this Weiner refers to the study done by Counts and Regan (1954) in which they give the age of onset for ninety-four chronic schizophrenic patients as 21·7 years, but 'the patient had been symptomatic but not "schizophrenic" for 12·9 years' (Bellak, 1958, p. 124).

The mode of onset can be twofold: There can be an insidious onset in which the illness presents the picture of a gradual degenerative organic disease. This may be called the schizophrenic process, or, as others prefer, the dementia praecox.

On the other hand, the onset of the illness may be abrupt or acute. It may then take the form of an episodic reaction to a situation and represent the only measure that can be exercised against the accumulating panic. This form of the illness may be called the schizophrenic reaction or, as some prefer, schizophrenia (in contrast to dementia praecox above). Initially the illness may have many different manifestations, but with the passing of time the illness developed through the acute mode of onset may degenerate into the illness developed through the insidious mode.

There is evidence to suggest that the illness with an acute mode of onset has a favourable prognosis, for it is still related to precipitating factors. Such a statement, however, is not to be regarded as exclusive.

THE FREQUENCY OF SCHIZOPHRENIA

There is the tendency to believe that with the increasing speed and stress of modern civilization there will be an increasing frequency of schizophrenia. But the accurate estimation of this frequency presents many problems. Already we have noted that the illness, in its chronic and episodic forms, is often elusive and complex. The criteria for its identification may range from the administration of objective psychological tests, to a 'praecox feeling' where the diagnosis is intuitive and subjective. It is difficult, therefore, to assess not only a given hospital population, but also the schizophrenic population outside the hospital records, and beyond this there is the task of determining the specific normal population to which the frequency-estimate may refer.

Having stated these difficulties, certain trends of frequency may be indicated.

It is estimated that out of every 1,000 children born, 18 to 20 will spend part of their lives in a mental hospital with schizophrenia. There is agreement that the disease occurs with similar frequency in all classes, but there is a slightly greater frequency in the lower socio-economic classes and in the more densely populated areas (Lemkau & Crocetti, 1958, p. 73ff.).

In the U.S.A., schizophrenia claims the largest proportion of patients under 35 years of age admitted to the mental hospitals. It was estimated by Bleuler in 1908 that schizophrenia claimed 75 per cent of the hospital beds; but this figure can be compared with the more recent figures of D. B. Klein (1951, p. 304) of 50 per cent, and of Lemkau of 47 per cent (op. cit., p. 75). Taking a figure as low as 40 per cent, this would mean that for the average-sized hospital of 600 beds, 240 would be occupied by schizophrenic patients.

It is also estimated that for the present-day population of Western Europe the frequency of schizophrenia ranges from 50 to 250 per 100,000 per annum, with a probable 290 per 100,000 ill with the disease at the one time; and of these, 150 will be in hospital (ibid., p. 71f., 80). This could mean that for a city such as Aberdeen with a population of less than 200,000, we could expect to find 300+ schizophrenic patients in the hospitals.

These figures, although general and approximate, portray to some extent the dimensions of the illness, and bear out the suggestion that schizophrenia is 'one of the major diseases of mankind' (ibid., p. 70).

HOSPITAL CARE: ITS NECESSITY

Although in certain cases the illness may be profitably treated on an out-patient basis, in general the symptoms are so pronounced and all-pervading that hospital care is essential.

The mental hospital is often associated with many fears and anxieties, the reality of which cannot be underestimated. It is not without considerable stress and emotion that the patient breaks with the real world, and the thought of the mental hospital evokes in his relatives (and often in the patient himself) the primitive (but real) and collective dread of insanity and all its associations. Frequently there is an overwhelming foreboding of failure and there is the unanswered question of why this has happened. There is also the anxiety for the future; that once having been on 'the inside' there will be no 'coming out' and that the stigma will always be with them.

Much can still be done to appease and correct these feelings and attitudes. Nevertheless, the position is clear – if the person is ill he must be cared for.

There are four general reasons why a person is brought to the mental hospital:

(a) that he may receive treatment, whether he appreciates the need or not.

(b) that he may be protected from the danger which he presents to himself and to others.

(c) that his relatives may be relieved of the responsibility of caring for him.

(d) that he may be given long-term care.

These will be considered in turn.

(a) *Treatment*

The general aim of treatment is to relieve the state of suffering and to bring the patient back into a normal contact with reality and his community. It is based on the presuppositions that schizophrenia is an illness – an inauthentic mode of existence – and that we who are regarded as normal have the right and duty to intrude on this mode of existence so as to induce the patient to change to a more authentic and acceptable mode. How this treatment is effected will be a subject for later discussion in this work.

(b) *The Danger of the Patient*

It is common to find that the schizophrenic illness has violent and self-punitive manifestations. There are suggestions however that there is a prior condition of sensitiveness which, when aroused, will lead the patient to make verbal and physical attacks on those about him or on himself. Although no one need purposely disturb him, his appraisal of the situation may be enough to evoke this behaviour. Hospital care is necessary as a relief to all concerned, though even then the patient's problems may not be over, for he will readily see the staff as adopting a negative attitude and again he will react. Unless this is checked positively it may lead, as so often in the past, to an atmosphere of 'therapeutic nihilism' which of itself will contribute to the chronicity of the illness, and the patient will become known as a 'typical institutional dement'.

(c) *Relief of the Relatives*

In general the schizophrenic is brought to hospital after a long period in which his relatives have tried hard to help, forbear, and tolerate. With the progression of the illness the patient presents increasing difficulties for the relatives and hospital care becomes necessary. But in addition to relieving the relatives of this physical burden, hospitalization may also provide a convenient solution to their feelings of guilt and their fears of solidarity which may surround the illness. The presence of the patient may be a continual source of uneasiness and embarrassment, but his removal to hospital may help to place these sensitive issues at a more comfortable distance.

(d) *Long-term Care*

As the illness becomes more pronounced, it may become inadvisable for the patient to leave the hospital even for short periods. But, regardless of the condition of the patient, the time will come when his next-of-kin will die out, leaving him with no place where he can go; the hospital will then become his home. Long-term care may do little more than provide a roof over his head, a place for sleeping and some food to eat; but usually the conditions are comfortable and the patients are encouraged to participate in the social and work activities of the hospital.

The average duration of hospital care for schizophrenic patients has been estimated as 13·1 years.[1] Although this could indicate a state of hopelessness, it is pointed out that it does not necessarily mean, for example, that four schizophrenics must remain in hospital for thirteen years to give this average. It could mean that three of them were discharged immediately, and the other one remained for fifty-two years, thus giving the average of thirteen years.

RECOVERY IN SCHIZOPHRENIA

It is only within the last twenty-five years that the concept of recovery has become meaningful for the schizophrenic illness. Previously, for any particular patient, there were only remote chances of recovery with the treatments available and spontaneous remissions were comparatively few. Today the prospects of recovery are much more hopeful, although the deteriorative course of the disease is still a matter of serious concern.

The possible course of the illness is depicted in a study by M. Bleuler (1955, p. 53), carried out over a period of fifteen years with 500 schizophrenic patients. His findings were as follows:

[1] Lemkau & Crocetti, in Bellak (1958, p. 75); *v.q.* Huston & Perpernik, in Bellak (1958, p. 534).

	Patients %
1. Acute onset with direct course to permanent deterioration	5–15
2. Chronic, simple course to permanent deterioration	10–20
3. Acute onset with direct course to permanent defect	under 5
4. Chronic, simple course to permanent defect	5–10
5. Acute, episodic course ending in permanent deterioration	under 5
6. Acute, episodic course ending in permanent defect	30–40
7. Acute, episodic course ending in recovery (social or complete)	25–35

In approximate figures, therefore, he found that 25 per cent of his patients reached a permanent deterioration, 45 per cent showed a permanent defect, and 30 per cent recovered.

The generally acknowledged trend towards an increased rate of recovery may be shown by reference to a study presented by Kramer and others (1956),[1] carried out in an American hospital over the period 1916–1950:

Period	*Schizophrenics released from hospital*	*Patients died*
	%	%
1916–1925	50	11
1926–1935	49	8
1936–1945	61	10
1946–1950	70	4

[1] Reported by Huston & Pepernik, in Bellak (1958, p. 533).

The rise in release from 1935 onwards may reflect the introduction of the active methods of treatment (particularly insulin coma and electro-convulsive treatments). But the increasing influence of individual and group psychotherapy of this period should not be overlooked.

Many suggestions have been made as to what might be considered favourable signs for recovery. Among these are included youthfulness, short duration of illness, an acute breakdown, external precipitating factors present, the person coming from high socio-economic classes, good education, steady church attendance, good marital adjustment, high intelligence, preservation of affect, and so on. But it has been found that although groups of factors seem to be associated with recovery, when these factors are tested individually the result is not always encouraging. It must be emphasized that factors given as favourable signs may not, by their presence, ensure recovery, nor by their absence preclude it.

There is a growing opinion that the actual factors which may lead to recovery *underlie* the other factors of age, duration of the illness, and so on. The view held by many, and supported by the present writer, is that the atmosphere and attitude of the patient's treatment and his situation will play a decisive part in his recovery. It is acknowledged that insulin, E.C.T., and other similar treatments have helped to transform our whole outlook towards mental illness. But it is to be noted that more than physical factors are involved in these treatments. There is the air of hopefulness and expectancy which is conveyed to the patient, there is the increased physical and emotional contact and so on, all of which make their contribution to the patient's recovery.

Although 'recovery' seems to be a fundamental concept for any illness, its meaning is subject to wide interpretation. Traditionally, psychiatry has thought of it in terms of removal and relief of signs and symptoms; more recently social and occupational criteria have been introduced. But some circles now go beyond this to suggest that recovery is not necessarily a matter for objective validation, but that its meaning is found through an intensive exploration of the inner experience of a particular patient. The present writer, while supporting this viewpoint, would suggest that even more fundamental to our understanding of recovery is an acceptance of a distinctive anthropology and an appreciation of the basic structures of human existence. Recovery thus becomes meaningful as we discern what man is and what he is meant to be. It would seem that psychiatric treatment could not lose by its closer consideration of these issues.

CHAPTER IV

Modes of Treatment

Prior to the introduction of the modern forms of treatment, a vast number of experiments were carried out on schizophrenic patients. These experiments varied from surgical operations on the endocrine glands and jejunum, to blood-letting and fever therapy, as well as many others. Although certain hopeful changes towards improvement or recovery were sometimes observed, it was probable that these changes were due more to the unpredictable and variable nature of the illness than to any particular treatment employed. On the whole the outlook for the illness was melancholy. When it became apparent in any given case that time was passing and no improvement shown, it was assumed that an irreversible process had become established, and both relatives and staff prepared themselves for the prospect of permanent invalidism. In general a policy of custodial care was adopted and where patients showed a marked disturbance or inaccessibility, measures of strict supervision and protection from all dangerous implements were employed. In some cases heavy bromides and other toxic sedatives were administered over long periods of years until the secondary effects of these were added to the original illness. Thus, the overall picture presented an atmosphere of hopelessness, which seemed to contribute significantly to the perpetuation of the disease.

The introduction of modern forms of treatment – insulin coma, electro-convulsive therapy, etc., brought widespread changes to mental hospitals. In their application to schizophrenia they have produced excellent results in terms of recovery, improvement, shortening of the episode, and making the patient more accessible. Unfortunately they are effective only in some cases and long-term studies have shown that there must be a reappraisal of the early expectations vested in these methods. In its own way, this only reiterates what is already well known in psychiatric circles – that there is no single treatment universally effective for schizophrenia.

It may be said at this point that, along with the changes of outlook and treatment which are taking place in psychiatry, a new social and religious awareness of mental illness and of the mental patient is developing. In the past, society in general tended to stand apart from mental abnormality and, at most, thought that so long as reasonable conditions were provided other issues would take care of themselves. Religious circles have also participated in these attitudes of detachment and aloof benevolence. There were those who believed that the patient's recovery would depend on his repentance, but the more general viewpoint thought of the issues in wide and undefined terms, and the concept of 'the love of God' was interpreted casually as ensuring every man's felicity and salvation.

In more recent times there has been a re-awakening to the issues and ramifications of mental illness and this has prompted religious circles to reconsider their approach with greater care. It is now understood that schizophrenia may so transform the meaning and significance of ordinary experience that language of hitherto accepted usage no longer adequately applies. It would appear therefore that even in religious circles there should be a genuine attempt to apprehend and understand the schizophrenic experience so that some meaningful communication might be made to the patient in his condition. This means that a way must be found whereby it is possible to speak with the schizophrenic in his world and at his level of experience without unduly imposing another level of experience, i.e. without throwing the Christian message at him 'like a stone'.

It is hoped that later chapters of this present work may give some indication of the way in which this might be done. The work will then be open to questions from both disciplines (those of psychiatry and theology), and it may be said that here it is theological and has no implication for psychiatry, or that there it is psychiatric and has no relevance to theology. It is suggested, however, that this attempt may contribute to a greater and more effective co-operation between the two disciplines, for in placing its emphasis on the experienced world of the patient and his emergent possibilities of self-fulfilment through relationships, it implies that all treatment of schizophrenia should be considered within the wider context of self-fulfilment as a religious phenomenon.

The methods of treatment of schizophrenia employed in current psychiatric practice fall into four main categories:

(i) prophylactic methods
(ii) institutional care
(iii) physical and physico-chemical
(iv) psychotherapy (including group psychotherapy).

The emphasis of this present work falls on the fourth category. Some brief reference, however, will be made to the other three at this point, and some guidance given regarding the relevant literature.

(i) *Prophylactic Methods*

Our limited knowledge of the illness restricts the knowledge and effectiveness of prophylaxis, but some principles emerge. The accumulating number of studies on the schizophrenic patient and his family point to the fact that adverse conditions in early life bear some relation to the development of the illness. Stressful situations in early and in later life may play some part, but prophylactic measures are often nullified by the stress and conformity of the age in which we live.

It is known, however, that the schizophrenic, before breakdown, is frequently an unusual person who needs special understanding at home, at school, at play, and at work. Child guidance clinics, vocational guidance services and other counselling and therapeutic bureaux can be of immense value, bringing out the best in the individual and helping him to withstand those stresses to which he is vulnerable. Similarly, education and training of teachers, ministers, and doctors and those having care of the young, should include practical instruction to help them to be alert to the presence of incipient disorders.

A discussion of prophylaxis would be incomplete without reference to religious faith. There is little doubt that a religious faith can be of great value to a person in helping him 'to relate himself meaningfully to the totality of Being' (Allport, 1955, p. 96). Properly conceived, it can transform his outlook and behaviour in a stressful situation, although it must be stated that this does not mean that a religious faith provides an immunity to illness or breakdown. A religious faith apprehended within the context of the community-of-believers may well have a prophylactic effect in that it turns the individual towards his divine Centre and towards his fellow-believers; but regardless of any prophylactic effect, if he feels that he is always held in the intimate regard of this Community, the desire for gain (prophylactic or otherwise) will be subordinated to what he will regard as more fundamental principles.

The significance of belonging to an accepting Community cannot be overestimated. We are beginning to experience the impact and meaning of such a Community in the Cairnmillar Institute in Melbourne: first through the League of Friends of the Institute, and secondly through the various group activities which have become part of the Institute's programme.

(ii) *Institutional Care*

The form of institutional care can have decisive and far-reaching consequences for the welfare of both the acute and the chronic patient. It is agreed that the rate and certainty of remission in the acute breakdown and the attitude and behaviour of the chronic patient depend to some extent on the atmosphere and the policies of the institution.

Institutional care can take one of two general forms:

(a) An active form of institutional care, in which the patient is encouraged and helped to take a positive interest in people and things about him. This form of care is now widely accepted and is being increasingly developed. Activities include work groups, occupational therapy, art therapy, dancing, indoor and outdoor sport and so on, and these always stand over against and challenge the patient's tendencies towards self-preoccupation and subjectivism.

(b) A passive form of institutional care, in which the patient is retained in hospital, given his meals and perhaps expected to do light manual labour. This form of care is associated with the gloom of older styles of nursing and is being replaced by the more active methods (Goffman, 1961).

(iii) *The Physical and Physico-Chemical Methods*

The physical methods which have brought new hope to mental illness include electro-convulsive therapy (E.C.T.), insulin and, in lesser use, Cardiozol and Metrazol, drugs (chlorpromazine, reserpine, and a constantly widening variety of others), and psychosurgery. In the original dissertation, the author elaborated in detail the development and effectiveness of these forms of treatment, but for the present work such an account is unnecessary. The reader may refer to the relevant literature on this subject.[1]

[1] *E.C.T.*

v. Hoch & Pennes, in Bellak (1958, pp. 424, 426, 431f.); *v.q.* Bleuler (1955, p. 60f).

Theories. v. Bleuler (1955, p. 58ff.); Hoch & Pennes (op. cit., p. 453).

Results. Bleuler (op. cit., p. 55); *v.* Hoch & Pennes (op. cit., p. 446f.). They cite Staudt and Zubin's study (1957), in which a correlation was made between the time after E.C.T. and the percentage of patients recovered or improved. Results:

Immediate effects	52 per cent
After one year	48 per cent
After two years	46 per cent
After five years	39 per cent

These results are to be compared with findings after five years of non-specified treatment – 42 per cent improvement.

INSULIN COMA THERAPY

cf. ibid., p. 398.

Results. ibid., p. 417f.; *v.* Sechehaye (1956, p. 2); *v.q.* Bleuler (op. cit., pp. 59f., 68); cf. Mayer-Gross *et al.* (1954, p. 283); Patterson (1958, p. 461).

DRUGS

Chlorpromazine. v. Freeman, in Bellak (1958, p. 478); ibid., pp. 489–93; *v.q.* Arieti (1955, p. 500).

Reserpine. v. Arieti (op. cit., p. 497f.); cf. Savage & Day (1958, p. 595f.); *v.* Freeman, in Bellak (1958, p. 478f.); *v.q.* Arieti (op. cit., p. 498).

Results. v. Freeman (op. cit., p. 481f.).

Permanency and Habituation. ibid., p. 487ff.

It is of utmost importance for the reader to understand that the physical and pharmacological methods of treatment have literally brought a revolution to the treatment of nervous and mental disorders. It is impossible to estimate the wide dimensions of relief and cure which have come as a result of their use. The present work in no wise seeks to belittle their importance – far from it! The author omits a detailed consideration simply because the focus of this work is on a form of psychotherapy. It must be stated unequivocally that in some cases this form of psychotherapy would not have been possible without the concurrent use of certain drugs.

(iv) *Psychotherapy and Group Psychotherapy*

The vast number of studies carried out on somatic methods of treatment have made notable discoveries. The fact cannot be overlooked, however, that within recent times more and more interest has swung to psychotherapy as a method of treatment for schizophrenia. Psychotherapy in general embraces many different forms and expressions, but essentially four main categories may be designated:

(a) The classical Freudian analysis which, while having an effective application to some conditions, has experienced difficulties with the schizophrenic condition. Freud abandoned psycho-analysis for schizophrenia because it was too difficult to establish and sustain an adequate transference relationship.[1] Later workers were, to some extent, able to overcome these difficulties, but they then experienced a problem of handling the fluid unconscious material so abundantly present in the consciousness of the schizophrenic (Hill, 1955, p. 180). In addition, the analytic situation itself presented a difficulty. The patient, turned

---

PSYCHOSURGERY

v. Paul & Greenblatt, in Bellak (1958, pp. 501f., 527ff.); *v.q.* Arieti (op. cit., p. 491f.); Bleuler (op. cit., p. 64f.).

Results. v. Paul & Greenblatt (op. cit., p. 514f.); cf. Mayer-Gross *et al.* (op. cit., p. 289f.); *v.* Bleuler (op. cit., p. 66).

Indications for Psychosurgery. v. Arieti (op. cit., p. 495); cf. Bleuler (op. cit., p. 65).

[1] Freud (1949 ed., p. 31); *v.q.* Fromm-Reichmann (1939, p. 412); Sechehaye (1956, p. 5).

away from a face-to-face encounter with the analyst, is thus not encouraged to forsake his autistic world; rather the situation can sometimes contribute to his autism.

(b) The parameters or variations of the Freudian method have come more and more into practice, and especially in view of the fact that the classical Freudian method had many inadequacies. Some of the exponents of these variant methods are Federn, Sullivan, Fromm-Reichmann, Rosen, Sechehaye, and others; but further reference will be made to these workers at a later stage.

(c) The eclectic methods which attempt to give a broad consideration of the various schools of psychotherapy, adopting features from any or all of them, reconciling their inconsistencies, improving upon their methods and in general attempting to develop a consistent workable system.

It may seem that the eclectic can make the most of the best elements in all schools. In practice this is not always so. Psychotherapy concerns wider and deeper issues than those of therapeutic cure; ultimately it concerns the way a man lives and his way of life. Eclecticism, far from giving the therapist a clear orientation, can reflect the therapist's own inability to discover some definite *Weltanschauung*, and to commit himself to it (Cantril, 1950, p. 101).

(d) The other forms of psychotherapy which do not develop from any particular theoretical system but nevertheless, through their application, provide significant beneficial therapeutic effects. Examples of these forms are occupational therapy, work therapy, art therapy, social therapy, and so on.

Psychotherapy may be mediated through individual and group situations. In all its forms it provides a situation in which the patient may directly or indirectly reveal and ventilate his problems, and in which he is assisted to a re-orientation of his attitude and behaviour. The general overall aim of psychotherapy is to bring the patient to an awareness of his internal psychic mechanisms, to assist him to a more socially acceptable contact with the external world and to help him to re-learn ways of participation in it.

In all, the importance and centrality of the personality of the therapist should be held in careful regard.

The present work concentrated extensively on group psychotherapy. This form of psychotherapy is becoming more widely employed and its value increasingly recognized both generally and in its application to schizophrenia.

Frequently the suggestion has arisen that the schizophrenic illness precludes a group-belonging, and thus group psychotherapy (group therapy) is greatly restricted or indeed impossible. Some writers, having worked with the illness for long periods, have concluded that no group formation emerged. It is recognized that the schizophrenic shows himself afraid of close relationships and shows a preference for seclusion and camouflage. It will be seen, however, that the group situation can be utilized not only to therapeutic advantage, but to the advantage of the schizophrenic, for in addition to providing a way by which he might abandon his isolationism, the group can also provide a protective cover into which the patient may from time to time withdraw.

The general principle behind group therapy may be twofold: on the one hand it may be employed for its empirical value, i.e. on the grounds that it saves time and produces therapeutic results. On the other hand, it may be employed for its intrinsic value that, irrespective of its empirical pragmatic value, the pattern of therapy in itself is of worth. The present work, in stressing the significance of the basic patterns of relatedness, stresses also the intrinsic value of group therapy, though the implicit empirical value is not thereby disregarded.

Group therapy is not intended to supplant the individual therapy, but it may gainfully supplement it. Whereas individual therapy has its limitations in engendering a relatedness to the world or a change in the person's behaviour, group therapy has the advantage of offering a wide range of possibilities to the patient. The group itself can assume immense significance, particularly as it is accepted that a primary human motivation is the desire for group-belonging, and that this group-belonging can have a far-reaching influence on the person's behaviour, his hopes and fears, his attitudes and beliefs. If this is generalized to psychotherapy, the group can become not only the medium of change, but the target and agent of change.

Compared with the individual therapeutic situation, the group situation is closer to the real-life situation – where one strives with the other for status and recognition, where one finds in the other a common need and understanding. The group situation in fact provides a type of miniature world situation, permitting a variety of expression and wide possibilities for identification, for evasion and release of tension and for relatedness. This regained relatedness within the group and the strengthened confidence found thereby can form the baseline for a reorientation of attitude and a renewed relatedness to the world.

In group therapy the therapeutic process may have different emphases according to the therapist's orientation. It may be concerned with the *intra-psychic mechanisms*. Here the therapy is directed towards the individuals within the group, and thus it becomes a form of individual therapy conducted in a group meeting. It generally has a psycho-analytic framework, seeking to uncover the individual's frustrations and conflicts, and to relate these to his early development.

The therapeutic process may be concerned with the *interpersonal relationships*. The stress here is placed upon the relatedness and socialization, self-expression and self-esteem, of the here-and-now. While not disregarding the intra-psychic processes, the focus of therapy is on the present meanings, the present experience, and the present decisions.

The therapeutic process may be concerned with the *group experience* or *group tension*.

Whatever the manifest content of the proceedings of the group, there is always an underlying group tension. Whenever individuals act together in a group there emerges this distinct and unifying phenomenon which may well be turned to therapeutic gain. It is an 'ebb and flow' phenomenon, influenced *by* the group members, and in turn exercising an influence *on* the group members.

In practice, to make these clear-cut distinctions as to where the therapeutic process lies is a fallacy, for the situation has about it a mark of unity which does not readily submit to reductionist schemes to study the isolated individual, or the interpersonal relationships, or the group tension. In addition the therapeutic process is not always easily discerned or directed, and often may be global and diffuse, so that while the therapist may purpose to make a specific emphasis, he should be aware of other processes which may be simultaneously involved.

It is necessary for the patient to experience that he belongs to the group. 'Not belonging is the worst contingency man can experience' (Dreikurs). At first the patient may not desire or apprehend this belonging and the group and therapeutic process may require 'structuring' to develop a formal belonging. In this development the patient experiences the rivalries and struggle of the other, as together they find their belonging and position in the group. From interaction and conflict there emerges the positive gain of a group cohesion: a force or pressure which unifies and binds the patients together such that the desire to belong to the group exceeds the desire to contract out of it.

The psychotherapy adopted in the present work differed in many respects from other forms of psychotherapy. Its background may be found in certain notable features of the work of some therapists who themselves have deviated from the classical Freudian school. In particular, reference is made to Paul Federn, Harry Stack Sullivan, Frieda Fromm-Reichmann, J. Rosen, Silvano Arieti, and M. Sechehaye.

The significant feature of *Federn*'s theory for this work was his postulation regarding the ego and its boundary. For him, schizophrenia was a disturbance of the ego and its cathexis. The ego itself is invested with libidinal energy which gives its experience of vitality, meaning and 'mine-ness' (Federn, 1953, pp. 222, 242). The ego-boundary is also libidinally charged, and it designates the limits of the ego. In schizophrenia this charge becomes withdrawn or defective; the ego-boundary may become diffused and may disrupt or breakdown. This is accompanied by a false reality, by an inability to distinguish thought from reality, by a regression to earlier states, and by an emergence of unconscious material.[1]

Psychotherapy must therefore seek to re-cathect the fluid ego-boundary. Federn abandoned the techniques of free association and the analysis of resistance on the grounds that there was an abundance of unconscious material already present. Instead he found a re-repression was necessary. The positive transference was essential and so he discouraged attempts to analyse it. He suggested also the desirability of a skilled woman-helper to facilitate a mother-transference. (Other workers have also adopted this measure.) For Federn, the aim in therapy was to appease the instinctual and emotional conflict and to help the patient with his deep wounds from which he had sought this defence of schizophrenia. To do this he suggested the non-psychotic part of the ego should be strengthened and the psychotic part 'spared' and thus, through this strengthening of the weakened ego, the possibilities for a new relation with reality may emerge (Federn, op. cit., pp. 144, 155, 161ff, 171, 192).

The significant feature of *Sullivan*'s theory for this work was his emphasis and insight regarding the interpersonal relationships.[2] Similar theories have been woven deeply into the 'warp and weft' of philosophy and theology for a long time. It is surprising that psychiatry has taken so long to embrace the valuable aspects of these theories. For Sullivan, schizophrenia, while manifesting intra-psychic and regressive phenomena, developed from disturbing interpersonal relationships, particularly as experienced in childhood. The person suffers a blow to his self-esteem which provokes panic and anxiety, and, later, distortions appear in his interpretations of the relationships into which he enters. The illness or condition seems to be motivated in the direction of some security so traumatically lost in the interpersonal relationship.

Sullivan's psychotherapy concentrated on helping the patient to re-experience the security of interpersonal relations. His psychotherapy was thus not so much a matter of observation and

[1] Federn (1953, pp. 160ff., 187, 235); *v.q.* Storch (1924, pp. 22, 24); Bychowski (1952, p. 105).

[2] Sullivan (1947, 1950a; in Arieti, 1955, p. 33).

treatment of a 'patient' but participation with another person. For him the therapist no longer could sit at a distance while the patient relived his conflicts on a couch, but psychotherapy entailed an active encounter and participation on both sides.

In this work I was deeply interested in *Fromm-Reichmann*'s writings regarding the loneliness of the schizophrenic and his longing for human intimacy.[1] She also emphasized the need for greater awareness on the part of the therapist of his own feelings and fear of loneliness. Without a deep understanding of the therapeutic relationship it could so easily degenerate into a pseudo-social relationship which, in her experience, could lead to therapeutic failure. The therapist must stand as a 'reliable bridge to reality' (Fromm-Reichmann, 1952).

I was also greatly interested in *Rosen*'s 'direct analysis' (1953). In this he provided the patient with a direct and straightforward interpretation of his behaviour; the interpretation being psychoanalytically phrased and addressed to the patient's regressed level. It was argued that the patient's sudden confrontation with his libidinal and psychosexual strivings would, in effect, shock him out of the psychosis. It is interesting that many workers have attributed the immediate success of Rosen's work (the long-term results were not encouraging) to his involvement with the patient – 'to the convincing, consistent, intentness of purpose, attitude, speech and tone of voice' with which he related himself to his patients (Fromm-Reichmann, 1952, p. 100).

The aspects of *Arieti*'s work which most affected this present work were, first, those concerning his theories of schizophrenia and, secondly, those which concerned the schizophrenic's thought forms. He argued that schizophrenia has its origins in a severe state of anxiety experienced first in early childhood and reactivated in later life (Arieti, 1955). As the defences against this anxiety crumble, some changes must take place – either in reality or in the person. A change in reality is not possible so, as the illness develops, it brings with it a change in the person causing his perception of reality to become more tolerable. Schizophrenia,

[1] Fromm-Reichmann (1939, p. 413f.; 1959, p. 1–15); *v.q.* Fromm-Reichmann (1953); von Witzleben (1958, p. 38).

then, for Arieti is a purposive regression involving a reversion to behaviour characteristic of an earlier phase in the patient's life history (ontogenetic) and an earlier phase of the racial developmental history (phylogenetic). In this regressive state, the schizophrenic abandons the normal forms of thinking and the normal Aristotelian logic and adopts a form of paleo-logic.[1] Thus, instead of following identical subjects the thinking follows identical predicates (von Damarus' principle), e.g. the horse is black; Mrs Smith's hat is black; therefore Mrs Smith's hat is a horse. One common feature may be sufficient for a person or object to be identified with another person or object.[2] The capacity for connotation and conceptualization may be lacking, and the normal laws of causality, contiguity, and similarity and the experience of time may undergo marked changes.

The schizophrenic loses his ability to participate in the world. There is a 'retreat from society'. In this he relinquishes the processes of socialization and symbolization which are the highest forms of evolutionary development (Arieti, 1955, p. 279). He may go into a world rich in symbols (paleo-symbolism), but these symbols lack social content and may be meaningful only for the person in whom they are found. Arieti also argued that the impoverished or incongruent emotion was related to the schizophrenic's regression to a paleo-level (ibid., p. 308).

This summary of Arieti's theories regarding the possible laws which underlie the schizophrenic behaviour and thinking should not be allowed to divert our attention from the schizophrenic's gross lack of integration and constancy and the wide disturbance of thought which can be most difficult to interpret and understand.

In psychotherapy Arieti suggests that the therapist should always attempt to participate in the patient's life and experience in an attitude of 'devoted acceptance' (ibid., p. 436). Therapy should aim at assisting the patient to relinquish his individualistic preoccupations so that he may turn again to the world as we know it. The therapist should be extremely sensitive to the whole

[1] Arieti (1955, p. 186f.); *v.q.* Arieti (1948, p. 326f.; 1950, p. 46f.).

[2] cf. Jung (1936 ed., p. 20); Storch (1924, p. 14f.); Schilder (1942, p. 266).

situation, which includes himself, for it is well known that the schizophrenic can discern the feelings of the therapist long before the therapist does so himself (cf. Brody, 1952, p. 44; Hill, 1955, p. 33).

Sechehaye brings further attention to the symbolism of the schizophrenic but, being more aware of the existentialist approach, she places greater emphasis on understanding the illness in terms of the patient's experienced world (*Erlebniswelt*). For Sechehaye, the schizophrenic has 'suffered an acute, agonizing sense of his very being about to founder in nothingness' (1956, p. 25). This arises out of the frustration of a basic need in his early infantile development.

The schizophrenic condition into which the person may 'deliberately' turn has a twofold function: it can provide a way whereby the patient can make further despairing attempts to re-live the infantile trauma and thus overcome it; it can provide the way of escape into fantasy and subjectivism where alleviation and satisfaction of the frustrated need may be found in symbolism. The schizophrenic turns from the real world as a defence against further emotional upheaval and as a regressive attempt to gain satisfaction in the symbolism of an earlier phase of development.

Sechehaye presents a comprehensive picture of the thought forms and mechanisms of the schizophrenic and she sees as fundamental those which she terms 'pre-symbolic magic participation' (ibid., pp. 140–148). Under this term she includes little that was not already known about schizophrenic thinking – the confusion of 'the symbol with the signified, the word with the thing, the thought with the object' (ibid., p. 146). But in her development of this term she goes beyond what was previously known and attempts to show that the psychotherapy of schizophrenia will depend on a more adequate grasp of the meaning of these symbolic forms of thinking. Without this, much of schizophrenic behaviour will remain meaningless. The importance of Sechehaye's viewpoint may be illustrated by her own example:

> '. . . When a patient cries, "I am the principal key", expressing his wish for freedom, the key literally represents the

freedom and independence he wants and not their emblem. It is enough for him to hold an old key in his hands or to draw the picture of a key to believe himself free. . . .'[1]

Sechehaye sees that the schizophrenic illness and behaviour are invariably associated with feelings of great sensitivity. The patient breaks with reality only with intense emotion, and likewise any revoking of the schizophrenic condition will have strong emotional investments. Having broken with reality he avoids any further contact for fear of the other person (e.g. the therapist) or for fear of evoking his own uncontrolled and sensitive emotions. Thus he may adopt defences of indifference, negativism, agitation, a fixity of gaze, and so on.

Although Sechehaye acknowledges the danger of any over-emphasis of purposefulness in such a complex disorder, she nevertheless sees a general purposefulness both in the regression into psychosis and in the behaviour *in* the psychosis.

For psychotherapy she stresses the intimacy of the therapist-patient relationship, but she has gone beyond most other attempts to bring this into practice. She treated one female schizophrenic patient for a period of approximately ten years, seeing her for the best part of every day. Sechehaye's awareness of the existentialists enabled her to articulate the significance of the 'meeting' and to refer to it as an 'authentic and exalting communication' (ibid., p. 25). She presented herself to the patient in a maternal role, and through the patient's acceptance of this good mother-image, she (the patient) was drawn out from her own world to a renewed contact with the external world.

Sechehaye sees that it is essential for the therapist to be accepted by the patient and to understand the possible reasons for the patient's regression into the schizophrenic world and the reasons for refusing to relinquish it. There should always be an awareness of the patient's 'fragility', and the need for time for the patient to re-experience the possibilities of living in the world once again.

Fundamental to Sechehaye's psychotherapy is her method of

[1] Sechehaye (1956, p. 147). For the schizophrenic the symbol can become reality (ibid., p. 125).

symbolic realization (or pre-symbolic magic). Here the therapist attempts to discover in the patient the frustrated basic need of early childhood and tries to satisfy this need on a concrete level in terms of pre-symbolic magic. The therapist does not attempt to impose external reality upon the patient, but attempts to enter the patient's experience and, in his language, to introduce him to a more 'gentle and tolerable reality' (ibid., p. 7f). Later, when the patient himself is ready for it, an attempt can be made to help him to regain his contact with the external world.

As well as a knowledge of psycho-analysis and genetic psychology, the therapist must possess an 'intuition' to feel the patient's 'deep hidden desires and basic hungers' (ibid., p. 9f, cf. p. 113). Sechehaye sees it as a difficulty that the patient may have many frustrated needs, but she (somewhat inadequately) overcomes this by saying it is the vital and basic need which must be satisfied.

The method of symbolic realization may be illustrated by the following example:

> Her patient Renée would eat only apples. On one occasion she came to Sechehaye and pointing to Sechehaye's bosom said, 'Renée . . . wants real apples, mama's apples.' By a flash of intuition, Sechehaye discerned the symbolism, and at once gave Renée a piece of apple, saying, 'It's time to drink the good milk from mama's apples; mama is going to give it herself to little Renée.' In receiving the apple Renée re-lived her early frustration of oral hunger, and received satisfaction on a concrete level, but in symbolism (ibid., p. 18f).

It may be questioned whether or not the essential feature of this therapy was, as Sechehaye suggested, in the symbolic realization – whether or not it was in what Sechehaye gave and the symbolism which may have been behind it. The essential feature may have been that Renée saw in Sechehaye one who was intimately concerned for her, one *giving* something to her, the unwanted one.

This discussion of Sechehaye's work and existential orientation leads us now to a more comprehensive discussion of the existentialist contribution to psychotherapy and schizophrenia.

CHAPTER V

Existentialism and Psychotherapy

I

In Germany, Switzerland, France, Austria, and Holland it is becoming easy to point to schools of psychology and psychiatry where there is an active awareness of the significance of existentialism. If it were a matter of one or two schools, then perhaps we need not be very concerned. If it were a matter of a few dubious practitioners here and there, then we could dismiss the matter hurriedly and get on with the job. Such, however, is not the case. Manfred Bleuler, for example, is one who has clearly commended existentialism as a new contribution to psychology and psychiatry. Existential analysis has opened new possibilities. Speaking of schizophrenia, he goes on to say: 'Existential analysis has more than just an academic or theoretical value in relation to schizophrenia; it also helps – and this I find in my own daily work – in the treatment of schizophrenics. . . . There is hope that a systematic psychotherapy can be built upon the basis of a thorough existential analytical examination of the patient' (Bleuler, M., 1955, p. 45).

Other names, such as Binswanger, Storch, Strauss, Boss, Kuhn, and Zutt have now become familiar names in this field. There is also Frankl of Vienna who is establishing a form of therapy called Logotherapy which represents a variant form of existential analysis.

Psychotherapists in Europe were early in acknowledging the significance of the existentialist movement. They recognized the inadequacies of other forms of psychotherapy. There is little doubt, however, that this realization and the turning towards existentialism were influenced by the era through which Europe was passing. Although the existential crisis has a universal significance, it assumed greater proportions for Europeans as chaos broke into the apparent order and peace of human society and 'all the ordinary stabilities of life' were shaken. Under such conditions questions about human existence and human history took on 'a new urgency' (Niebuhr, 1940, p. 8). The philosophy of crisis, as also the theology of crisis, came as an attempt to formulate some answers to this situation.

In America, existentialism has not been assimilated into psychotherapy with such rapidity. But after an age of unparalleled prosperity, there are suggestions of a growing uneasiness in man about himself. More and more people are becoming interested in the existentialist movement. Names such as Farber, Weigert, Colm, Will, May, and Kors are being linked with this movement, and as their forerunners we could name Harry Stack Sullivan, Frieda Fromm-Reichmann, and others. The official *Handbook of American Psychiatry* counts the existentialist movement as sufficiently important to devote a chapter to it.

In Britain and the Commonwealth, the existentialist movement has been received with much less enthusiasm. Although many years have passed since Binswanger published his important work demonstrating the possible significance of existentialism for psychotherapy (and since then there have been numerous contributions to the field) the majority of psychiatrists and psychologists remain uninformed on these issues. Published works in this field are limited virtually to those by R. D. Laing. The existentialist movement is, however, a growing movement, and has long passed the stage where it could be regarded as an ephemeral whim (Kuhn, 1951, p. ix).

> 'Existentialism, which has been called a philosophy of crisis, of the crisis of modern man caught in the cogwheels of his ever dehumanized civilization, is rapidly turning the designation into a title of honour by its achievements in diagnosing the nature and depth of the débâcle and by discovering, at the

bottom of the Twentieth Century whirlpool of evanescent realities, despairing man's forgotten power to *be*' (Sonnemann, 1954, p. ix).

These events in Europe, America, and Britain are of such significance that some searching questions need to be asked. Where does this existentialist movement come from? What is its history?

Some might reply, 'We don't care where it comes from; all we know is that it must go. It is nothing more than an intrusion into psychiatry by some queer philosophical trend.' I hope that, with greater understanding, it will be seen that this movement is not a philosophical *intrusion* into psychiatry. The history of psychiatry shows how psychiatry has always depended to some extent on philosophy. It stands to benefit from its continued listening to what philosophers are saying.

Existentialism had its origins in the 1840s when Kierkegaard protested against the Hegelian exaltation of objective reason and its identification with reality.[1] The nineteenth-century climate of thought was noted for its emphasis on science as the all-powerful panacea for the ills of mankind, and its emphasis on objective reality, methodology, universal principles, and abstract ideas. There was a general disregard for the uniqueness of the individual and his subjective processes.

Kierkegaard criticized Hegel and his followers for their apparent exclusive emphasis on objectivity and objective reason, and he pointed to the inescapable importance of the subjective processes. He postulated an existential attitude demonstrated in the involvement or participation in the situation with the whole of one's existence. He also developed an existential philosophy, the content of which was to interpret the human situation.

Nietzsche, at a later stage, dramatically and prophetically pointed to certain aspects of human existence, and his work has played an important part in the existentialist movement. In spite of progress and advance, and the promise of the earlier period, Nietzsche underlined the growing meaninglessness and despair of human existence. The themes of meaninglessness, nothingness,

[1] *v.* Tillich (1944, pp. 44, 55; 1957, p. 24); Heinemann (1953, p. 12).

emptiness, despair, have become dominant themes with later existentialists as they have tried to examine human existence and specific human situations.

A further reaction to the objectivism of the nineteenth century came through Sigmund Freud. Freud belonged to two worlds – the world where objectification and categorization were very important, and hence he tried to retain his scientific standing and scientific acceptance; and the world of humanitarian and phenomenological concern. He saw that the Kraepelinian categorizations tended to exclude the uniqueness of the person. Freud turned to the phenomena, to the non-rational biographical issues of the patient's life.[1]

The modern existentialist movement has developed out of many factors. There has been the continued attempt to find the intelligent balance between objective factors and subjective processes. There has been the continued protest against the exaltation of objectification and the treatment of the other person as an object to be labelled or categorized or classified. There have been the Romantic and Bohemian influences from which, perhaps, Sartre and his followers emerged. In addition there have been notable cultural factors. Since World War II, 'existentialism' has become a common word; it is significant that many psychotherapists now adopting this frame of reference emerged from concentration camps. There have been the cultural factors of crisis and chaos which have swept Europe; there is the growing flood of literature, productions in art and music which depict man's homelessness, emptiness, and despair. Other writers highlight the depersonalizing forces of technology and modern society, and the loss of identity and individuality.

The stress of the existentialist movement falls on the careful and sympathetic appreciation of human experience; its reality and meaningfulness or the lack of reality and meaningfulness. The historical character of objective reality is not abandoned, rather are objective reality and objective meaning subordinated to the subjective reality and subjective meaning. With this

[1] For a more comprehensive study of these reactions – Kierkegaard, Nietzsche, and Freud – see Allers (1961).

emphasis, existentialism attempts to widen the scope of any appraisal of reality. Its concern is with human existence, with the fact that a person *is*, that he exists. What he is in essence is a secondary consideration. This stands over and against the Platonic doctrine in which essence (i.e. the Form, the Idea) takes precedence over existence (the manifestation or embodiment of the Idea or Form) (cf. Tillich, 1957, p. 21ff).

In attempting to appreciate the nature and experience of human existence, existentialism directs us to the unique person in his freedom, and to the primacy of the inseparable relation between him and his world. Man is thus always man-in-the-world, as opposed to man-in-isolation. The awareness of this dialectical relationship between man and his world reduces, to some extent, the subject-object dichotomy which provoked the initial protest of the existentialists (cf. Tillich, 1944, p. 56).[1]

For existentialism, to exist means to be in the world; it means to stand out of non-existence (*existere*: 'to stand out'). But in standing-out of non-existence, it also stands-in (Tillich, 1957, p. 20). Existence is always overshadowed by non-existence which manifests itself relatively as man partially surrenders to it, and absolutely as he finally surrenders to it in death. Existence therefore always implies the presence of this crisis: the crisis in which man (in the totality of his being) is struck by the possibility, the anxiety, and the dread that he will cease to be, that he is doomed to non-being. There arises within him the disturbing knowledge of his aloneness and finitude on the one hand, and of his freedom and possibilities on the other. He can choose to resign to the despair which threatens to engulf him, or he can choose to take the despair upon himself and face the future. The existentialist viewpoint is that it is only out of this encounter with despair and nothingness that man can turn towards being.

> 'By revealing the inevitable shipwreck of all earthly happiness suffering opens the way to existential fulfilment and the illumination of Transcendence.'[2]

[1] May (in May *et al.*, 1958, p. 11) suggests it is possible to 'cut below' the subject-object dichotomy. This is not easily facilitated, and in some circumstances is not desirable.

[2] *v.* Grimsley (1955, p. 175) for a discussion on Jaspers.

II

Many are uneasy about existentialism entering into psychiatry and psychotherapy. What significance could this approach have? It has to be stated emphatically that the existentialist approach has its greatest significance for psychiatry and psychotherapy when it is adopted as a *method of research*. It is a method of research springing from dissatisfaction with our present knowledge of various conditions of mankind and from dissatisfaction with various methods of treating these conditions. Technically, existentialism is not a 'school of psychotherapy'. It neither claims to be *the* answer, nor is it the whole of psychotherapy. It stands as a method of research (Laing, 1960a, 1960b).

The existentialist approach affirms the fundamental priority of the person and emphasizes the detailed historicity. It studies in painstaking detail the subjective states, moods, and emotions. It attempts to lay bare the fundamental structures of human existence and seeks to determine in which way a particular person appropriates or distorts these structures. In all, the existentialist approach is concerned with a person's mode of being, his being-with-others, his being-in-the-world.

With the existentialist approach (which I shall call existential psychotherapy), the context and aims of therapy, the means of discovery, and the interpretation may all show important and necessary deviations from other forms of psychotherapy. The patient's existence, even when he is ill, is always regarded as a being-in-the-world, having its own unique structural patterns. In some illness, however, the experience and the meaning of this being-in-the-world may be lost or distorted. The aim of therapy is to lead the patient to the rediscovery of these, and to experience a courage whereby he can face his possibilities and accept the fact of his being. Thus the aim of therapy may not be 'recovery' as such, but the achieving of an experience within the patient whereby he is brought to understand the meaning of his being and of his illness. In this understanding and therapy, therefore, the patient's existential reality assumes precedence over reality as it is generally conceived, and the therapist attempts to see the patient's world through the patient's 'eyes'. The context of therapy will then follow from these overall aims.

The method of discovery in therapy may follow the general principles of psychotherapy, but over and above this it brings a greater stress to the fact that discovery need not only be a means to therapy but may be therapeutic in itself. Thus discovery and therapy become experiential for the here-and-now, and this calls for the therapist's involvement and participation (as against a spectator-attitude), and a need for understanding to precede any employment of techniques. At times this may mean 'being-with' the patient as he recalls and lives earlier experiences; at other times it may demand a mutuality and participation in unspecified creative situations involving 'reciprocal value-judgements' (Cantril, 1950, p. 114; cf. Roberts, 1950, p. 150; May *et al.*, 1958, pp. 10, 76f). The method of discovery is inseparably related to the overall forward movement of the patient towards his possibilities.

Interpretations in existential therapy will be based, in general, on the existentialist motifs and framework. These interpretations will be directed towards the patterns of existence and the meaning-structures of the person's life and illness. There is a danger that interpretations can become little more than an imposition of the therapist's own ordered patterns on to the unordered world of the patient. This might help to make the therapist more comfortable while the patient, in many cases, will seem better for the interpretation, whether it is valid or not. But this kind of imposition is not far removed from propaganda. Unwittingly, psychotherapy can become imposed propaganda. This may seem very erudite but in fact it is much more difficult and more exasperating for the therapist to *be with* the patient and participate in a genuine dialogue.

The general psycho-analytical viewpoint in making interpretations is to analyse and bring to awareness the conscious and repressed components of the neurotic defences. This viewpoint is a deterministic one which ultimately absolves the person from responsibility and it says nothing about the forward-moving creativeness and transcendence. To analyse the neurotic defences does little for the future potentiality. It is at this point that the existentialist approach has made a notable contribution.

The relationship in therapy plays an important part here also, and although the therapist is bound to retain the therapeutic situation, he cannot be entirely without a standpoint in it. The therapist will clarify his assumptions and values so that the patient can work out his attitude for or against them. The more the therapist tries to hide these behind impartiality and objectivity, the more the patient is exposed to what Buber calls 'sublimated violence' (Buber, 1957a).

The patient is always regarded as a being in-his-totality, even where there is obvious fragmentation. He is an indivisible being-in-the-world, and thus the dichotomy, introduced in interpretations of conscious and unconscious processes, becomes less significant, although it does point to a necessary widening of being (of which the term 'unconscious' is the symbol) (cf. Sonnemann, 1954, p. 191f.).

The themes of existential therapy as stated above may appear generally acceptable. But the fact remains that the widespread attitudes towards the method are those of suspicion or indifference. It may be that these attitudes arise from the present-day preoccupation with techniques and management, or from the unwillingess on the part of psychotherapists to have psychotherapy inundated with the tenets of philosophy. This, however, does not explain why some psychotherapists appear to regard existentialism in a light similar to that in which some men regard a religious experience. Their attitude often seems to be associated with an emotional aversion, not least from the fact that existentialism does require a form of 'conversion' in that, before it becomes meaningful, the therapist himself must experience an encounter with the existential crisis.

The influence of existentialism on psychotherapy may be traced systematically in the following ways:

(a) *The Adoption of an Existentialist Attitude*[1]

This is the first and most obvious development of existentialism

[1] cf. Tillich (1957, p. 26; 1952, p. 117f.); Heinemann (1953, p. 165).

in psychotherapy. As already hinted, it concerns the attitude of the therapist to himself, to the patient, and to the world. With the whole of his being and out of an intimate concern, the therapist reaches out to the patient, becomes involved with him, and attempts to 'participate' in his experience. The existential attitude thus goes beyond the precise *knowledge* of the person which can be gained in detachment, to a *knowing* of the person in his relatedness to the world.

(b) *The Adoption of Concepts and Motifs*

Up to the present time existentialism has not led to any formulation of a systematic method of psychotherapy, but some psychotherapists have found certain of its concepts and motifs to be helpful. Examples of these are as follows:

(i) *The existential neurosis* This is regarded as an illness arising out of the loss of meaning to life. The person, to some extent, surrenders to a form of existence in which ultimate questions are either avoided or disregarded, and despair is imminent or present. The problem for therapy is to re-open the way of an authentic existence wherein despair may be faced positively and meaning found.

(ii) *The encounter* Encounter is the decisive meeting between two persons, and in this meeting the whole of one's outlook may undergo profound changes. Although the concepts of transference and counter-transference are involved in this encounter, the concept itself is more comprehensive.

(iii) *Kairos* This is a critical moment in a person's life, and denotes a decisive change for better or worse. It may arise from within, or it may be precipitated by the judicious intervention of the therapist.

(iv) *Dasein* Man's being-in-the-world has the distinctive character of his 'being there', which is marked not only by its temporality and spatiality, but also by its personal uniqueness. In the consideration of Dasein, the structures of being (in general), as well as those of the personal being of any individual, assume an added significance for psychotherapy.

(v) *Nothingness* Despite the actuality of prosperity, or equanimity, man's being is always pervaded with the possibility that it will founder on nothingness. Being goes hand-in-hand with the threat of non-being. The increasing pressures of depersonalization and annihilation have contributed to the meaningfulness of this concept of nothingness, and psychotherapy, in adopting it, has gained added insight into man's condition.

(vi) *Transcendence* Existentialism, in its attempt to discover the structures of man's existence, has discerned that a fundamental feature of his being is his capacity to transcend his situation. His freedom leads to a vast range of possibilities. Although this viewpoint is not foreign to psychotherapy, the existentialist influence has helped to bring a clearer articulation of man's forward-moving potentiality as distinct from his present actuality.

> 'We can understand another human being only as we see what he is moving toward, what he is becoming' (May *et al.*, 1958, p. 71).

(c) *Phenomenology*

Phenomenology is a third way by which existentialism has influenced psychotherapy, and perhaps represents the early stages in the development of existentialism as a therapeutic method. Psychiatric phenomenology (as distinct from philosophical) arose when some psychotherapists considered that the techniques available were inadequate for any full appreciation of the individual's experience. They pointed to the fact that the patient lives in a different world and that an attempt should be made to grasp the reality of his subjective experience.

Following Husserl's sense of the term, phenomenology concerned itself with an unbiased observation of phenomena; in this it was to some extent analogous to the Freudian basic rule in psycho-analysis. Although phenomenologists have followed differing paths, the underlying theme of the method is one which seeks to study the individual experience under consideration with care and sensitiveness, reckoning no nuance or shade of delineation and description too subtle to be unworthy of note.

Some of the forms of the phenomenological method will be noted:[1]

[1] For this categorization, see Ellenberger, in May *et al.* (1958, Ch. 3).

(i) *Descriptive method* Here the patient gives a full account of his experience to the therapist who, while not expressing any value-judgements, attempts to empathize, or become involved with the patient in his experience. The method was used first by Karl Jaspers, but had its limitations in that the patient could neither remember the full depth of his experience, nor express it adequately in words. This led to the method developed by Minkowski.

(ii) *Genetic-structural method* Minkowski attempted to find the central unifying experience or event in the person's life-history, and to orientate the person around this. Thus there developed the idea of meaning-structures in the person's life. We have already seen that the loss of these structures lies at the heart of the existential neurosis. The aim of this genetic-structural method was to disclose the meaning-structures. It can be seen here that phenomenology *per se* has been broadened to embrace interpretation.

(iii) *Categorical method* The phenomenologist, in attempting to reconstruct the person's life or his manner of experiencing inner and outer reality, may relate this experience to the categories of time, space, substance, and causality. In the study of schizophrenia these categories have become particularly significant, not only for the phenomenologists but for the wider field of existential therapy generally, e.g. Binswanger shows considerable interest in the manner in which the patient experiences these categories.

(d) *Existential Analysis*

The existentialist influence in psychotherapy has been most pronounced in that form of psychotherapy which has become known as 'existential analysis', of which one of the main exponents is Ludwig Binswanger. Existential analysis, like phenomenology, attempts to appreciate and reconstruct the patient's inner world of experience; but it does this in a more comprehensive and distinctive manner, for in addition to representing a wide blend of phenomenology, existentialism, and psycho-analysis, it adopts as its central framework the overall ontology of Martin Heidegger. It is thus distinguished from all other forms of existential psychotherapy.

Other writers have given considerable attention to Binswanger and his method and have accentuated the difference between his therapy and all other therapies. Further reference will be made to this issue in the next chapter (under the discussion of Heidegger). Meantime, it may be said that there are clear indications that this distinction is false and that Binswanger's method is, in fact, a development of the eclectic existential therapy discussed under (b) above. Although such a criticism may appear radical, in actuality it does not discredit the value of Binswanger's appropriation of existentialism into psychotherapy. His work is an impressive contribution and reflects a painstaking attempt to move forward in the elucidation of the issues in this difficult field of study. It is not surprising, though regrettable, that at times his work becomes obscure and involved in tedious detail.

POSTSCRIPT

A lucid and systematic account of existentialism as applied to psychotherapy is to be found in Werner Wolff's work. Although existentialism has found its widest application in the study of schizophrenia, Wolff (an American psychologist), in giving an overall survey of what existential-psychology means, seeks to apply it directly to neuroses. His work is methodical and stimulating, but it has not been widely read and his book has now gone out of print.

In the work of R. D. Laing we find a further and more recent attempt to apply existential insights to the issues of schizoid and schizophrenic conditions. His intention is to bring about a thorough integration of existentialism and psychotherapy, and he does this with great care for detail and accuracy.

CHAPTER VI

An Expanded Approach

It has not been easy to translate the modes and themes of existentialism into an articulate psychological method. Most workers in this field have tended to follow, in general terms, the approach of Heidegger. To one trying to understand their attempts, it seemed that in place of understanding and hope there was much obscurity and despair. Despair, of which Heideggerians speak so much, seemed to pervade both the psychotherapeutic method and the communications about that method.

Psychotherapy is not only a very complex process, it is also a very human process – an inter-human process. Is there any good reason why it should not yield itself to simple terms and simple descriptions? In this expanded approach, an attempt is made to move beyond the difficulties and obscurities of a Heideggerian atmosphere, to embrace a simpler and more systematic consideration of the inter-human themes. Here, Buber and Tillich are of immense significance. Although the influence of Heidegger was inevitable, the present work was stimulated and inspired by Buber and Tillich. It will be helpful to give a brief summary of the work of these three men – beginning with Heidegger – and focus attention on those trends of their thought that contributed to the background, orientation, and method of the present study on schizophrenia.

MARTIN HEIDEGGER

Heidegger's phenomenological analysis of Being (Dasein) is original, ingenious, and penetrating, but it is often obscure, and the claims which he makes for its all-sufficiency are unacceptable. Nevertheless, his intentions and some of his concepts and motifs can bring a beneficial and necessary emphasis into psychotherapy.

He asserts that man is thrown into the world without choice or decision and his being is always a being-in-the-world in a primary and inseparable relationship. Man-and-his-world is an entity, and this unity renders vain any attempt to study man-in-isolation or to reduce him to an object of observation.

The reality of man's subjective experience of being-in-the-world is characterized by the fact that his being is indubitably his: it is possessed by a quality of mineness (*Jemeinigkeit*), but this mineness is not always acknowledged, and is, to some extent, lost or hidden in all men. Man's existence is always faced with the pressures of depersonalization which would submerge his being into the anonymous collective (*das Man*) where his mineness is also jeopardized. His being is always threatened by these pressures, always falling under their influence, so his being is marked by its fallenness, making him anxious and fearful.

Two modes of being-in-the-world are open to him: the authentic and the inauthentic.

His being is always to some extent inauthentic in that he is always under the sway of *das Man*, and that his being is characterized by chatter, curiosity, and the ambiguity that confuses authenticity with inauthenticity. He tends to avoid the meaning of being, to surrender to despair, and to deny the reality of his own death either by pushing it off in time or by restricting the possibilities of death to other people.

There is, however, the possibility of authentic being. Heidegger states:

> 'Inauthenticity denotes a way of being in which man may go astray, and for the most part always has gone astray, but in which he need not necessarily and always go astray' (Heidegger, 1953, p. 259).

Authenticity involves man in accepting his possibilities and in making a decision. Fundamentally, the possibility which is uniquely mine is my own death.

'If I am cast into the world, it is in order to die there' (Grimsley, 1955, p. 63).

It is in his standing apart from the crowd in his confrontation with his death as his own most personal possibility that man realizes his authentic being. Lost in inauthenticity, man's conscience calls him. As it calls, he finds he is guilty – guilty of his inauthenticity, and in order to overcome his despair he must do with it as he must do with his death – recognize it and shoulder it with resolve and openness.

Clearly time and the time process (*Zeitlichkeit*) are important for Heidegger. Authenticity is achieved when man turns towards the future with resolve (and particularly as far as his death is concerned). It is achieved when he accepts his guilt and thus resolves to be his past; it is achieved when he turns away from his fallenness and accepts his past into his present, and from this projects himself into the future. Personal Being (Dasein) is always ahead of itself.

Man alone is given this capacity. He alone can ask the question of his existence; he alone can apprehend his own death and face it; he alone can transcend his own concrete being and every other concrete being.

Heidegger and Psychotherapy

Heidegger's analysis is not directly concerned with psychotherapy, but in its attempt to disclose the fundamental patterns of man's existence, it provides certain implications. It should be pointed out however that while Heidegger and psychotherapy are both concerned with the experiential level of man's being (this is called the *ontic* level), their concern leads in different directions. For Heidegger the experiential level is significant in that it reveals the fundamental structures of Being (this is called the *ontological* level), but for psychotherapy, the experiential level is important for its own sake: e.g. Anxiety (Angst) is an ontic fact of man's existence – Heidegger sees it can give valuable insight into the fundamental structures of Being. But the psychotherapist is concerned with this particular Angst, why it is coloured in this particular way, how it shows what is ailing the man in his living in the world, and so on.

It is difficult to delineate clearly the precise nature of the influence and relevance of Heidegger for psychotherapy. Many psychotherapists have found his concepts and motifs of great value in their work, and others have attempted to go beyond this to base their psychotherapy on an Heideggerian framework. Although in some cases these appropriations of Heidegger have been legitimate, it would seem that in other cases the implications have not been fully apprehended. But all are aware, for example, of Heidegger's insistence on the all-sufficiency of his system which he claims gives an exhaustive plan of the ontological framework of man's being.[1] (See above for the meaning of 'ontic' and 'ontological'. Ontology refers to the fundamental structures of Being and all their possibilities. The term 'ontic' refers to levels of experience which may be a reflection of the deeper structures and patterns of Being.) Psychotherapists therefore should exercise care lest in their acceptance of the acuteness and profundity of Heidegger's insights they also implicitly accept the exclusiveness of his system as a whole. To make this error not only indicates a lack of appreciation of their own position, but also to some extent invalidates it.

In this regard it is pertinent to allude to Binswanger and his acceptance of the Heideggerian ontology whereby his form of existential analysis is distinguished from all other 'schools'. But Binswanger, while accepting Heidegger's ontology, finds it necessary to add to it.[2] (He includes contributions from Martin Buber (I-Thou, I-It relationships) and then adds some further concepts and thoughts of his own; he gives centrality to love (allowed-to-be) and includes concepts of *Umwelt* (drives, needs, instincts), *Mitwelt* (inter-relationships with other persons), and *Eigenwelt* (the basis on which we relate to the world); he includes

[1] Note, for example, Heidegger's claim of all-sufficiency (1953, p. 180): 'Faith and Weltanschauung in so far as they make statements of one kind or another . . . will have to have recourse to the existential structure set forth (by me) if they wish their statements to make any claim to *conceptual* intelligibility.'

[2] *v.* Ellenberger, in May *et al.* (1958, p. 121f.); *v.q.* Binswanger's analysis of 'The Case of Ellen West', in May *et al.* (1958, p. 269ff); Sonnemann (1954, p. 148f.).

modalities (dual: the extension of the I-Thou relationship; plural: formal relationships; singular: man with himself; and the anonymous: in the collective).)

These additions are not ontic but are additional ontological structures and point to the insufficiency of Heidegger's ontology. Binswanger (*v.* May *et al.*, 1958) acknowledges his divergence from Heidegger, but justifies this by saying that he attempts to work out the Heideggerian ontology within the special ontic-field of psychotherapy (op. cit., pp. 192, 269). There is a parallel instance in theology where Bultmann justifies his use of Heidegger in a similar way, but it seems that Bultmann also is unaware that he is re-writing Heidegger's analytic.[1]

As in Bultmann, so in Binswanger, this appropriation of Heidegger is not legitimate. It is not possible to add Buber and Binswanger to Heidegger in this manner and still retain the basic ontological analysis of Heidegger. Binswanger here is in direct conflict with Heidegger and thus, as mentioned earlier, it is wrong to claim that his Daseinsanalyse represents a new and different form of existential therapy because it, too, falls into the category of therapy which seeks eclectically to apply existentialist concepts and motifs.

We have noted already that Heidegger's analytic is concerned with man's Being in general, and thus it is not surprising that he has nothing to say about schizophrenia as such. But here again his work can be helpful in the interpretation of the illness and therefore in its psychotherapy. In common with most psychotherapists, Heidegger regards man's existence as patterned and purposive. Man, in driving forwards towards his future and in relating to his present and past, is a man of time, inseparably related to the world. These conditions, being ontological and therefore universal, will still obtain for the schizophrenic, but it seems that his actual ontic being must be seen as a negative, inauthentic mode of these ontological structures of relatedness. His illness blocks and distorts his experience as a man-in-the-world. We may say that his total

[1] Reference may be made to Bultmann's article 'Die Geschichtlichkeit des Daseins und der Glaube' (1930), and also to Cairns (1960), who refuted Heidegger's claims, and Bultmann's appropriation of Heidegger.

being founders under the impact of his being thrown into the world (thrownness); under the pressures pulling him into *das Man* (fallenness); under his incapacity to accept the possibilities of decision (existence). The quest for meaning is lost; chatter, curiosity, and ambiguity may predominate; and the 'mineness' of his death is jeopardized. The call of conscience is no longer made or heard and his capacity to respond to it has gone.

To regard schizophrenia as an inauthentic mode of being not only raises the problem as to when inauthenticity leaves sanity to enter insanity, it also raises the further problem of the schizophrenic's incapacity to turn from inauthenticity to authenticity. Heidegger claims that authenticity is found only through resolve – a unique capacity of man experienced as he stands apart from all other men and faces his own death. This may well imply that in so far as the schizophrenic has lost this capacity, he is no longer a man; and yet clearly he is always a man-in-the-world. Psychotherapists, however, will attest to the fact that the schizophrenic cannot 'decide' on his own account to revoke his psychosis. Although he may always retain the possibility of turning to authentic being, it must be seriously questioned whether, on Heidegger's individualistic framework, these possibilities could be actualized. To suggest that man's capacity for authentic being rests in himself, in his conscience and resoluteness, is inadmissible for the sane man; how much more is this inadmissibility accentuated for the *insane* man! Thus, the claim of universal validity of the Heideggerian system again meets with criticism.[1]

Man – sane and insane – needs more than the *call* to face his possibilities. He must have the possibilities placed within his grasp (Macquarrie, 1955). This might lead some to a religious viewpoint, and indeed there are aspects of Heidegger's thought which might have led him to an appreciation of a religious belief:

> 'His deep understanding of the fallenness of man, and of man's impotence so that responsibility already implies guilt, are factors in his thought which seem to demand for their completion a doctrine of God' (Macquarrie, 1955, p. 149).

[1] cf. the introduction (by Kluback and Wilde) to Heidegger's *The Question of Being* (1959, pp. 12, 15).

But his individualistic self-sufficient philosophy does not lead to this point. As far as Heidegger is concerned 'God is not yet'.[1] In this, too, he further depreciates the significance of man's relatedness to his fellowman.

I contend that the appreciation of the divine economy, including man's relatedness to man, is fundamental to an understanding of human existence and also, it follows, to psychotherapy. But here Heidegger falls short, and we are led to Martin Buber.

MARTIN BUBER

Buber, while stressing the immense value of the individual, nevertheless sees every man as a son of God. The fundamental fact of human existence becomes man's relation to man, and what takes place between man and man. Self-hood, according to Buber, cannot be achieved by man as he stands apart from other men (nor, for that matter, as he becomes submerged in the collective), but self-hood can be achieved only in the meeting, in the dialogue, in the turning towards the other.

'Through the *Thou* a man becomes *I*.'[2]

Buber suggests that man's experience holds two fundamental relations, and these are distinctively designated as the 'I-Thou' and 'I-It' relations. The I-Thou relation obtains between one person and another or, under certain circumstances, between a person and specified objects of the natural world. The I-It relation, on the other hand, is the manipulative, mechanical, observing relation which obtains between man and objects, as for example in the natural sciences.

The I-It relationship is a necessary relationship in man's daily experience, but sometimes it extends to all his relationships. Every person, every thing, even his own life can become an *It*. In so far as this tendency prevails, a man's life is artificial and irresponsible. He uses the other, talks about the other, but does not enter into a

[1] Macquarrie (1955, p. 136); *v.q.* Kuhn (1951, p. 153); Heinemann (1953, p. 107).
[2] *v.* Buber (1937, p. 28); *v.q.* Friedman (1955, p. 60).

personal relation, and therefore he loses his manhood and becomes an object himself.

> 'Without *It* man cannot live, but he who lives with *It* alone is not a man' (Buber, 1937, p. 34).

For Buber, certain I-It relationships can become so intensely personal that they become I-Thou relationships. The ocean can assume a personal significance, as can a man's dog, or his tools. This leads to some confusion, however, for Buber states that an I-Thou relationship must have mutuality and responsibility, but it is clear that the ocean, for example, can assume these only in a mystical or metaphorical sense. This has provoked suspicions about the immanental aspects of Buber's doctrine of the meeting with God, and raises the question as to whether this is a meeting as of a person or as of the ocean.

Along with the I-It relation but over against it there is the I-Thou relation in which there is a mutual turning of one towards the other in the fullness of being, and finding in the other the fulfilment of the self. In the dialogue arising between the *I* and *Thou* all other possibilities are placed aside in the interests of this exclusive relation, and amidst all other possible directions the dialogue takes its direction – one turned to the other. It involves claim and counter-claim, demand and response, discipline and responsibility. The one enters into the event from the standpoint of the other, but each retains his identity and autonomy. In the turning towards each other for genuine dialogue, each reaches out beyond the special sphere of each to what Buber calls the 'between'.

Genuine dialogue is frequently absent and instead there can be either a technical dialogue (which should obtain only for objects, I-It relations) or a monologue disguised as dialogue. In the latter, genuine dialogue is avoided by a protective cover of seeming and appearance. Genuine dialogue, in contrast, is open and aware of the other, seeking the other for his own intrinsic value and worth. It says in effect: 'I seek not thy goods but thee alone' (*v*. Pfuetze, 1954, p. 153).

Although silence and gesture can play their part in the dialogue, speech is of great importance. It is the means by which one contacts the other and communicates with him. In addition, speech or the spoken-word can become intrinsically meaningful, the bridge from man in his isolation to the other, and also the bridge from God to man. The Jew did not see God so much, but he heard his word: 'Hear, O Israel!' In this word God calls to man, and man in answering finds his real self. The genuine dialogue, therefore, reaches beyond the man-to-man dimensions to God, in whom it finds its source, its centre, and its direction (Buber, 1947, p. 15; 1953, p. 45).

According to Buber, it is only in this God-centred existence that the human dialogue and human life find their meaning and significance. Three integral and important issues are to be noted here:

First, it is necessary to apprehend and experience the fact and person of God standing over and between and in every I-Thou relationship.

> '. . . We look out toward the fringe of the eternal *Thou*; in each we are aware of a breath from the eternal *Thou*; in each *Thou* we address the eternal *Thou*' (see Buber, 1937, pp. 6, 75).

The responsibility involved in the dialogue becomes a responsibility to the Thou, and also to the eternal Thou. Man becomes aware that in this hour a demand is placed upon him, and he knows that God requires him to respond.

Secondly, it is necessary to apprehend and experience the fact that genuine dialogue constitutes the bond of true community which only obtains in so far as God is at its centre.

> 'It is not the periphery, the community, that comes first, but the radii, the common quality of relation with the Centre. This alone guarantees the authentic existence of the community' (Buber, op. cit., p. 115).

This community stands in contrast to all groups, all classes, all aggregates which centre themselves on their aims or objectives, or on what they achieve. In the true community, for Buber, man stands, not side by side, but *with* man and, turning towards the other, together they find their being in God.

> '. . . I cannot legitimately share in the Present Being without sharing in the being of the other'.[1]

In this way man becomes aware that there is meaning in the world.

Thirdly, it is necessary to apprehend and experience the fact that man has a special place in God's concern and that he has been chosen by God to participate in the redemption of the world. God, who is transcendent and raised above man, is present with man and turned towards him. God is present, and at all times and in all places exercises a redeeming influence in which he chooses to use man.

> 'He has formed for himself a partner in the dialogue of time, a partner who is capable of holding converse' (Buber, 1946, p. 23).

Man can choose to reject his part in this redemption, but in so far as he participates in it he participates in a process of rediscovery and recreation of his own self, and re-experiences the meaning of being.

As he meets with the other and as he meets with the eternal Other who is also eternal Same, man finds hope for this hour.[2]

Buber and Psychotherapy

It is becoming increasingly recognized that Buber's work has immense significance for the psychotherapist and for psychotherapy generally.[3] There are indications that we are as yet in the early stages of the assimilation of his thought into psychotherapy. As to be expected, his influence stems from his discernment of the meaning of being and from his careful and penetrating analysis of the nature, depth, and possibilities of man's relatedness.

Before psychotherapy discovered Buber, there was an awareness of the importance of relation, but there is no doubt that he has

[1] Buber (1947, pp. 61, 65); *v.q.* Friedman (1958, p. 178f.); Miller (1956, p. 48); cf. Brunner (1937, p. 295).

[2] *v.* Buber (1957b, p. 228; 1947, p. 205); Friedman (1955, p. 282).

[3] cf. Farber (1956a; 1958); von Witzleben (1958, p. 42). Note also the influence of Buber on Binswanger's work (Binswanger 'The Case of Ilse', in May *et al.* (1958, Ch. 8) and 'The Case of Ellen West' (op. cit., Ch. 9). Note also that the Washington School of Psychiatry (of which the official journal is *Psychiatry*) is becoming increasingly aware of the significance of Buber's thought for psychotherapy.

brought added insights, the full meaning of which has yet to be understood, not only in psychotherapy but generally. The emphasis of his thought implies for psychotherapy, however, the need for opening the patient to the meaning of his being and to the discovery of himself as he meets with the others. A psychotherapeutic situation is thus implied where patient and patient, patient and therapist, move together towards an open and direct dialogue in which mutuality, responsibility, and self-realization will be found. It therefore points to a spontaneous turning of one towards the other in community; community which finds its true expression and experience as it becomes aware that its source and centre and being are in God.

If Buber's thought is followed and accepted in psychotherapy – as it is in this study – the medium of the group assumes a fundamental role and significance, for it is in such a setting that the sick man might realize himself and rediscover the meaning of his life in the world (cf. Buber, 1957a(ii), p. 105). It is true that individual psychotherapy (involving only therapist and patient) can also contribute to this realization and rediscovery, but there is a greater tendency here for the relationship to become a technical relationship of I-It; and this is particularly so where attempts are made to employ techniques. The group becomes of special significance because it provides wider possibilities for spontaneity and relation, and it provides the setting in which the basic patterns of existence may be experienced. Although it may begin as an aggregate, with tendencies to emphasize success and cure, the vestiges of the community will manifest themselves as the group relation is regarded as having intrinsic value.

Buber's thought may also be regarded as having relevance for the schizophrenic illness. In the person suffering from this condition we may see varying degrees of negation and distortion of all that is implied in Buber's community, dialogue, and I-Thou. Relation is diminished and reciprocity virtually lost. The *It* tends to predominate in its talking-about, manipulating, observing, and experiencing the other without entering a relation. Meaning and significance of life either are absent or undergo distortions involving the categories of time, space, causality, and substance.

In considering the work of Heidegger, the question was raised as to man's status as a man when he is suffering from schizophrenia. A similar question arises with Buber, but whereas on the one hand he says that a man who withdraws from the dialogue and community falls from being a man to an 'individual', on the other hand he makes it clear that the worth of the person is never lost. The man farthest from God cannot cut himself off from God.

> '. . . When God created man he set the mark of his image upon his brow and embedded it in his nature, and (that) however faint it may become, it can never be wiped out' (Buber, 1946, p. 21).

PAUL TILLICH

Tillich, one of the ablest of present-day Protestant theologians, goes beyond the attempts of other writers to present a systematic analysis of the fundamental patterns of human existence which he illumines with the relevance of the Christian Message. He stresses that although the theologian should certainly be aware of the content and universal validity of the Christian Message, he should also be involved in correlating this Message with the human predicament.

> 'Theology moves back and forth between two poles, the eternal truth of its foundation and the temporal situation in which the eternal truth must be received' (Tillich, 1951, p. 3).

There must always be a correlating process between the 'questions implied in the situation' and the 'answers implied in the message' (ibid., p. 9). Thus, we might say that before the theologian can make any realistic attempt to bring the Christian Message to the schizophrenic, he must be aware of the schizophrenic's situation. For this task, Tillich's systematic analysis of human existence can be immensely helpful, and it is to a summary of some aspects of this analysis that we must now turn. Although the general orientation here will be towards 'normal existence', this should provide a basis for a later discussion of the schizophrenic existence.

The Self-World Structure

Any analysis of the patterns of man's being must begin with an awareness of the central significance of man's encounter and relations with the world.

> 'The self having a world to which it belongs – this highly dialectical structure – logically and experientially precedes all other structures.'[1]

The self-world structure is thus the fundamental structure of man's existence, and in Tillich's analysis of it, six elements are relevant to the present study:

(a) man's estrangement
(b) man's finitude
(c) anxiety
(d) the polarities of existence
(e) the categories of existence
(f) man's courage to be.

(a) *Estrangement*

To exist is to be in a state of estrangement. This is an ontological element of man's being and cannot be derived. Estrangement therefore does not imply a deliberate fall from a pristine glory, but it represents a tragic and universal condition.

> 'The state of existence is the state of estrangement. Man is estranged from the ground of his being, from other beings, and from himself' (Tillich, 1957, p. 44).

In addition to this universal predicament in which actualized creation and estrangement are one, there is an individual appropriation of estrangement in which, by a personal act, man turns away from that to which he belongs. In its tragic universality and in its individual appropriation, estrangement manifests itself in three ways:

[1] Tillich (1951, p. 164); *v.q.* Tillich (1952, p. 40; 1957, p. 60); cf. Schilder (1942, p. 365).

(i) *In unbelief* By a total act of the person, man turns away from the source and ground of his being, i.e. God, so, losing unity with it, turns towards himself and the world.

(ii) *In making himself the centre of his world* (*hubris*) Man's being is centred in the self, to which all parts of his world converge. But there is the temptation to accentuate this centredness. In doing so man not only attempts to avoid his finitude, his weakness and dependence, but in effect elevates himself to the divine.

(iii) *In attempting to draw the whole of reality into himself* (*concupiscence*) Man, set between the finite and infinite, strives to recover union with the whole from which he is separated. His poverty drives him towards abundance, irrespective of any person who may be involved. This may be observed in his desire for material power and wealth, for the satisfaction of his bodily appetites, and so on. In his estrangement, man becomes unaware of his condition and tends to avoid the fact that he is a finite and limited being having a source and centre in God.

(b) *Finitude*

Man's existence is always overshadowed by non-existence. At every point man is limited by non-being, which is expressed by the 'no more' or the 'not yet', having relative and absolute manifestations. The whole structure of man's being, therefore, implies that he is finite. He can, however, move out beyond his finitude into a potential infinity, so that while man looks at himself in his finite being he can also imagine infinite possibilities. It may be thought that this implies that man's attempts to transcend himself and his situation are merely manifestations of his infinite possibilities to avoid his finite actuality (his finitude). Tillich, however, does not subscribe to this view; for he sees that the capacity for self-transcendence is beyond the finite-infinite polarity, in 'being-itself' (*v.* Tillich, 1951, p. 191).

Man's awareness of his finitude is his anxiety which, like estrangement and finitude, is an ontological element of his being.

(c) *Anxiety*

Anxiety, arising out of the awareness of man's finitude, is always present, though often latent. It arises out of the threat of non-being which itself may become manifest in three aspects of man's being:

(i) Non-being may threaten the 'basic self-affirmation of a being in its simple existence'. Relatively, this threat is that of fate, but absolutely it is the threat of death.

(ii) Non-being may threaten the spiritual self-affirmation. This may manifest itself relatively in emptiness, and absolutely in meaninglessness.

(iii) Non-being may threaten the moral self-affirmation. The anxiety from this threat manifests itself relatively in guilt, and absolutely in condemnation (*v.* Tillich, 1952, p. 39ff.).

Tillich distinguishes between existential and pathological anxiety. The former pertains to the nature of being; it cannot be removed and is therefore something with which we must come to terms. If anxiety becomes accentuated to such an extent that it virtually takes possession of man's being, then it becomes pathological. The defences constructed against it are usually fanatical and brutal, and certainly destructive – destructive both towards people who have come to represent the threat implied in the anxiety, and towards the self. This destructiveness may be manifest in feelings of despair, of condemnation and meaninglessness, and in drives towards suicide. The power of non-being becomes so prevailing that man is unable to affirm himself or find any affirmation of his being.

(d) *The Polarities of Existence*

Human existence involves three main polarities, all of which reflect man's estrangement, his finitude and anxiety. These polarities are as follows:

(i) *Individualization and participation* Man's relation to the world is a dialectical one, involving man as an individual on the one hand and his participation in the world on the other. These poles are interdependent:

> 'Without individualization nothing would exist to be related. Without participation the category of relation would have no basis in reality' (Tillich, 1951, p. 177).

Man, however, oscillates anxiously between the two poles, threatened with isolation and loneliness on the one hand, and submergence in the collective on the other. If one pole is lost so, too, is the other.

It is this polarity that is so central to man's discovery of himself as a person able to enter into communion with another person. Through participation with others a man finds himself, but it is only as he finds himself that he is able to participate.

(ii) *Dynamics and form* This polarity is expressed in the fact that in order to be, man must have form, but this form, not sufficient in itself, always reaches out beyond itself. Form is that which 'makes a thing what it is, its contents, its *essentia*, its definite power of being' (Tillich, 1951, pp. 178–182; 1957, pp. 64–65). Dynamics, on the other hand, are the potentiality of being, retaining the present form and stretching out to further being. Being thus conserves and transcends itself.

Dynamics can give way to a 'formless urge for self-transcendence' (*v*. Tillich, 1957, p. 64) and can become an end in themselves. On the other hand, form can lose its dynamics and become rigid and static, and attempts to break through may result in chaos. Thus:

> 'Man is anxious about the threat of a final form in which his vitality will be lost, and he is anxious about the threat of a chaotic formlessness in which both vitality and intentionality will be lost' (*v*. Tillich, 1951, p. 200).

(iii) *Freedom and destiny* The description of the ontological structures reaches its fulfilment in this category which reflects the fact that man 'transcends the essential necessity of being without destroying it' (see Tillich, 1951, p. 182).

Freedom is found in man's ability to decide, to deliberate, and to be responsible; and every part of man participates in this freedom – not just his will. Destiny is that out of which the decision arises and becomes personal, i.e. *my* decision. Destiny is not that which determines my future, but it is 'the basis of my freedom' (ibid., p. 185).

Man may try to preserve his freedom by 'arbitrarily defying his destiny' (ibid., p. 200) and he may try to preserve his destiny by surrendering to his freedom. When destiny is lost there is the tendency to make freedom absolute, but in man's finitude such freedom 'becomes arbitrariness and falls under biological and psychological necessities' (ibid., p. 201). Thus one of man's unique features may be his freedom, but this can only obtain as it is in interdependence with his destiny.

(e) *The Categories of Existence*

Man apprehends and meets his reality according to certain 'categories' of which Tillich names four:

(i) *Time* Time is the central category of man's finitude, for he is always under its threat; and complementary to this it is within time that the affirming answer to its threat is found. In his estrangement man experiences a diminishing tolerance for his temporality; in guilt he remembers his past, in his transitoriness he knows his present, and in apprehension he looks towards his future. He tries to prolong his time, to perpetuate his memory, to ensure his immortality, and in his resistance and despair time takes on a demonic and destructive power.

(ii) *Space* To be means to have space; the space of one's body, or the space involved in having a home, or the social space of profession, society, or group to which one belongs. But space also is always under threat; and this can give rise to an 'ultimate insecurity'. Against this threat man strives to preserve his space, for he is restless under the thought and experience of homelessness and spacelessness.

(iii) *Causality* The cause of an event implies its dependence on something else and its inability to rest on itself.

> 'Everything is driven beyond itself to its cause, and the cause is driven beyond itself to its cause. . . .' (Tillich, 1951, p. 196).

But the awareness of causality gives rise to anxiety, for it is thus that man realizes his dependence and the lack of necessity of his being. 'He might not be! Then why is he?' As an answer to this anxiety man may attempt to make himself an absolute cause.

(iv) *Substance* All finite beings are anxious over the loss of their substance, both relatively in the continuous life process and absolutely in death. This loss is associated with the threat to one's identity and 'the power of maintaining one's self' (ibid., p. 198). In an attempt to escape this anxiety there is the tendency in man to make himself an absolute substance.

In this summary of Tillich's position, the emphasis has so far fallen on man's dependence on his situation and the anxiety and despair he experiences. It is necessary however to consider a further element of man's existence.

(f) *Courage*

Whereas most existentialists would have us pitch our tents in the wilderness, Tillich provides a way to the 'promised land'.

Courage, for Tillich, is 'the self-affirmation of being in spite of the fact of non-being' (see Tillich, 1952, pp. 147, 163). It is not something which can be derived, but it is something which is given – it is ontological. Through this courage man finds a satisfying alternative to the way of despair. Although some forms of courage may be actualized as man identifies himself with a group or collective, or as he asserts himself regardless of any participation in the world, Tillich claims that genuine courage is found only when man abandons these attempts to find courage through these ways of self-salvation, and turns to God and receives it from him. Courage can come only from God, for only God stands over and above the threats of non-being.

> 'Courage needs the power of being, a power transcending the non-being which is experienced in the anxiety of fate and death, which is present in the anxiety of emptiness and meaninglessness, which is effective in the anxiety of guilt and condemnation' (ibid., p. 147).

Since God is the 'creative source of everything that has being' (Tillich, in Kegley and Bretall, 1952, p. 341) (he is Being itself), he is not, therefore, subject to finitude and estrangement. In him is the power to resist non-being in all its forms, as experienced both through the polarities and through the categories of existence.

But although he is almighty and transcendent, he is a God of relation and manifests his relatedness to his creatures and creation. His holiness shows not only a holy power, but also a holy love which forgives and accepts the unacceptable. It is by faith in this God, who in power transcends but in love accepts, that 'self-affirmation in spite of non-being, i.e. courage, is found.

For Tillich, however, the experience of this courage cannot be attained until there is an apprehension of the New Being as revealed in Jesus Christ. In him, God, as the essential man, participates in the human predicament and conquers it. This is the paradox of the Christian Message and it stands opposed to man's accepted interpretation of his existence.

> 'It is an offence against man's unshaken reliance upon himself, his self-saving attempts, and his resignation to despair' (Tillich, 1957, p. 92).

Jesus as the Christ becomes the New Being, for he stands over and against the merely potential character of essential being, and over and against the estranged character of existential being. Subjected to existence, he conquered.

It is given to man to participate by faith in the power of this New Being or New Creation, and in doing so the destructive consequences of estrangement are re-interpreted and overcome. Courage-to-be therefore involves more than an apprehension of an historical event. It involves a personal encounter and a faith to accept that we are accepted, even though unacceptable.

Courage-to-be and man's salvation are, therefore, closely related. Indeed, salvation means to be; it means to find unity where once there was estrangement; it means the recovery of the lost centre of being; it means the reconciling of God and man, man and his world. Salvation means a reclamation of the old and a bringing in of the New, in which the ultimate meaning of existence is revealed and fulfilled.

Thus through participation in the New Being, through the acceptance of the New Being, and through being-transformed by the New Being, man is given his salvation and, simultaneously, his courage to enter into the human predicament.

Tillich and Psychotherapy

In the foregoing discussion, the unmistakable affinity of some of the themes of Tillich with those of psychotherapy will have become evident, and it is hoped that further attestation of this fact will be found in the succeeding chapters.

His penetrating understanding of human experience and the human situation generally has won him the friendship and acclaim of many psychotherapists. This is not surprising when we read from T. M. Greene's summary of Tillich's position:

> 'Paul Tillich is, I am convinced, the most enlightening and therapeutic theologian of our time. He analyses our conscious problems and our unconscious needs more profoundly, and he shows us how these problems can be solved and these needs satisfied more constructively than any recent or contemporary thinker' (Greene, in Kegley and Bretall, 1952, p. 50).

Certain features of his thought require brief comment:

His approach to the human situation is of immense importance. It indicates one who comes to the situation, not with clear-cut formulated answers, but with an attitude and intention of partnership and participation, of waiting and listening from within that situation. Tillich makes it abundantly plain that neither solution, meaning, nor hope comes through any attitude of detachment or separation. Thus there is a constant correlating process of the questions which arise from within the situation and the answers which may be relevant to it.

This points to the centrality of the human experience and of the relatedness of one to the other within it. Experience is the medium both of the questions of the situation and of their answers, and it may have a reality regardless of objective observation and, indeed, in the given-ness of its nature, regardless of subjective appraisal. This speaks straight to psychotherapy and underlines the need for a more sympathetic appreciation of the experienced world of the particular person, and of experiential reality generally.

In his analysis of experience, Tillich discerned that certain patterns or presuppositions were implied, and these are reflected in his distinctive ontology. This ontology has relevance for psychotherapy in that it discloses, in a systematic way, man's existentiality and points to the New Being as the sufficient answer to the threats which this existentiality contains. Tillich depicts – perhaps more clearly than others – the fundamental structures of man's being and shows that in his finitude and estrangement man may negate and distort these structures. In addition, he brings a fresh insight into the categories and concepts of existence; and while emphasizing the overall meaning-structures, shows that here also conditions of a demonic character may obtain. It may be asked, however, what advantage such an analysis has over any given psychological analysis. Here only a general answer may be given, and this seems to be that, whereas a psychological study deals more with the ontic and 'preliminary' level of man's existence, Tillich's analysis is concerned with the ontological and 'ultimate' level.

The peculiar and rightful task of the psychotherapist is revealed in Tillich's distinction between the pathological and the existential. Applying this distinction particularly to anxiety, Tillich hastens to acknowledge that it is the psychotherapist's function to cure the pathological condition. But he also points out that anxiety, in so far as it is existential and ontological, can never be removed, nor should psychotherapy aim to do so. In its existential form it is something with which man must come to terms. But how? This is the problem constantly before the psychotherapist, not only in the numerous 'borderline' cases who come under his care, but in the vast population of 'normal' people who come to him from time to time. Tillich claims that the only satisfactory answer to this existential anxiety is in the person's discovery and acceptance of the divine acceptance, and this in turn implies an acceptance, by faith, of the power of the New Being.

For Tillich, therefore, the psychotherapist fulfils a vehicular function (*v.* Tillich, 1951, pp. 12–13). He must always direct the patient towards the ultimate goal of accepting the divine acceptance. The therapeutic cure thus represents a preliminary stage towards this discovery of the 'ultimate meaning' wherein the person becomes aware of his life-structure centred in God, from whom he receives the grace which he needs. This does not depreciate the achievements of psychotherapy – so long as it directs the patient towards this goal which, for Tillich, is of crucial importance. To receive what is implied in this goal is to receive salvation. To lose what is implied is to lose the centre of Being, and this in turn means loss of self, and loss of communal relatedness.

Psychotherapists may express some resistance to Tillich's overall viewpoint, yet they may find certain aspects of his analysis or certain of his themes apposite and helpful. But care must be taken lest, in applying these themes in a specialized way on an ontic level, their real meaning should be lost. For example, the concept of courage may be adopted by some psychotherapists, but because of hesitancy or because of their indifference to the overall theocentric standpoint of Tillich, they may attempt to 'apply' the concept on a level where the divine grace is disregarded. It must therefore be emphasized, for psychotherapy and generally, that, although the application of these themes on an ontic level is appropriate, this application must be related to Tillich's overall ontology.

POSTSCRIPT

The salient points of this 'expanded approach', which arises particularly from Buber and Tillich, may be recapitulated as follows:

1. Its emphasis is on experience: both experiential reality in general, and the unique experience of a particular individual.

2. It seeks to discern the meaning-structures of existence and to relate the ontic level to the ontological (as found in Tillich's ontology).

3. This ontology is theocentric; it reflects man's existentiality, but points to his despair until he is directed towards the ultimate meaning, the core of which is the divine life and divine grace.

4. This ontology, while pointing to man's actuality, also emphasizes his potentiality, and provides a solution whereby man can transcend the actuality of his predicament. Transcendence and self-fulfilment are marked by their given-ness, and are received

in man's turning towards the other with the intention of dialogue and community.

5. The emphasis of this expanded approach is always on the unrestricted participation in the human situation.

CHAPTER VII

The Schizophrenic Experience

This survey of Heidegger, Buber, and Tillich brings us to a position where it is possible to make a reappraisal of the schizophrenic experience. There are difficulties in this, for schizophrenia in its mysterious and complex nature often eludes the attempts to describe it in the available language and terminology. Four aspects of the condition will be noted here:

1. Schizophrenia and estrangement
2. Schizophrenia: a mode of being
3. The schizophrenic and his decision
4. The loss of the determining Centre.

1. SCHIZOPHRENIA AND ESTRANGEMENT

From Tillich we have seen that every man participates in the universal tragedy of estrangement from God, from man, and from himself; and that every man, to some extent, actualizes this estrangement. With schizophrenia, the estrangement may be catastrophic and irreversible. In some ways it would seem that the condition is not necessarily caused or derived but rather, in its development and manifestations, it reflects a latent or underlying ontological pattern, which under certain circumstances may become actualized, e.g. a renewed encounter with the threat and stress involved in an experience of early childhood may be sufficient to warrant a schizophrenic destiny. There are writers who believe that schizophrenia may be one response to the basic threat of man's being – the threat of non-being – wherein the child or person in the totality of his being realizes that he might cease to be, that there is no necessity for him to be, and that there is no reassuring word coming back to him from the world.[1] He thus experiences the anxiety of an ultimate insecurity. Certain people, re-encountering the stress of this insecurity in later life, become schizophrenic, others do not. Those who do, it seems, find themselves bound in a situation of acute anxiety where the assurance of their being-in-the-world is either absent or confusing in its contradictions.

The person who becomes schizophrenic is thus involved in an accumulating loss of confirmation of his being-in-the-world, and as an answer to this he surrenders to the on-driving forces of estrangement. This surrender to some extent represents his way of escaping the anxieties of the self-world structure of his being, but since this can only be finally escaped in death, the schizophrenic becomes involved in far-reaching changes to this structure, as if to make it more tolerable.

His participation in the world is diminished or grossly distorted. On the one hand he may believe that he is merged with the cosmos and this provides licence for an indiscriminate transcendence and for all forms of behaviour, scattered in their inconstancy and irresponsibility. The *mineness* of his being becomes diffuse and his experience of reality (in terms of the ontological categories of time, space, causality, and substance) reflects his aspirations and self-attributions of absolutism whereby he places himself above the categories of finitude. On the other hand the self, although chaotically divided, may assume the centre of existence, and the schizophrenic attempts to draw all things into it. Here the *mineness* of his being may become so accentuated that he abandons his relations with the world as such and becomes morbidly self-preoccupied. His experience of reality in this case may be reflected in this withdrawal into himself where he appears to be overwhelmed by the world and frightened by his finitude, and where it seems that he is persuaded that self-fulfilment can only be found by and in and through the self.

We may say, therefore, that the schizophrenic, in his mis-

[1] *v.* Weigert (1949, p. 400); cf. Tillich (1957, p. 20f.; 1951, p. 195).

carried attempts to make something of his self-world relation, falls into an extreme state of estrangement wherein both the self and his world suffer tremendous upheavals. (All this goes to confirm the view of Sartre and many others that to tear yourself from the world is to tear yourself from yourself.) It would appear that these upheavals lead the schizophrenic to a position where he no longer can believe in the other person. In effect he negates his own possibilities of love for fear of the consequences; and he negates the possibilities of others loving him, not only because of *his* unworthiness but also because of theirs. Thus, in abandoning all 'turning toward the Other', he abandons all turning toward the Eternal Other, i.e. God, and the self not only loses its legitimate self-centredness, but loses its centre in God. As a concomitant of this, or as a consequence of it, the self-world relation is led to chaos, and eventually to ruin.[1] As he becomes increasingly estranged, the schizophrenic succumbs to the power of the ultimate insecurity and the way of 'courage' is removed from him.

Since all men participate in estrangement, the question arises as to when this estrangement crosses the boundary of schizophrenia. There have been figures in history, e.g. Napoleon and Hitler, and in fiction, e.g. Citizen Kane, who have exhibited extremes of estrangement – in their denial of God, their self-centredness, and their ruthless attempts to draw all things into themselves. Despite their estrangement they could not be called schizophrenic for, in the first place, they did not exhibit the characteristic pattern of symptoms. In addition to this fact we note that in schizophrenia the person's self and his world tend to fall into fragmentation and confusion, his capacity to organize and relate meaningfully is lost, and in the chronic stage of the condition he becomes a 'ruined man'. Not so with these figures in history and fiction, for they have exhibited a capacity to organize both people and things to an extent unknown in schizophrenia. Thus there seems to be more to the schizophrenic's destiny than his actualization of estrangement.

[1] Tillich, in a private communication, referred to the schizophrenic as a 'ruined man'; cf. Buber (1947, p. 80f.).

A note should be added regarding other men who, while not exhibiting the grandiose tendencies of those figures cited above, would nevertheless question the statement that the loss of Centre, i.e. God, involved loss of the self. They either deny or conceal any religious belief but, in so far as they seek some power of being to transcend the power of non-being, they are implicitly seeking a religious root. Many, however, find this power of being as resting in themselves or in some aggregate; but such a solution is inadequate and misplaced and the people concerned should be asked to study their situation once again.

2. SCHIZOPHRENIA: A MODE OF BEING

Through the centuries countless people have lived and died schizophrenics. In spite of the distortions, schizophrenia was their way of being-in-the-world, and indeed it reflected in an inarticulate and peculiar way their answer to the demands and questions of their existence.

Schizophrenia as a mode of being differs markedly from all other modes, for it may show no constant and predictable pattern. We have noted that it may manifest wide variations from one time to another, and may fluctuate from apparent normality to the extremes of suffering and insanity. The schizophrenic's meeting with people and with the world generally seems to indicate that a deep-seated fragmentation has taken place so that he sometimes behaves as if it were possible for only part of his person to be present in the meeting, or different parts at different times. There are a confusing number of possible streams of relatedness open to him, but frequently he is unable to select the one which should be his, and at times it appears that he is involved in different streams simultaneously.

This, nevertheless, is his way of meeting the world; it is his meeting, and although the early stages of the condition may be accompanied by great distress and even verbalized desires to return to normality, as the condition progresses a form of adjustment may take place. Although there are known exceptions, he may actually assert that he has never been happier, which may support the suggestion that possibly schizophrenia is more than a pathological condition – that it is a pattern of existence actualized in answer to some situations.

This pattern of existence has its own purpose and its own possibilities. It represents a way by which the schizophrenic can preserve some sense of security without entering into mutual and responsible relations. The schizophrenic, unable to present a centred and unified self to the world and often torn by fears involved in the self-world relationship, attempts to distance himself from his world, and even from himself. His mode of being becomes an 'existence-at-a-distance'[1] wherein he is able to retain his awareness of people and of his world, but wherein also he attempts to become immune to the stress and anxiety which they entail.

> 'We have that frequent picture of the schizophrenic who succeeds in partially relating to other people through his intellectual functions, but who is emotionally distant and desocialized' (Arieti, 1955, p. 298f.).

Closely related to this existence-at-a-distance is the schizophrenic's sensitivity. Beneath the external appearance of detachment or deterioration it sometimes becomes apparent that he is extremely sensitive. On the one hand he craves a close and intimate relationship, and he may reveal intense positive and negative feelings over any change he perceives. On the other hand he may attempt to flee from any relationship and indulge in repulsive and disturbing forms of behaviour in order to preserve some distance. Falsity, concealment, and diffusion are frequently the prevailing features of his being-in-the-world; he may be present and not present; he may adopt an incomprehensible and seemingly inconsequential language; he may laugh uproariously when it would be more appropriate to weep; he may place distance not only between himself and others, but also between himself and his own body. He may renounce the world as we know it and attempt to find his satisfaction and security through symbolism,

[1] cf. Arieti's description of the 'schizoid personality' (1955, p. 61); cf. Fairbairn (1952, p. 26), who also refers to the schizoid.

and through channels which are sometimes more typical of his earlier personal development, or of an earlier racial development.

Relationships with people seem to be sought not for any inherent worth of the people, but almost exclusively for the passing pleasure and satisfaction which may be derived from them, directly or indirectly.

The pertinent fact is that this is his reality which, although false to us, is to some extent meaningful to him. His behaviour may not be so bizarre and capricious as was once thought, but it seems to be a mode of being, directed towards the preservation of some security. It is, nevertheless, an 'inauthentic' mode of being. This term 'inauthentic' is applied here in a more comprehensive sense than that attributed to it by Heidegger. It includes the capitulation to the collective (*das Man*), it includes chatter, curiosity, and ambiguity; but it goes beyond Heidegger to include the distortions in the fundamental self-world structure and to include also those 'decisions' of the total being beyond those of moral, deliberate actions. We note also that this inauthenticity can be so pronounced that the person cannot turn to authenticity of his own accord, but generally requires intensive psychiatric treatment to assist him to do so. If we accept the premise, however, that schizophrenia is a mode of being, the question may be asked as to how and why it should be changed to a different – so-called authentic – mode of being. This is usually answered in terms of criteria established by the culture in which we live.

Certain implications emerge for those who want to help the schizophrenic. It is clear that he must be addressed consistently as a person in his world, and that his schizophrenia is to be regarded not so much as an ontic variant of normal Dasein (Personal Being) but as a characteristic mode of being with its own ontological structures and its own possibilities. Objective observation must play its part, but communication should be directed toward the unique and specific person in his own peculiar world.

> 'We must begin with the patient at the place where he is and communicate with him in his own conflict-ridden language. . .'[1]

[1] Wexler, in Brody & Redlich (1952, p. 198); *v.q.* Sonnemann (1954, p. 243); Sechehaye (1956, p. 84); Hill (1955, p. 18).

Thus an attempt must be made to understand how the world looks to him and how his symptoms play a part in his way of living in the world: e.g. in the consideration of the schizophrenic's delusions, although it is clear that attention should be directed towards their scientific note and towards their removal, it is suggested that there is much to be gained from an approach which, from a deep insight into the whole of man's being, attempts to see how this patient comes to have these delusions and what part they play in his world.

So long as the patient is treated at-a-distance his need to remain in the schizophrenic world becomes greater, and the possibility of him turning again to the world as we know it becomes less and less. More than any ordinary person, the schizophrenic needs to be loved and in this we must set out to be-with-him, and thus rediscover the spontaneous person in the world.

> '. . . Whenever a psychotic feels that you understand him – he is yours' (Federn, 1953, p. 141).

3. THE SCHIZOPHRENIC AND HIS DECISION

In the treatment and rehabilitation of the schizophrenic, or in any casual meeting with him, the issue of his ability to make decisions soon obtrudes and we quickly discover that in this regard he is far from reliable. Indeed, the facility by which he is able to change his decisions, or entertain mutually opposing decisions simultaneously, exasperates and bewilders all who attempt to become involved with him.

It is commonly found in the schizophrenic – more so than in any ordinary person – that he may take a course of action directly opposite to that on which he had previously decided, or in fact he may not act at all on a decision which he had made, and he may justify this by saying that the action took place in his mind. Frequently he will make impassioned speeches about how he has decided to renounce his psychosis and turn again to the world; but even after seventeen years some are still making these speeches.

It is evident, therefore, that schizophrenia as an ontological structure is not annulled by verbal and intellectual decisions. Resolve and responsibility are no longer meaningful concepts. In this sense the schizophrenic may be regarded as being in a 'decisionless state'.[1] He is unable to make reliable decisions, and those he does make are rarely effective. This decisionless state, however, may be replaced by a more positive decision-making when the schizophrenic becomes involved in the therapeutic relationship, and particularly where he perceives that this relationship will provide him with some satisfaction.

A survey of the literature, or even the foregoing part of this chapter, may lead some to think that the schizophrenic, or the person who will become schizophrenic, is not so decisionless, and that in fact he turns to psychosis by a conscious and determined choice. We may read, for example, that he breaks with reality, that he creates false conceptions of reality, that he denies reality, that he deliberately turns away from society, and so on.[2] But the psychosis is not contracted or revoked by any deliberate and intellectual action on the patient's part. The inadequacy of language sometimes makes it necessary to adopt mythical or analogous descriptions which will inevitably give rise to some misinterpretation. These descriptions, however, could imply that more than intellectual faculties are involved here: that in fact it is the whole of the schizophrenic's being which decides to enter psychosis. This 'decision' is not something for which the person is morally responsible – in the same sense as if it were an intellectual decision – rather it seems to pertain to a sub- or pre-moral basis, involving the total being in its interdependence with its world. Decision in this sense is not individualistically limited, but embraces also the universal and tragic estrangement which is so much a part of the person's being-in-the-world. Certainly, as a result of his encounter with the world, he has taken destructive forces into himself and these help to actualize the decision he will

[1] cf. Smith (1959, pp. 20–27). Describes his experience and 'decisionless' condition, after being 'A Sunday with Mescaline'. Note that Mescaline can evoke a 'schizophrenic-like condition'.

[2] *v.* Bleuler (1950 ed., pp. 393, 396); Federn (1953, p. 187); Blau (1957, p. 609); Sechehaye (1956, pp. 25, 131).

make; but there are also the destructive forces of the universal estrangement, and to some extent these condition the decision he will make. Although it is *his* existence, and he alone distorts his freedom to bring this destiny, it all takes place within the universal tragedy of the human predicament. As such, the schizophrenia is his *Geworfenheit* ('thrownness', i.e. he finds he is thrown into this kind of existence) rather than his *Schuld*, i.e. his particular action, offence, or sin. In his 'decision' to enter psychosis he is no more guilty than the rest of us who contribute to the tragedy which actualizes his estrangement.

4. THE LOSS OF THE DETERMINING CENTRE

If it is thus argued that the schizophrenic condition reflects the person's *Geworfenheit*, the question will be raised as to the part this plays in the divine economy. Even here the picture is very confusing: on the one hand the development of schizophrenia may bring little or no change to the religious life of some patients. On the other hand the changes may be vast and many – an atheist may suddenly hear God speak to him; a Protestant may begin to recite novenas to the Virgin Mary; another patient may believe his thoughts are in direct contact with heaven; and another may deny any possibility of divine grace and assert that he is the Godhead himself.

If we examine these conditions more closely we may argue that, in so far as the fundamental structures of being have undergone distortions, something must also have occurred with regard to the divine determining Centre which gives these structures their meaning and coherence. Theoretically it may be suggested that the determining Centre is lost, and this entails the person falling to pieces, and also his world (see Tillich, 1957, p. 61). Practically, however, this is more difficult to support for, in addition to the fact that the Centre is not always so categorically lost from the schizophrenic, we are once again faced with the problem of distinguishing between the loss of Centre, which seems to leave the self as a responsible agent – as in atheism or practical Godlessness – and that loss of Centre which is so complete that the self as a physical unity disintegrates or never forms. Our present knowledge does not offer any solution to these problems; we can simply say *that* they obtain.

According to the definition given by Tillich, a man who does not find his determining Centre in God despairs in his quest for courage to be. This does not mean that he is a coward, but rather that he founders in the futility of his own attempts to achieve some salvation. In the schizophrenic the loss of courage devastates his whole being and, while some religious apprehension may be retained, it is devoid of authority and effectual meaning. (Here again it is difficult to distinguish the condition adequately from any average state of estrangement.)

Where there is an awareness of the possible manifestations which the loss of the determining Centre may entail, the tendency may be to vindicate the effectuality of a religious belief as a prophylactic and rehabilitative agent. But while it is a misplaced belief which is held only for its calculated gain, we can go beyond this to suggest that some forms of religious belief actually may be harmful and, instead of leading the person to fullness of being, may lead him into greater estrangement – e.g. where the person does not apprehend the significance of the polarities of existence and accentuates one pole over another (say, individualization over participation) the inevitable consequence of this distortion is greater estrangement.

We cannot escape the fact, however, that in man's universal estrangement, corporate belief, while sound in theory, becomes a difficult possibility in practice. The ordinary believer tends to become more individualistic in his religion. So long as he is prosperous or enjoying good health, the condition of others may not strike him with any urgency – indeed he tends to leave the schizophrenic to work out his own salvation. But it is my thesis that the schizophrenic cannot stand alone in his condition, for we who are to some extent involved in his estrangement must stand with him.[1] If he is to rediscover the determining Centre and the structures of his being, so must we; for while in one way

[1] cf. Buber (1957b, p. 97): 'A soul is never sick alone, but always a between-ness also, a situation between it and another existing being.'

or another we may speak to him in his condition, he also speaks to us in ours, confronting us with the urgent necessity to regain our awareness of the corporate significance of redemption. The clue to this seems to be by means of participation; it is only by our participation that the schizophrenic will be led to believe in people, that he will discover the Centre of his being and find the courage to turn again to the world.

In the following chapter I try to describe something of what this participation means in the midst of a schizophrenic world with schizophrenic people.

CHAPTER VIII

Meeting and No-meeting

Participation and involvement, interpersonal relationships and being-with-others, are of paramount importance in any walk of life. But when we are involved with schizophrenia, they assume even greater importance. In the schizophrenic there are notable distortions in his relationships with other people and his world, and in the apprehension and appropriation of reality. Perhaps it will help him if we set the stage for his fresh encounter with reality. In the group – which played such a crucial part in this work – the person is turned towards the external world, and he is helped to experience himself and the other person in the simple situation of 'being with' others. The group provided the situation in which rediscovery of the self and the other could readily take place, and it opened the possibilities of spontaneity and relatedness. The group is, in fact, a biological necessity for, in addition to all theories, or apart from them, a man needs his fellow-man: in order to live they must live with each other. But the group has an added significance – psychologically and theologically. Psychologically it has an instrumental value in contributing to the person's health and normality. Theologically, it has an intrinsic value in that existential fulfilment resides in the corporate relations of the one and the other.

Out of this meeting and no-meeting, one with the other, in that gulf of uncertainty, confusion, and paradox, a way of talking and a number of terms began to emerge.[1] These greatly helped

[1] These terms will be described by referring to various incidents and events of the groups. Some of the examples used in this chapter have been quoted already in Chapters I and II.

my awareness and understanding of what it means to participate in a relationship, and particularly where that relationship was with the schizophrenics who were so intimately involved in this work. Out of the encounter with anguish and despair, where nothing seems certain, we can become aware of the possibilities of choosing an authentic existence. This is not always possible for the schizophrenic, particularly the chronic schizophrenic, but it remains a possibility always to be borne in mind.

Throughout this work reference has been made to the issue of 'being with others' or 'turning towards others'. In the practical work something more specific arose from this being-with-others. This was the specific impact of the encounter.

1. ENCOUNTER

> 'If we go on our way and meet a man who has advanced towards us and has also gone on *his* way, we know only our part of the way, not his – his we experience only in the meeting' (Buber, 1937, p. 76).

The encounter has a dual character, yet in this duality there is an essential unity:

(a) the other person meets me, I meet the other person.

(b) arising out of this meeting, there is the added encounter with the existential reality.

(a) *The Encounter as a 'Meeting'*

Although the therapeutic relationship may begin with a casual meeting and may in fact appear casual to the patient for some considerable time, therapy must be the unfolding of the levels of the encounter beyond this casual (I–It) relation until one can meet the other in 'mutual dialogue'. Thus the 'encounter' involves the meeting with the other in the fullness of relation. This 'fullness of relation' in turn involves the self-attributions of the one, and the endorsement of these by the other; it involves a partnership wherein the one meets the other and both are confronted with the reality which each represents for the other.

Clearly this extends considerably beyond the casual and first meeting and indeed may obtain only when therapy has been successful. Nevertheless, existential therapy aims to bring the patient into this genuine meeting where the therapy may move from the patient's strong identification with the therapist to the discovery of his own capacity once again to 'face the world' (cf. Colm, 1953, p. 103). It may not be so much 'what' the therapist does but 'how' he does it. Essentially it is a matter of one meeting the other with the purpose of bringing him out of 'distance' into 'presentness' and 'relation', out of the world of dream and fantasy and self-construction into the world of reality. The therapist comes as a representative of the world and seeks a meeting with the patient. He virtually summons the patient to respond to the 'address of Being over against him' (*v.* Friedman, 1955, p. 189). Hans Trüb said:

> 'Only genuine partnership can save the sick person who has withdrawn from dynamic encounter with the world into isolation' (*v.* Colm, 1953, p. 103).

In this work it became evident that the schizophrenic had fallen away from genuine encounter with the world and with his reality. He no longer lent himself to a genuine meeting of himself and the other, but eluded the meeting or, being there, distorted the other into that which in the totality of his being he preferred him to be, or feared that he was.

> e.g. In Session 118, Group II, I asked Walter where Norman was. Walter received the message but could not allow himself to enter into a 'meeting' with me. He turned to Arthur. He did not want to 'meet' Arthur, so he distorted Arthur into someone else, and he said, 'Where is he, Davis?'

The whole study resounds with the unfolding of the depths of the meeting one with the other. Out of the encounter in the group situation there would burst a fresh awareness of their capacity to encounter the world.

> e.g. Norman: Whenever Norman was home he refused to take his meals with the family. Either he would sit down at the

> table, gulp his meal and leave, or he would take his meal into another room. He also lacked confidence to speak with any visitors who came to the home. After a period of this form of therapy, his relatives reported with conviction the change that had 'come over him', and they could see him regaining his confidence. Towards the end of the therapy his mother, now a very old lady, came to me and said: 'I always prayed that I would be spared to see him well – and now I have.'

This was not a matter of wishful-thinking on the part of his aged mother. Norman began the sessions with the conviction that he was 'there' to help the therapist. After his continual encounter with reality and the meaning of the relationships formed, he apprehended that his place was not 'in here', but 'out there'. After 9·4 years since his last admission to hospital, or after 10·5 years since his first admission, he was able to receive his discharge.

There was not a patient in Group II for whom this encounter of person with person did not hold an accumulating meaning and an emotional investment.

> e.g. Consider also Davis. When he first began therapy with me he could enter a 'meeting' with the others only with obvious discomfort and fragmentation. He would fidget and tremble and perspire, and his speech was often very confused. Later in the therapeutic sessions he was able to stand up before the group and with composure enter into the meeting with them.

(b) *The Encounter with the Existential Reality*

Here there is a confrontation with elements of one's self or one's world, or with elements in the self-world relation. It is possible that these elements were present all the time, but there had been no active awareness of them. There is an 'unwillingness of man to admit the curious predicament of his existence by reason of his simultaneous involvement in, and transcendence over, temporal flux and finiteness; or more exactly [there is an] . . . unwillingness to admit that there is no escape from this predicament even on the level of the new life' (*v.* Niebuhr, 1943, p. 132). Existential therapy attempts to bring an awareness of existential reality, but in doing so the therapist must himself be alert to the appropriate moment for confrontation (*kairos*).

This form of encounter may be described by reference to examples in the group sessions.

In Group II Walter seemed to experience considerable discomfort whenever his relationship to his mother was discussed. On some of these occasions Walter would tear his finger nails deeply into his flesh until he was bleeding freely; on other occasions he would plainly avoid the encounter with this sensitive issue of his life. In Session 11, when Arthur asked him about his mother, Walter did not reply. Edward then asked, but still Walter did not reply. After a long silence Walter said, 'I'm a bittie deaf.'

In Session 161 Edward distorted his own dynamics and form so that he became convinced that he was God as well as Edward. His encounter with the concreteness of reality came through the encounter in the group. He was helped to see the distortion he was making, and this, together with the relation which had already formed, seemed to contribute to the relinquishing of this conviction.

In Group I, although there were numerous instances of this encounter, one that well illustrates the point was found in Session 65. Mona thought the therapeutic session was just a casual meeting, but was suddenly struck by the shock of the encounter with existential reality. This involved not only an encounter with the word which was spoken, but also an encounter with the person who spoke it, i.e. myself. Although I had misgivings at the time, it so happened that the course of the patient's illness changed from this encounter. (The nurses and doctors agreed with this finding.)

In Session 183 Barbara also was confronted with the truth and reality of what in her total being she had already sensed I thought of her. Again, in consequence of this encounter, there seemed to be a clear change in the course of the patient's illness.

The last example which might be given concerns Margaret, Session 190. She had made every attempt to conceal her fear and anxiety over matters of religion. She feared with her whole being that she was condemned to burn in hell. In the therapeutic meeting she concealed this and contrived to avoid any discussion of it. The encounter with reality must have been painful to her as I said to her, before she had time to seat herself properly, 'Why do you keep wearing that Cross?' It is noteworthy that it was not until four months after her discharge that she was able to face her anxiety over this issue in a way which I considered positive. (During these four months I had regular weekly individual sessions with her.) She is now an enthusiastic and sensible member of a church youth group, and whereas she was unable to tolerate the thought of going to church, she now goes.

It seems therefore that the encounter in its twofold aspects assumes a fundamental importance in the therapeutic process. It was seen that out of this encounter self-realization could be gained or lost.

2. PRESENTNESS

> 'The "making present" increases until it is a paradox in the soul when I and the other are embraced by a common living situation and (let us say) the pain which I inflict upon him surges up in myself, revealing the abyss of the contradictoriness of life between man and man' (Buber, 1957 a(i), p. 103; 1951, p. 112).

Presentness means to be present in time and space, but since it is also a presentness-for-a-relation, it involves intentionality, and thus the three polarities of individualization-participation, dynamics-form, freedom-destiny, are involved. When one man is present to the other there can be no semblance – each makes himself present in the fullness of his personal being. There is no imposition of one on the other but one must influence the other in his unfolding. It is in this 'presentness' or 'being present' with one another that the bonds of relationship find their beginnings and orientation. Only that man who is prepared to be genuinely present with the other can know the experience of communication. If the other can experience that I am 'present', and more especially present *to him*, he can begin to experience his own self-becoming or his own self-realization.

Already we have seen that the schizophrenic can distort this presentness in time and space and in intentionality. He does not present himself to the world in his fullness but distorts the self-world relationship, so that this presentness becomes fragmented and regardless of time, space, and intentionality. In extreme cases the polarities are lost.

Existential therapy strives to bring the schizophrenic into presentness again. This demands the unreserved involvement of the therapist, for the initiative falls on him to be present and constantly available. Partial presentness (semblance) is unacceptable not only in that it may be interpreted as hostility, but because communication can be so subtle and tenuous that a deeper relationship may be precluded.

The whole of the therapy of this work is geared to the principle that man cannot attain self-realization, cannot become himself, through some inner or personal integration. The peculiarities of schizophrenia make it evident that even the relationship of patient-therapist is not in itself sufficient. The patient requires to be caught up in a 'presentness' on a greater scale, involving him in greater possibilities of creativeness and spontaneity; hence the group medium.

On the practical level this study attempts to portray the importance of 'being present' and the ways of 'making present'. From the beginning, no matter what else was happening – no matter what the patients said or did and though they may not have been present to me – I strove to be present to them. Out of the realization of this presentness the groups found their life and meaning.

e.g. Group II, Session 118. It is not 'obvious' to me what the actual contents and meaning of this session were, but I believe it was of fundamental importance that I was there, there with them. If this were not so, the events of this session would never have occurred, and the forces in 'play' would never have been promoted.

As early as Session 3, the concept of presentness was inculcated. Walter spontaneously recognized the absence (lack of spatial presentness) of three members. It may have been only the physical presentness with which Walter was concerned, but it also could have been that in the presentness of the group as a whole he experienced the group-ethos, which helped him to be present and thus controlled his desire to be 'absent', as were these three members. It was evident that the remainder of the session was concerned with something more than physical (spatial) presentness; but the patients' inhibition toward the encounter and their semblance in it were apprehended.

It seems unnecessary to elaborate on the fact that, the schizophrenic condition being as it is, presentness did not always obtain. There were, however, many interesting distortions wherein presentness could take on different meanings. Here we may note two instances:

In Session 86 Walter saw himself as so 'present' to me that he said, 'Any speech coming out of my throat is in direct contact with your hearing'. This, for him, was a mark of a 'confidential communication', and so by this form of presentness of himself, he was attempting to transcend the presentness of the others.

In Session 146 again Walter was involved. He thanked Arthur for being chairman of the group in my absence, and thanked him also 'for bringing Mr Macnab's thoughts to us'. The fact that Arthur was chairman in my stead was sufficient indication that my thoughts were present through Arthur.

In Group I, Session 6, we found an example of the reluctance to be 'present' in the group. Stella said:

> 'Once I was in the joy of life; then I became ill; now I am well again, and I want to forget all about it.'

Far from well, she was attempting to avoid the anxiety that would necessarily be a part of her being 'present' to the group.

A further example of this reluctance to be 'present' was found with Marie and Margaret in Session 152. Note Marie, particularly – how she sat like a sphinx in order to avoid being 'present'.

In Session 154 Margaret avoided the encounter with her existential reality and tried to depreciate its significance. In Session 155, however, she became 'present' to me as she wept over the 'horrible' past, and faced the apparent hopelessness of her situation.

In Group I generally, there were many examples of this presentness. One additional example may be noted from Session 29, where Kerry made herself 'present' to the group, and disclosed her feelings and fears; to find that Stella was ready to share these experiences, and thus to be 'present' also.

Presentness sets the situation for a genuine self-disclosure.

3. SELF-DISCLOSURE

> 'The basic movement of the life of dialogue is the turning towards the other' (Buber, 1947, p. 22).

In the relation which obtains between one person and the other, self-disclosure is a prominent feature, for in turning towards each other there must be openness and directness. It is out of this intention to 'know' and 'be known' that a genuine and mutual dialogue may take place. In the movement towards this genuine dialogue, self-disclosure comes from the person as he actually is – the person who is spontaneous and unaffected in his entering the relation, and not clamouring (overtly or covertly) to preserve his esteem in the eyes of others.

The self-disclosure can undergo many distortions, most of which seek to conceal the person as he actually is, and attempt to have him appear as something else. In this the self-world structure undergoes distortions. This man-in-mask frets over the impression he makes with others, or alternatively, in his estrangement, he loses all the concern he once had for them.

In schizophrenia, self-disclosure cannot lead to a genuine relation for it is either blocked and inhibited on the one hand, or unwieldy and chaotic on the other. (Here again the polarities of existence have undergone considerable loss.)

Existential therapy attempts (in its own way) to help the patient 'dare' to be a real person, and thus tries to open to him the way of courage, whereby he may turn towards the other in self-disclosure where all appearances are put aside and 'deep calls to deep'. It involves the relinquishing of the defences by which the patient protects his self, and by which he conceals the genuine or actual self. Buber says (1957a(ii) pp. 107–108):

> 'It does not depend on one saying to the other everything that occurs to him, but only on his letting no *seeming* creep in between himself and the other.'

Self-disclosure is thus not an uncontrolled opening of the self, nor is it an open discharge of tension. When these forms of openness do prevail, however, it should not be overlooked that, as well as reflecting possible pathological conditions, they may be the attempts of the patient as he 'dares to be a real person'; but he is hindered by the fact that he does not know how.

In this work the self-disclosure of the patients was not limited to that which takes place between patient and therapist. Although the self-disclosure obtaining between the two may be genuine, and although the therapist, in some way, represents the real world, this self-disclosure may not be generalized to other relationships. The patient may disclose to one, but may be in semblance with the rest of the world. Thus the group assumed vital significance, for it represented more faithfully the shock of self-disclosure to the patient's world.

It is true that this self-disclosure could be made only where there was a trustful commitment, otherwise there would be a possibility of a precipitation of a greater anxiety than if the disclosure had never occurred. Here the therapist played a crucial role, for each member of the group had to see in him the epitome of trust and commitment, and as this became more and more their experience, so it was reflected in the group. The therapist, although not disclosing himself, nevertheless had to be ready to disclose what was relevant to the relationship, and his disclosure had to be genuine at all times. Just as the therapist tried to bring the patient to 'dare' to be a real person, so he had to 'dare' to be a real person himself. Different therapists may have their different frames of reference for this, but I found my own theological frame of reference particularly helpful here.

In this context the patients could speak and, speaking, speak boldly. This was the boldness of men and women 'in-community'.[1]

> e.g. The self-disclosure was particularly significant for Group I, where the traumatic past was still intensely meaningful. In Group II, the self-disclosure was applicable in a different way, for the past was no longer so painful to them. Here, there was a greater concern for the self-disclosure of the present relation and the present moment. Perhaps it was true that their response to the present was conditioned to a large extent by the traumatic past, but this past was either rigidly concealed or no longer obviously meaningful. Whatever the solution to this may be, it should be noted that so often the category of causality was greatly distorted.
>
> Reference may be made, however, to Norman when he was encouraged to ventilate his past. His relationship to his mother and his earlier social relationships were discussed. Causality seemed to be taken into account here, but there was no evidence of a traumatic charge. This may have been due to a psychotic denial, but it was significant that Norman himself regarded it openly. If this were true, the question must be asked if there would be any gain in retraumatizing a suspected area when it appeared that the trauma and its meaning had passed and the patient was living on another level of reality.

In Group I the self-disclosure meant turning oneself towards the other and, stripped of all semblance and in trustful commitment, disclosing to the other and to the world the content of one's guilt (the past), the content of one's feelings (the present), and the content of one's hopes and anxieties (the future). This did not occur without considerable discomfort. In Session 2 they confessed their anxiety and derived some comfort from the fact that I also was anxious. It seemed that Kate might have wished me to go further in my self-disclosure when she asked why I was wearing a Fraser tartan tie, when in fact there was a Macnab tartan. (i.e. 'Who are you – what are you – ?)

[1] cf. ἡ παρρησία of the People of God.

But this was only the beginning of the disclosure, and later in the sessions there was a noticeable readiness to lend oneself to this relation.

Reference however should be made to the painful self-disclosure of Sophie in Sessions 47, 50 and to the defiant but sensitive self-disclosure of Marie in Session 146, and so on.

In Group II it was particularly significant to note that the self-disclosure did not always pertain to the words which were spoken, but to what went on *between* those who spoke. Often there was little evidence of turning towards the other, and speech was monologue – see Session 55, where Walter and Arthur spoke on regardless of one another.

The self-disclosure did not seem to be limited to words but pertained to the whole person as he stood up before the group, or as the group turned towards him. (See Session 7 – Walter.)

There were times, however, when the self-disclosure did approach that found in Group I. Arthur, for example, showed distinct signs of a psychotic denial regarding the separation from his wife. In the group he was able to take a large step towards the disclosure found in Group I.

It was stated above that self-disclosure was relevant not only for the patients but for the therapist also. There were occasions when, through my failure to disclose the nature of the relationship, the course of therapy was hindered. After I had made the disclosure, however, the changes or comments which followed sometimes indicated that the patients had discerned my feelings long before I had disclosed them.
e.g. In Group II, Session 125, Walter perceived my undisclosed annoyance over his and Edward's negativism, and he said: 'A time bomb is going to explode.' Later I realized that I had been concealing my wrath and so, in the next session, I began to clarify my position to them. Edward interrupted and said that he knew I had been angry – 'It was not what y' said in particular, but I felt you were angry, I *felt* it.'

4. PARTICIPATION

> 'Participation is essential for the individual, not accidental. No individual exists without participation, and no personal being exists without communal being' (Tillich, 1951, p. 176; *v.q.* Cantril, 1950, p. 159).

The basic movement of participation as it is used in this immediate context is the 'turning towards' the other or the world in thought and actuality, with the intention of entering into a mutual and responsible relation. Participation depends on man's individuality just as his individuality depends on his participation, and therefore it follows that participation involves not only the differentiation of the other from the self, but it involves also a discovery of the self and one's individuality. The person, in participating with the other, meets the resistance of the other and thereby discovers himself and his finitude. But there is also the interdependent act whereby the person, in order to participate with the other, places him at a distance both in the sense of distinguishing between what is self and what is not-self (his own individuality), and in the sense of becoming aware that the other is an object who may become a 'Thou' of relation.

We have noted that in schizophrenia this polarity of participation-individualization can and does undergo various distortions, as do also the capacities for distance and relation. Participation on the one hand may be lost or negated, or on the other hand it may become demanding in its attempts to enter or avoid a relation. Individualization on the one hand may become absolute or on the other hand may become fragmented and lost. It follows also that there will be a confusion and distortion in distancing and relation.

In the form of therapy used in this present work, the group set the situation for participation and relation, and encouraged their actualization. Distancing manifested itself in three ways:

(a) *There was the distortion in distance such that individuality was blurred or confused*

e.g. In Group I this was evident in Emily (Session 5) where it seemed that she could not clearly distinguish herself from her girl-friend's manager. We saw also that Kerry (Sessions 25, 38–39) had tendencies to confuse her identity with a windmill. In Session 25, she said, 'I thought I was a windmill. I thought I was not human any more, but was just something somebody used.' In Session 38 she said, 'It is just as if I can see and hear, but everything is strange, . . . and I think I am that windmill.'

In Group II these distortions occurred frequently. One of the best examples was found in Walter, in Session 176, where I asked him about his greatest fear. Walter replied, 'I'm afraid of the sea.' Note the ensuing discussion:

ARTHUR: 'I'm surprised at that – why? Help me to understand you.'

WALTER: 'Are you afraid of the sea?'

ARTHUR: 'No.'

WALTER: 'You are – you are.'

ARTHUR: 'No – only in a storm; but not normally. . . .'

WALTER: 'You're frightened to tell anyone else.'

ARTHUR: 'Why are you afraid?'

WALTER: 'Why are *you* afraid?'

Walter protested further that it was Arthur who was afraid of the sea. I asked about himself. Walter replied, 'I'm not afraid of the sea.' I reminded him that this discussion had begun with him saying that the sea was *his* greatest fear. Walter replied, 'Did I say that? Oh, I didn't know what I was saying.'

It could be argued that through his distortion in distance Walter had experienced a diffusion of his identity with Arthur.

This diffusion of identity, possibly explained through the collapse of the ego-boundaries, either seemed to bring with it a disregard for the patient's own individuality (and thus he could become merged with anything at whim) or it could bring an accentuated preoccupation with the loss of individuality. In either case participation was inevitably affected.

(b) *There was distancing in order to avoid a relation*

e.g. in Group I, particularly in the early sessions, the patient would attempt to keep other people at a 'safe distance'. Kerry, in Sessions 14, 30, placed a chair between herself and me so as to preserve her from any direct participation. Margaret, in Session 132, stared at me in silence as if to turn me to stone.

The seemingly detached gaze was also experienced in Group II. Walter's gaze toward the therapist was of particular note. It seemed that in this gaze there was not only a desire to turn the therapist into stone, but also a desire that he himself could turn into stone (thus avoiding a relation). In addition, however, there was also the desire *for* a relation. Here again, we find something of the paradoxical nature of schizophrenia.

We noted that Edward had mute or catatonic phases. In these it appeared that he had abandoned all contact with the world, and found an absolute distance between himself and all that was other. A session later he would recount all that had occurred during his stuporose state (Session 21).

(c) *There was distancing in order to enter into a relation*

In Group I this distancing developed on a more or less normal level as the group progressed. It was clearly demonstrated by the fact that the patients entered into relations with each other, showing that recognition of each other's individuality had taken place. It was particularly notable that each group which was formed also met and formed a group outside the group-room. After discharge from hospital it was a common practice for the groups to meet independently of the therapist. They would meet in each other's homes, they would go shopping together, or they would go out to entertainments together. Frequently other members of their families would also be involved in these reunions.

In Group II the distancing for relation took different forms. There was the distancing that seemed to imply a relation: if Walter showed himself to be disturbed over something, it seemed to be a great comfort to him to bring his chair close to mine (see Session 184). This was also noticeable with Edward (Session 72). The reduction in physical distance seemed to convey a relation or relatedness, as it does with an infant when a mother holds it in her arms.

There was a further form of distancing which seemed to convey some security before any participation would take place. This was particularly noticeable with Norman. See Session 9, where he had to sit in a certain position and face in a certain direction before he would participate or enter a relation with Edward. He had refused my suggestion to sit face-to-face at close range.

As the therapy progressed with Group II it became evident that distancing approaching the normal was taking place. This can be seen by reference to any of the later sessions of the group. See, for example, Edward, in Session 137. Edward entered the room and was in a happy mood. He spoke to Walter with spontaneity. I asked Edward to tell the group about his early life. He told us he did the messages for his mother – 'groceries from the grocer, bread from the baker, coal from the coal merchant, with clockwork regularity'. He went on to talk of his schooling. Walter interrupted, 'Are you a defective, Edward?' Edward replied, 'No.' 'Did you go to a school for defectives – mental defectives?' Walter asked. Edward replied, 'No, I went to an ordinary school.' I asked Edward if he knew what a mental-defective school was. He replied, 'Yes, it's a school for imbeciles – backward children – children who can't hear –' (he laughed). I reminded Edward that there were times when he could not hear either. He laughed again and said, 'I know.'

Distancing, however, only sets the situation for participation and relation. Although participation can take different forms and thus lead to different forms of relation (which will be discussed in a later section), here we are concerned for the participation which will lead to a 'genuine relation'. In this genuine relation speech is very important, although the relation can take place even in the silence of communication. In the relation there is an affirmation of the one by the other that he is accepted, and the relation reaches its fulfilment when this acceptance is mutual, and when this acceptance is accepted in mutuality. The schizophrenic, to the extent that he loses his capacity for participation and relation, is unable to accept or tolerate acceptance. Like every other person, he has sought the warmth and intimacy of the human relation (perhaps more so than others), but after being subjected to the threat and trauma of its loss, he has found the prospect of further relation very frightening.

This was more evident in Group II.

e.g. Session 169: Edward and Fred, having established 'distance', then followed through with relatedness, which took as its content the issue of whether Fred was too 'close' to his mother. Walter was drawn into this. His desire for participation in the group had become increasingly noticeable, but on this issue he immediately sensed the danger that was involved, i.e. the discussion could turn to his own mother. He then attempted to distance himself from the group, but still retained an awareness of a relationship with it. He stood up and, addressing the group, began to talk incoherently (it was incoherent to me) about inviting his aunt to a party. Here I felt that R. D. Laing's suggestion was appropriate, namely, that this was 'red-herring speech'; but this view might be contrasted with the views of Arieti or Sechehaye who might see this language as having a symbolic meaning.

Often it seemed that the intention for relation and thus participation was present, but the patient did not appear to be able to 'go through with it', and excessive distancing followed. Walter, when entering the group room on one occasion, was addressed by a male nurse who had not seen Walter for a considerable time. Walter, hearing the nurse call to him, turned round quickly with an unmistakable expression of pleasure. He began to wave to the nurse, but before the gesture was complete, he broke it off and hurried into the room and quickly closed the door behind him.

It was not always clear that a relation was taking place, for distancing was often very great. Participation, although present, did not necessarily imply a relation, as will be seen in a later section. But the relation did not always take the form we might normally expect.

This can be illustrated by reference to the members' sensitivity that the group was to be terminated; to their awareness that six of them had to be present to make the group; or to their belief that the group would survive in a somewhat metaphysical way.

Arthur, discussing the fact that the group would soon be terminated, said,

'I believe that the discussion group is a group in itself and the things said there we would never say to anyone else . . . but only in the group. I was genuine in that group. Others say it is only the daily routine, but I believe they (the group) were all genuine in their interest.'

On another occasion he spoke of how the group, though ended, would continue, and in a letter to me on the last day of the group, he was the only member who did not make explicit reference to the group ending. Instead he spoke of 'endeavour', 'ambition', 'ideal', 'the help of Mr Macnab'. These events seemed to be indicative of the sensitivity of the relation, and of its loss.

Reference has been made to Edward's attempts to avoid relation by his muteness. This was also facilitated by his hallucinations and delusions. It was nevertheless a moving experience to see this man discover himself in the group. Although apparently lacking in all the desirable qualities, Edward was appointed the chairman of the group. Up until this point he would oscillate with rapidity between the levels of psychosis and non-psychosis, and he showed no desire to participate or enter into relations with the group. After he became chairman, and this was acknowledged by all (Norman would always address him as 'Mr Chairman'), Edward's enthusiasm could not be mistaken.

When it was announced that the group was to be finally terminated, Edward fell away into his psychosis again. (Note Sessions 187, 188). He had told us at a much earlier stage that he had 'swallowed' a stone. Now Edward, who had shown an amazing ability to hold the office of chairman, suddenly reverted to his earlier delusion. It seemed that he wanted to keep the therapist with him; it seemed that he did not mind being deprived of his individuality or the therapist being deprived of his. Edward was intent on maintaining the pole of participation with this therapist who had been a Man Friday to this Robinson Crusoe. (Terms he used in Session 105.) I suggest that Edward managed to solve his problem by swallowing the therapist, but this was 'uncomfortable' and painful, for unlike the warm milk of a mother's love, I had become (for him) a stone (Sessions 187, 188).

Participation, as it has been discussed so far, has pertained only to the patient. In this regard it should be stated that participation, like individualization, is not something a person can or must do, nor is it something a person is able to attain. The polarity itself is a fundamental of existence, and contains or implies a 'given-ness'.[1] It cannot be caused or derived, but seems to arise out of the meeting between the one and the other.

Participation is not limited to the patient; the therapist also must be aware of this polarity and the extent to which he is subject to it. But in therapy the therapist's participation extends beyond that which is generally meant by the term. Although he retains his individuality as a real person in the world, in his participation he attempts to experience the patient's world, to understand something of it, and to see what meaning it has for him.

> 'He must put his arms round the vexatious world . . . only then do his fingers reach the realm of lightning and of grace' (*v.* Buber, 1947, p. 65, also p. 192).

For my own part, this participation of the therapist takes on a new level of significance when I realize that God – the Centre and Source of everything that has being – is 'the principle of participation'.[2] In his atoning activity he not only participates in existential estrangement with all its destructive consequences, but he gives to man the capacity and intention to participate in his (God's) participation. This participation does not remove the

[1] 'The *Thou* meets me through grace – it is not found by seeking' (Buber, 1937, p. 11).
[2] This term is used by Tillich (1951, p. 245).

'finitude and anxiety, ambiguity and tragedy' (*v.* Tillich, 1957, p. 134), but having its source in the transcendence and participation of God, it stands in contrast to perseverance; and, for me, provides the Courage (in Tillich's sense), and the desire to participate in the negativities of existence and find there some meaning for the patient's life, and for mine.

> 'The principle of participation implies that every question concerning individual fulfilment must at the same time be a question concerning universal fulfilment.'[1]

5. CONFIRMATION

> 'The basis of man's life is twofold, and it is one – the wish of every man to be confirmed as what he is, even as what he can become, by men; and the innate capacity in man to confirm his fellow men in this way' (Buber).[2]

'Relation', 'Identity', and 'Distance', lead us to the issues of confirmation; to mutuality, non-mutuality, and pseudo-mutuality. Confirmation is a central concept in the therapy adopted in this present work and it is necessary, therefore, to consider it at greater length.

Man is thrown into the world. His life consists of constant attempts to find out who he is; to find out what is over against him; and, in face of all that he finds, to actualize himself. He attributes to himself a certain role and a certain status – he assumes something about himself. In a more mythical way of speaking – it is as if he stands on the edge of a vast canyon and in his loneliness directs himself to the other side. He calls and waits for some reply. Martin Buber writes:

> '. . . sent forth from the natural domain of species into the hazard of the solitary category, surrounded by the air of a chaos which came into being with him, secretly and bashfully he watches for a Yes which allows him to be and which can come to him only from one human person to another' (Buber, 1957a(i), p. 104).

[1] *v.* Tillich (1951, p. 270); *v.q.* Brunner (1937, pp. 566–67) – reference to the faith which stands in the context of the Consummation; cf. Tillich (op. cit., p. 245).

[2] Buber (1957a (i), p. 102; *v.q.* 1951, p. 110); Friedman (1955, p. 81).

Confirmation therefore has three aspects in unity:

(a) the aspect of self-attribution, the striving for self-identity and self-actualization

(b) the aspect of endorsement which can come only from another person

(c) the aspect of mutuality which must reside in both (a) and (b).

It is true: if I confirm him who is outside my self, and over against my self, I then must wait for him to give this its mutuality before a relation can take place, but at least I demonstrate my presentness and my availability. So far as my personal relations are concerned I am not confirmed until the mutuality is there; it is a matter of encroaching on another person, claiming something from him which cannot be found in myself alone. Confirmation will therefore entail the encounter, the anxiety, and the conflict, which are so much part of the dialectics of participation. It will entail subterfuge, shock, and uncertainty; but these reflect the 'world' with which we must come to terms and are certain indications that a satisfactory solution can never be found in individualism.

Confirmation cannot take place in any other milieu than that in which one man and another commit themselves to community. Standing over against any collective or aggregate, this community implies that the intention, at least, must be towards encounter, presentness, self-disclosure, and participation. Confirmation in community, therefore, is more than mutual gratification or mutual compliance, for it represents a constant challenge to develop both oneself and the other. Out of this mutuality, both move forward to the experience of enjoyment of life.

But man, being in estrangement, knows or should know that the 'menace of non-complementarity' is always present. Mutuality may never obtain, or it may fall into pseudo-mutuality or non-mutuality. Unless some positive way of transcendence is found, that for which a person sought endorsement may become a matter of fantasy and unreality.

The schizophrenic, in face of the mock confirmation about him, may discern the falsity before the normal person does, and indeed it seems that his sensitivity is such that his discerning may be more penetrating. There follows the tendency to distance others from him: he is the only one who confirms him (self) – his love is therefore precious to him, and in discerning the falsity he not only fears the love of others, but fears to release his own love on them because of the possible consequences (*v.* Fairbairn, 1952, p. 26).

Although there were many examples of this in the present work, reference may be made to Margaret in Group I. Note the straightforward incident of Session 180. Why this pressure on the therapist, why their exasperation and apparent resentment? Had they found no confirmation in this situation? Then Margaret found evidence to support what she had sensed to be true. 'It's all false. They're not sincere!' she said.

It is reasonably certain that the staff do not yet perceive the falsity and insincerity, nor would they realize that this was discerned by the people who were their patients.

When Margaret and Barbara were transferred to the convalescent ward their attitude changed. Two sessions later they said they felt they were regarded 'as persons' again, and this was in contrast to their feelings about their previous ward. In the convalescent ward they were 'confirmed' in that they were given a task and left to perform it in trust, whereas previously they pestered me for their discharge, they now accepted the situation and said they were happier.

Genuine Mutuality

Genuine mutuality, so fundamental to confirmation, is described by Wynne and colleagues, as follows:

> 'Each brings a sense of his own meaningful, positively valued identity, and, out of experience or participation, together mutual recognition of identity develops, including a growing recognition of each other's potentialities and capacities.'[1]

e.g. In Group I this was experienced again and again, but was most clearly manifested in the endorsement of each other's experience. In Session 136, Margaret endorsed Marie as Marie

[1] *v.* Wynne *et al.* (1958, p. 207); cf. Tönnies (1955, p. 57).

told of her resentment for her mother. To justify her resentment, Marie said, 'You just can't sit there and let things hurt you again and again without it making you feel resentful.'

Margaret endorsed her by saying, 'Yes, and your mother can hurt you where it hurts most. She does not have to hit. She knows what words to use.'

A similar endorsement is seen in Session 163 where Marie, having told about herself in a form of self-disclosure, then received Margaret's support, 'I believe all that Marie said . . . I felt exactly the same way. . . .'

I suggest that there is more than an agreement or an endorsement of words in these examples. Rather there is an endorsement of the whole person in her being-in-the-world.

In Group II the tremors, and more, of genuine mutuality were experienced.

e.g. Norman was acclaimed as the best artist in the group. He accepted this role and proceeded to develop it. There were times, however, when he exceeded the endorsement given by the group, and the group members felt their identity and individuality were thereby being lost. Arthur did not object to Norman's pervading dominance in the mural painting. But in the last mural which was entitled 'Disintegration' (Session 186), Norman decided to paint the title in large coloured letters across the top of the mural. It was then that Arthur felt his identity was being lost, or encroached upon by Norman. This action of Norman's not only implied an accentuated individualization on his part (to the exclusion of the others and to the exclusion of participation in the group) but implied that he was taking possession of the mural. Arthur complained that the art therapy session was a matter of each putting his own ideas down on the mural and that the group, as such, had been lost. The art therapist told me that when Arthur saw Norman writing the title on the mural he demanded that it be removed or he would 'walk out'. In fact he stood back from the mural (and the group) until Norman had erased his attempts to 'steal' the mural and embody the identity of the group in himself.

A further example of genuine mutuality may be cited in Sessions 161, 162. Edward told the group in 161 that he was 'kept going' in life by the fact that he was not only Edward but also God. Fred did not confirm Edward in his role of God. Indeed, there was no confirmation in this respect, but there was a genuine mutuality directed towards his being. Arthur told him that in the previous session he (Edward) had come late, and in spite of the group rule that any late-comer would not be admitted, the group had relaxed the rule in his case and admitted him. Arthur pointed out that such a mistake and such a submission to the group's condescension conflicted with any aspiration to be God!

The mutuality was experienced in their recognition of their identity one towards the other; in their recognition that identity in individuality had come to terms with the identity of the other; and in their each turning towards the other in openness and intention. Arthur participated with Edward with obvious endorsement; but Arthur rejected Edward's self-attribution. It was noteworthy that arising from this Edward abandoned this self-attribution.

Pseudo-mutuality

In pseudo-mutuality it appears that any awareness of the impact of solitariness is dulled, and the crisis that the centre of life has been lost (and there is Nothingness) is avoided. In pseudo-mutuality a person does things because it is expected, and although he does not enter a relation, he tries to maintain the sense or impression of relation.

There are two aspects, therefore, of pseudo-mutuality which make confirmation false:

(a) the lack of awareness of one's estrangement and of one's actualization of estrangement

(b) the attempt to maintain some semblance of relatedness.

The manifestations of pseudo-mutuality are widespread throughout our culture and society. One example is as follows: Person A, carrying a bunch of flowers, stops to pass the time of day with person B. A says to B, 'Do you see my lovely flowers? They have a beautiful perfume.' A hands the flowers to B with the intent that B should inhale their fragrance. B does so, but just as she takes the flowers (and she had already thought that they are not really very beautiful) A's attention is distracted, and so A does not witness B smelling the flowers. B comments, 'They're just lovely!' But she looks up and discovers that A has not witnessed her demonstrated interest. In order that there is no misunderstanding, B awaits the return of A's attention, and then B repeats the smelling of the flowers and repeats her words of 'appreciation'.

The attempt to retain the semblance of relationship is obvious. The chatter and avoidance of self-disclosure point to B's unawareness of her actualization of estrangement.

Pseudo-mutuality is a widespread phenomenon of our society, a fact we often overlook. We observe a person attempting to avoid all depth in relationship, and generally masking his true feelings. We might see this as a further symptom of his illness, rather than as behaviour in keeping with established patterns within his family and his society. There is little doubt, however, that pseudo-mutuality, and the falsity and anxiety which go with it, are significant issues in the development of schizophrenia and the later course of the condition. People with any predisposition to schizophrenia, and the schizophrenics themselves, are very sensitive. They readily perceive the shadows of falsity and react to them.

To support this, reference can be made again to the situation of the 'double-bind' in which the person finds himself in an enclosed situation which affects him through its falsity on the one hand and its reality on the other. It appears that though the 'double-bind' is very widespread, its impact is greatest when it obtains between the parent (mother) and the child. It involves on the one hand a primary injunction or directive, but this is contradicted by a secondary injunction which is usually communicated non-verbally. In addition, there is the tertiary injunction prohibiting the person from leaving the situation.

An example of the 'double-bind' can be found in Group I, with Desma, but the example in question occurred after she was discharged from hospital. The event could have been a recapitulation of many similar events in her earlier life, but this is supported by the impression which Desma's father made upon me.

It will be recalled that Desma was engaged to Paul. At one stage Paul was temporarily employed with Desma's father's firm. This set the situation for a severe family quarrel. Desma's father, we had already seen, 'always had to be boss in the home', and although this was tempered somewhat while Desma and her mother were in hospital, after Desma's discharge she again became concerned about her relationship with her father. As an appendage to the quarrel which had taken place, he said to Desma, 'Oh, and by the way, you can tell Paul that we are seeing far too much of him. I see him all day, and I see him all night. I'm sick of him!' Desma later told Paul about this. Paul said he would solve Desma's father's problem by resigning his post; then, at least, he would not have to 'put up with him' during the day. The next morning Desma told her father of Paul's intention, and he replied, 'Can't you take a joke?'

We see here the articulated primary injunction followed by an articulated secondary injunction with an implicit non-verbal communication that this is not an 'I-Thou' relation, but an 'I-It' relation, i.e. as perceived from Desma's point of view. The tertiary injunction was also non-verbalized – she could not leave the field as far as her father was concerned, and she could not leave the field as far as Paul was concerned.

It is possible that this double-bind represents a precursor to a state of sensitivity in a person's relationships, and this sensitivity reaches such intensity that the schizophrenic contracts out of the situation by 'falling' into the schizophrenic mode of life. In this mode of being, he also resorts to forms of pseudo-mutuality or non-mutuality, wherein by means of behaviour strange to any normal person, and language sometimes, apparently, strange even to himself, he manages 'to throw dangerous people off the scent' and thus avoid the pains of relatedness.

In the present work the group itself and the existential therapy adopted were in constant opposition to the mock-confirmation manifested in pseudo-mutuality. It seemed that pseudo-mutuality was often more painful than the total absence of endorsement.

Session 61: Sophie, in the silence, would look back and forth from Mona to me, as if unable and unwilling to receive the full impact of the silence or solitude. In Session 63, it will be seen how this exasperated me. It was clear at the time that Sophie was disturbed lest she fail to maintain some semblance of relation, and disturbed also at the silence which set the situation for an encounter with her emptiness and dread.

In Group II, the aspect of pseudo-mutuality by which they avoided a genuine relation (and thus avoided the shock of their existence) was frequently evident. The bursts of raucous laughter were not as empty as they may have appeared. In Session 187, Edward told the group with pathos that he was to be eaten alive:

EDWARD: 'They mean to say they'll eat me alive . . . I want to get out of here – and get to Foresterhill.'

Previously he had associated Foresterhill with the place where he would be given an injection and thus killed. Asked about this he said, 'There I'll be needled to death.' Walter looked at Edward and laughed loudly.

Pseudo-mutuality was also to be seen in Arthur in Session 7. Arthur knew that all eyes were on him, but he avoided any serious talk by rambling over his experiences in the Forces. Norman discerned his chatter-in-order-to-maintain-a-relation. and said, 'Arthur, you're just like a newspaper!' He explained what he meant by saying, 'A newspaper has nothing to say, but it manages to be full!'

It was Norman also who, in his appraisal of the world-over-against-him, discerned with unmistakable clarity the mock-confirmation. In Session 161 he said of 'the general public',

'Now, as far as other people are concerned – well – if it's a summer's day, it's hot, and if it's a winter's day, it's cold.'

Here in symbolic language he was depicting the lack of

genuine concern of the general public, or people in general, for him. If they meet him in the street, and if it is a cold day, they will say, 'Aye, aye, cold day – ' and walk on. Alternatively, if it is a hot day, they will say, 'Aye, aye, it's a hot day – ' and walk on. There is no involvement and no relation, but only the semblance of a relation. There is no serious talk, but only talk that in fact avoids the encounter and relation, and avoids any awareness of estrangement.

Non-mutuality

Here there is no effort to enter into a relation, and there is no effort to preserve the semblance of relation. One person becomes an object to the other. There is no concern for the other's life, or for the other's encounter with my life (cf. Wynne, *et al.*, 1958, p. 220). Thus there is an attempt to accentuate individuality to the detriment of participation.

In the group this was more obvious at the beginning of the therapy. In Group I, for example, it was common to begin a therapeutic group with a total non-mutuality. Note in Session 8, Kerry was still avoiding the helpful presence of others, and pleaded for an exclusive relationship with the therapist.

Even as late as Session 40, Emily's 'meeting' in the group remained one of non-mutuality. When Kerry and Stella were professing their need for help, Emily chipped in to define her position, 'I'm just here to keep them two company.' she said.

Non-mutuality was particularly evident in the last series of Group I. Note Session 131, where all the members refused to disclose themselves, and regarded each other as objects of curiosity – 'nosey-parkering', and so on.

In the group the non-mutuality of isolationism and distance was constantly challenged – challenged by the presence and tacit demands of the therapist, and by the actuality of the group itself. It was common for non-mutuality to give way to pseudo-mutuality by which means the patient concealed her real self and her actual thoughts and desires, and by which she hoped to become acceptable to the therapist.

In Group II it was necessary to participate constantly in the struggle against non-mutuality and the loss of confirmation altogether. Although this loss of confirmation was very much a matter of the present situation, I became aware that it seemed to have roots in the patient's past (perhaps in early childhood) where his being-in-the-world had not been confirmed.

In the group, non-mutuality took its most drastic form in mute or stuporous behaviour and in distancing which sometimes became so extreme that communication seemed to be lost. Note examples in Edward, Session 17; or in Fred's negativism and stereotypes: the extent of his participation would be limited to such expressions as, 'There is too much money spent on doctors.' 'Things are hopelessly out of date.' 'I have nothing to say.'

Arthur also showed another form of non-mutuality when he refused to allow a recording to be made of the group proceedings (Session 64). In effect he was saying that this was not to be trusted; he negated his confirmation of the group and the group's confirmation of him.

Existential therapy, as adopted here, was directed toward the confirmation of the person so that the 'I' would become concerned for the 'Thou', and the one would participate with the other, 'in the irrefragable genuineness of mutuality' (Buber, 1947, pp. 30, 51). To quote Emil Brunner (1937, p. 320):

> '. . . the Self no longer merely regards life from the point of view of the "I", but also from the point of view of the "Thou".'

Brunner enunciates three important points regarding this confirmation which were held in mind throughout the present work:

(a) the other is also an existing person in his individuality and he is given to us

(b) the other meets us in a relationship which demands at least that there should be listening

(c) one should meet the other out of intention.

In the following pages of this section an attempt is made to give some indication of the actual movements of the group to attain this confirmation.

Little need be said about *Group I*, for here confirmation followed on after the usual trends and principles of group therapy were exercised. The therapist himself participated; he was 'present', always encouraging self-disclosure and the commitment of the self to relationship in which there could be a recovery of the awareness of one's being-in-the-world and the confirmation which was available to it. The therapist was sometimes overtly rejecting, i.e. behaving as a 'real person', and this was particularly so as therapy progressed and neared its conclusion. But it was essential to demonstrate that, regardless of this overt rejection, there was still an unerring confirmation of the other person (the patient). It was noticeable that the patients seemed to reflect in the group the character that the therapist was displaying or disclosing towards them.

Not the least force in this confirmation-in-community was the awareness that they were homeless and unloved. No place could be regarded as their abiding place, for no place wanted them and, in a strange way, no place was worthy of them. In the group they found a unique belonging and in the hospital they became unique in the eyes of staff and other patients. In the group they found they were loved and in this setting they were then able to work out their relationships in and to the world – relationships which had become so distorted in the veritable upheaval that precedes and accompanies the schizophrenic onset.

Confirmation seemed to be a crucial issue. 'Am I a person?' or as Kerry so dramatically said in effect, 'Am I only a windmill?' 'Am I a person of genuine worth or am I just something somebody uses?' (Sessions 25, 38–39, Group I.)

The relatives' group played an important and significant part in this confirmation. This was manifested in two ways:

(a) By the simple fact that the relatives attended the relatives' group. In this illness it seemed that the patients had sent up a distress cry to the world. They wanted confirmation of their person and being. As they waited and listened for an answer to their cry, the attendance of a husband at the relatives' group brought the sign of relief as from one who was 'found'. (Note in Group I, Sessions 14, 21, and other places.)

(b) By the fact that, in the relatives' group, the relatives themselves were introduced to their present behaviour and introduced to what their behaviour should become. They were taught about the nature of the illness and shown the importance and necessity of confirmation. In other words, an attempt was made to open to them the possibilities of loving or of re-loving.

I did not neglect the possibility that the relatives, particularly the husbands, may have been in need of confirmation themselves, and this was possibly reflected in their attitude and behaviour towards their wives. There was little doubt that they were disturbed – naturally enough – that their wives were in hospital with a mental disorder. A loved one who perhaps remained a loved one in a different way, had suddenly become strange, frightening, and inaccessible. Shame, anxiety, and hostility towards the patient were all present. With these mixed feelings, the relatives came to the group, and I believe that not only were they helped to understand their relatives (the patients) but they found a necessary confirmation for themselves.

> Davis's mother said, 'You know I think these meetings help *us*!' This may be but a form of empathic support, but I felt that the effect went beyond this. In the group they found a confirmation that was not available and not found elsewhere. Kerry's and Stella's husbands had agreed outside the group, and now disclosed inside, that other than the group they had 'nobody else to talk to'.

The confirmation found in this group was demonstrated in many ways, not least that after each session the relatives would wait for each other and adjourn together to a nearby café for coffee. As another result of these group meetings I discovered that, in addition to meeting each other at my group session, some of the members were arranging to entertain other members of the group (and the patients) in their own homes.

In *Group II* confirmation came in many and diverse ways. In some cases it was clear that confirmation had taken place, while in other instances it was difficult to know what had occurred or if confirmation had taken place, but the overall effect of confirmation was evident. It was thus impossible, and at this stage contrary to the purpose of this work, to distinguish or analyse the prevailing group moods which all contributed to confirmation (or limited it), although an attempt was made to be aware of these moods.

In order to set the situation for confirmation, certain techniques and activities were followed, and cursory reference will be made to these.

(a) *Art Therapy*

Each Tuesday morning, Group II went as a group to the art therapist for painting. The art therapist gave each patient her interest and help and, when occasion arose, she would ask them to clarify verbally what they had painted. Otherwise, as far as the art therapist was concerned, they had liberty to do more or less as they pleased.

Prior to the group therapy session on Tuesday afternoon, the art therapist and I would confer about the proceedings of the morning and then, during the afternoon session, the patients would discuss their own and each other's paintings with me and give their attitudes and opinions. Discussion would also revolve around the topic for the next painting, and although I gave general direction here, I always looked and waited for suggestions to arise from the group. Suggestions from the group became more frequent and more realistic as the group sessions progressed. My own general direction usually concerned suggestions to paint people, e.g. mother, other members of the group, the group, the patient himself, myself, and so on; or movement, e.g. 'the group doing something', some person 'doing something', 'yourself doing something', and so on. As time went on, the patients became very sensitive towards 'the group' featuring in their paintings. In the Tuesday afternoon session it became commonplace to hear them speaking to each other about their paintings of the group; what 'the group' was doing; or 'what *we* are doing.'

It was thought that the art therapy would encourage a participation of each patient in his world, and of each patient in the other patients' world and work. For many weeks the patients made their own individual paintings, but as the group therapy sessions progressed I found they had become more aware and sensitive of the group and so the idea of a group mural was suggested to them and accepted. In all, five of these murals were painted, each one being completed in about three to four weeks. In the painting of these murals, as well as in the murals themselves, the moods of the group and of the individuals became evident. On the one hand there was enthusiasm, on the other aggression, and, occasionally, a request to return to the individual paintings.

When the art therapy was first begun it seemed that the painting represented and perhaps fulfilled a narcissistic need.

e.g. After the first painting (Session 23), the members of the group sat gazing at their own paintings, oblivious to anyone or anything else in the group.

In Session 41 there was a growing awareness of the other person's painting, and thus perhaps the other person himself. Norman attributed to himself the title of the 'best painter'. Edward, however, did likewise, but on my standards Edward's self-attribution was unrealistic. But Davis, Fred, and Walter all endorsed, at least overtly, that Norman did exist and that his painting was better than theirs. (Arthur voted for Davis's painting which was probably another way of voting for his own.)

In the group sessions in which their paintings were discussed and in the art sessions themselves, we saw something of the 'impact, antagonism, conflict and competition with others' (*v.* Goldstein, 1947, p. 203), which contribute to and accompany the process of confirmation:

ARTHUR: (explaining his painting) 'I've tried to get the whole meaning of the group into the painting. It's like the Forces, you have an emblem; there is a symbol, and within the symbol you have other symbols.'

FRED: 'Is this a house?'

ARTHUR: (with disgust) 'No, that is *not* a house! I thought you would know that!'

Arthur then spoke at length and concluded, 'Do you all understand what I am trying to portray in the painting?' (Session 49.)

Note his turning towards the group and his apparent quest for their word of affirmation.

In Session 57 Edward's painting brought some measure of confirmation. He painted his girl-friend. Walter laughed loudly and said, 'Too pot-bellied and bandy-legged!' Edward accepted, but Davis said, 'I've no business laughing. Mine is no better.'

In the group murals, the quest and struggle for self-actualization could be seen:

Note Sessions 112, 116, 120:

In 112, Walter, who had been 'scolded' at the art therapy session, now tried to achieve his self-actualization, not by winning the favourable regard of the group, but by demonstrating to the group his own unmistakable supremacy. In the first instance he did this by confusing the group with a word they did not understand, and in the second instance by an attack on Arthur's self-attributed honour.

In Session 116, Norman's attempt to achieve self-actualization by an individualistic assertion (and to the detriment of the others) was held in question.

In 120, it became evident that Walter had achieved his somewhat dereistic self-actualization by painting an immense clown in the centre of the mural. This commanded the central place in the mural, and though it was a matter of interest and consideration that Edward suggested it represented 'authority' (Session 116), it was noteworthy that Walter regarded the clown as the king. Although he did not actually identify this 'king', it may be significant that at one time Walter had his own self-attributed thoughts of kingship.

(b) *Drama*

This was not injected into the group in the same sense as the art therapy, but did arise from the group proceedings, and was developed and encouraged without any previous planning. It seemed to give considerable impact to the confirmation, particularly since I was involved in this confirmation. Group drama arose first in Session 3, and through this simple act I believe the beginnings of a group formation were manifested.

In Session 9 the drama reached a greater intensity and involvement. Here it arose from Norman's refusal to sit face-to-face with Edward, and from Norman's reference to the fact that he was reminded of riding in a motor-bus. There seemed to be little doubt that this event gave rise to confirmation, not only for Norman and Edward, but for the other members participating, and for the group as a whole.

In Session 14 they dramatized in their own way the Exodus from the film of the *Ten Commandments*. Perhaps the content of the drama was not so important as the group pressure and confirmation that accompanied it: e.g. note Walter's reluctance and refusal to proceed, but when Davis, Norman, and Edward called him back, he came.

In Session 79 the group discussed the fact that Edward was the only one of the group who had not been to the psychologist. (I had asked that each member visit the psychologist for psychological testing.) The group decided to introduce Edward to what he might expect when his turn came. Walter assumed the role of psychologist and Edward did the 'tests'.

In Session 84 the drama was very revealing. Here they acted the 'Kangaroo-Mouse' which had featured in films at the hospital. This drama, however, broke into 'trumpet-blowing' and 'changing-of-the-guards'. The extent of emotional involvement and the feeling which went with the one confirming the other are difficult to describe in words on paper: they had to be experienced.

Sessions 104, 105, pertained to the Easter Event. In 104, Walter and Edward enacted the Crucifixion with involvement and understanding. Note, however, Edward's confusion of 'Good Friday' with 'Man Friday' and of the confirmation Man Friday gave to Robinson Crusoe (Session 105).

The dramatizing of these religious events was of particular interest to me, for in addition to the confirmation which came thereby, the content of the conversation itself was very revealing. Further reference will be made to this in a later section of this chapter.

(c) *Singing and Other Sounds*

Although singing did not play a big part (nor was it purposely injected), when it arose in the group it was seized upon and an attempt was made to turn it to the fulfilment of the purpose of confirmation. I am aware that the way in which the singing arose, both in the first instance and later from time to time, may have been used by the patients to avoid the encounter with each other and with existential reality. A constant attempt was made, however, to direct this singing to the encounter within the group. It was thought that after a satisfactory confirmation had thus taken place, at a later stage the encounter with existential reality would follow. It will be seen from the sessions in which the singing occurred that there was an awareness of the presence of the others, and this became more meaningful to them.

e.g. Note in Sessions 6 and 7 Walter's conflict and struggle.

In Session 10 I taught them a song called 'The road through the heather'. This theme and song returned to the group again and again, and even after months when it had not been mentioned.

After each one had sung, or after a group performance, there followed an acclamation of some form (clapping, stamping, etc.).

It is noteworthy that Walter found satisfaction in being chosen as conductor, and this seemed to accord with the satisfaction he seemed to derive from allied roles on other occasions, e.g. the policeman in Session 9, the psychologist in Session 79, and so on. Although this patient was regarded as greatly deteriorated, and lacking in background, education, and culture, the facility with which he entered and eventually carried through these roles became very remarkable.

In Session 18, and again in 45, Walter introduced the topic of music. Before long he was playing a 'saxophone' – an instrument consisting of a chair turned upside down. Although he had experienced considerable difficulties on earlier occasions both in the act of singing and in keeping tune, here he 'played' 'Love's old sweet song', purposefully and tunefully. He stood up and bowed. The group applauded with animation. (It was interesting that Edward seemed to derive satisfaction from his delegated task of handing the 'saxophone' from one patient to the other.)

Frequently there was a noticeable reluctance amongst the group members to speak out loudly, or even to speak at all. This seemed to be associated with a fearfulness which was involved in the encounter one with the other – a fear that no confirmation would ensue. But there was also the fear that each patient had of himself, which was disclosed in his fear of his own voice. These fears (or when lacking their definite object – these anxieties) are interdependent. The voice or speech represents the participation of the self (though this is not exclusively so). In the fear or anxiety surrounding one's voice there is fear and anxiety surrounding the self. And in speaking there is the fear and anxiety vested in the other for his reception of what is said and his response to it. Here again the self-world structure and the polarity of individualization participation are centrally involved.

In the group this was noted in the extreme forms of muteness shown by Edward and Walter, and to a less extent in Arthur. With Arthur it seemed that he was afraid of and sensitive to himself, and on these occasions, and on the occasions where he felt he was being subjected to the group pressure, he would speak in a soft voice, such that it was very difficult to detect what he was saying. The fearfulness was noticeable; but it was to some extent overcome when they were encouraged to make noises: e.g., instead of applause, I frequently encouraged loud stamping of the feet. At other times we had competitions to see who could make the loudest noise and who could sustain the longest note. Thus in noise-making there was always a group participation. The competitive spirit was very notable. When I took them for a walk I would encourage calling out to each other, and in the group activity, as one competed against the other, I encouraged the 'spectators' to cheer. It is suggested that these events contributed to the necessary process of confirmation of their being- and participation-in-the-world.

(d) *Making Group Speeches*

From time to time the group members were encouraged to stand up and, with composure, address the group on some topic chosen by themselves, the group, or by me. As far as possible the topic was related to some event or person closely associated with the group. The change that occurred with these patients during the time of the therapy was remarkable. At the beginning these men showed frequent and widespread disturbance. Although this alternated with periods in which the disturbance was less noticeable, as time went on the alternations themselves became less frequent and the extent of disturbance less intensive. Each man could make his speech with composure and realism.

e.g. In Session 39 Walter spontaneously said, '*I'll* give them a speech.' Although the speech did not follow, his action (namely, his climbing onto the table and taking control of the situation) represented in a symbolic way some of the qualities involved in making a speech.

With the exception of Fred, all group members showed indications that the group was making its impact upon them. Fred's address to the group retained its stereotyped and blocking pattern with its general lack of animation and feeling. In contrast we noted that Davis, who in his earlier attempts to address the group could only do so with trembling, perspiring, and speech aberrations, was eventually able to make his speech with composure. Edward was the youngest in the group and frequently showed the greatest disturbance. As time went on these disturbances were noticeably less frequent.

Note his behaviour in Session 179, where Walter had failed to keep his individual appointment with me. Edward said, 'We said he would not be getting off, but I'm in favour of letting him off.' Norman said, 'I agree with you, so that should put him more at ease.' Edward went on, 'We'll have his opinion first; if it's a good explanation, we'll let him off.' Walter then entered. Edward stood up and said, 'Where was you at two o'clock?' Walter: 'I was seeing the doctor for a physical.' Edward: 'And where was you at half past three?' Walter: 'I didn't know the time was passing.' Edward: 'Oh, Walter, Walter, Walter!'

Note also the way in which Edward handled the misdemeanour of Norman and Fred – 'We think, gentlemen, that what's expected of you is for you to read out what you've written, and that's all – that's all we want of you. You can have a seat first. You speak first, Norman.' At the end of this episode, Edward said, 'So you are forgiven – on behalf of the group.'

Applause and congratulation played a large part but at the same time directness was exercised in order to avoid tendencies towards pseudo-mutuality. The group-member might be told he was 'not up to standard', that he was 'talking nonsense', that it was difficult to understand him, and so on.

(e) *Group Scrutiny*

Each member was subject to the group scrutiny. He would be asked to stand up before the group while other members would make comments about him, his demeanour, his dress, his looks, his contributions to the group, the possible reasons for his behaviour, and so on. This was begun in Session 3.

This varied in its comprehensibility, but it seemed that it contributed to a group-belonging which appeared to be interdependent with the confirmation arising out of this group scrutiny.

e.g. In Session 8 there appeared a constructive affirmation such as, 'He has not been talking as much as he was yesterday.' But on the other hand the group scrutiny became difficult to assess when Davis rose. Walter looked at him and laughed heartily, and looked at him again. He then said, 'He's like a horse!'

Walter, who in Session 5 was delighted that we had noticed

his haircut, was quick to inform us of this in a later session (Session 17), 'Not a bad trim, eh?'

The group scrutiny became more complex, and as time went on the group came to see that the real issue was not how people looked, but how they regarded the rest of the group.

Such pressure of group scrutiny was evident in Session 160, where Edward presented the group's feelings on the issue of coming late:

> 'If you don't come at half past three from now on, we'll take it that you don't want to come and the door won't be opened, so you'll have to turn back home.'
>
> Note that in Session 161, Edward himself was subjected to this rule; and in Session 176 Fred and Norman were involved.
>
> There is further evidence of this 'higher' form of scrutiny in Session 166, where the group rejected Fred's beard without rejecting him; and where the group rejected Edward's claim that the attendants in the hospital had three years to live. Here again in this latter case it was a rejection of the viewpoint rather than the person who held it, such that Edward still retained his self-esteem in the group, and he felt there was no need to call for their vote on the issue. (Earlier in the group sessions, rejection of a person's viewpoint implied rejection of the person, but with the group-belonging which had developed these two issues were not so inextricable.)

In this group scrutiny some attempt was made to rediscover the polarity of individualization-participation and also the polarities of dynamics-form, and freedom-and-destiny.

(f) *Group Leadership*

Group leadership mainly concerned Edward. Because of his lack of participation and his self-preoccupations, and because of his lack of appeal to me personally, I purposely chose him to be the group chairman. His role was overtly accepted by the group, but it clearly evoked aggression on many occasions. Throughout the therapeutic sessions Norman invariably referred to Edward as

'Mr Chairman', and although it appeard that Norman did this partly out of his own friendly disposition, at times it also appeared to arise from aggression, rivalry, and condescension.

At the beginning of the venture of having Edward as chairman, it was a very slow and tedious matter telling him, step by step, what he was to do and what he was to say. Sometimes it had to be repeated over and over again before he could grasp what was being said to him and before he could appropriate this to the group. As he became more and more aware that this was his role, given to him by me, and endorsed by the others, he began to make much more of it. His best achievement occurred when we went for a walk to Craig-Hill. He showed complete self-sufficiency for his chairman role and did not err (Session 165).

One of his delegated functions as chairman was to close the group each day. At first he could do this only with extensive stumbling and almost word-by-word assistance. As he assimilated this function into his role he carried it out without difficulty. This was not a mechanical or stereotyped function, for he showed animation and interest as he did it, and the extraneous events which arose from time to time were handled with versatility – for instance, after Session 176 had concluded he brought the group members back into the room. He had remembered that he had not announced their next meeting time. There is little doubt that Edward came to accept his role and in it he found some confirmation of his being-in-the-world.

Other members of the group were delegated to assume leadership on a temporary basis, i.e. for one session or for part of a session. At one stage of the group's life, each member took his turn to lead the group on some chosen topic. Here again, confirmation is seen to arise out of the rediscovery of the polarities of existence.

(g) *Outings*

During the group sessions four outings were arranged, and these all played a part in the confirmation.

(i) There was the hospital bus trip to Cruden (Session 143). For the group, *I* allowed them to go. As far as they were concerned, *I* had arranged for them to obtain seats on the bus; and they went as a group. All this had the unmistakable effect of confirmation.

(ii) Professor Millar came to visit them (Session 162). Although this was not an outing as such, it can be regarded here as equivalent to one, and certainly prior to another. They had eagerly anticipated this visit even though they were somewhat apprehensive about it. There was the question of his purpose in coming to see them, but when assured that he was genuinely interested in them, they looked forward to the visit. When Professor Millar arrived, Edward (as chairman) introduced each member and they all responded appropriately by rising and shaking hands. Professor Millar spoke to each one, and each in turn spoke to him. He then showed the group some card tricks and on the succeeding day there were attempts to reproduce these. Note their attitude to Professor Millar, and his suggestion of an invitation to visit him at Foresterhill (Sessions 162, 163).

It appeared that he had so confirmed them that their reactions to the invitation to visit him were mixed (compare Davis and Arthur in Session 163).

(iii) The group visited Professor Millar's Department. Note their anticipation of this in Session 165. On the day of the visit the event was met with enthusiasm. All awaited Professor Millar's arrival in his coach to take them on the ten-mile trip back to Aberdeen to his Department. They were all dressed in their best suits. On the way into the city, we stopped to pick some heather, and this provided a subject for frequent comments. Before going to his Department, Professor Millar took the group to morning coffee in a nearby café and, again, this was received with great satisfaction and awe.

Session 171 (Appendix) gives an abbreviated transcribed recording of some of the proceedings in the Department. There is also a short account of their attitude to the trip (Session 172 – Appendix).

Overall it seemed to be an excellent exercise in endorsement of their person: it was confirmation.

(iv) I took them for two walks: both over two miles in distance (Sessions 165, 182). On these walks I encouraged them to fall into different sub-groups to speak with me or with each other. In addition to this I had purchased a medium-sized ball which we threw back and forth. At the beginning it was like pushing a heavy weight to get them to participate with each other, or in the ball-throwing. It seemed that they were set on the destination and were regardless of what was happening on the way. With the ball I encouraged rivalry and competition and as time went on these actually developed. There were some scuffles to get the ball, and they cheered and clapped as one was successful. In addition I was able to bring their awareness to the fact that a lost ball meant *all* should look for it; or a man behind meant *all* should wait for him.

(h) *Written Communications*

Each day the group members were encouraged to make written communications, which could be directed to the group, to specific group members, or to me. Although there were wide liberties, frequently the group or I would set the topic for these communications. Topics were on items such as:

> The group standards and why I should accept them; We all long for mother-love; What I think mother-love should be; Four things life holds for me; Why I prefer to live rather than die; Should this group make decisions about my personal matters; What I think of the outside world and how I would improve it, and so on.
>
> Frequently the communication would be about a group member and his contribution to the group; or it would be in response to a 'story' told by a group member or the therapist.

Here again, the purposes were to assist my understanding of them; to see what type of communications they would make, if any; to encourage their awareness of my interest and presence, and their awareness of each other and the group.

> e.g. Arthur read his letter to the group while Davis was absent. When Davis arrived, Arthur suggested that Davis would not want to hear his letter so he would not read it again. Before Davis could reply, Arthur began to reread his letter (Session 129).

On the other hand there was an awareness of each other, even in the example cited above. A further example is as follows:

> They had been directed to write letters to one another, the recipient being designated in each case. Arthur 'forgot' that his letter was to be directed to Edward. After Arthur had read his letter, Edward noticed the error and said, 'Did you mention my name? – because the letter's supposed to be to me!' (Session 83.)

In these communications, considered as a whole, it became evident that there was a quest for confirmation. The content did not always give this indication (particularly those of Edward and Arthur) but the actual quest for confirmation seemed to be intimated in many ways – by the fact that they made the communication, or by the fact that they spoke about their failure to make the communication.

Some of the letters on the last day of the therapeutic sessions seemed to come from men who had received their confirmation. This was particularly so in Norman's letter. For him the group had come to an end and I had been removed from the personal realm into the officialdom of the administration. It was no longer: 'Dear Mr M.........' etc., but it was thus:

> My name and address His name and address
> Date
>
> 'Mr Macnab,
> Dear Sir,
> On behalf of the folks and myself too, may I convey my thanks in the work you have accomplished up to the present time. It is said you are leaving, and may I also add personally that the better climate [refers to my return to Australia] will

coincide with a better and substantial post for the future, all found.

I remain, Sir,
Yours faithfully,
N. Hawkins

The organization, the clarity, and the feeling of this letter are noteworthy, and stand in contrast to his earlier communications which were frequently confused, lacking in continuity and coherence, and devoid of any apparent feeling, e.g. the following was meant to be a personal letter to me:

'Norman Hawkins

1930s Identity Card Civil

1. Knit a complete heel of a sock.
2. Press or Street Maps.
3. 1 m. £ beach, 1959
A few extras in sites for new building.

Mr N. Hawkins
Army A 1940 H2
Aberdeen

Past Employment:
1. Building Trade 1930s.
2. Funeral Undertaker 1940s.

Sgd. N. Hawkins'

(j) *The Relatives' Meeting*

There was no doubt that these patients were keenly concerned about the relatives' group. It was a source of great contention and in some cases of certain confirmation. There were discussions on what this relatives' group meant; there were arguments over the failure of some relatives to attend, and there were pressures on members to approach their relatives about non-attendance.

It would be tedious to mention the number of times Norman raised the topic of relatives, and we may note how disturbed Walter became if we dwelt for any length of time on it. (See Sessions 58 or 115.) Davis was horrified when he learned that his mother had not attended the group after having stated that it was her intention to do so. But his satisfaction was clearly evident when he was told that his mother had resumed her attendance.

(See Session 113.) It was significant that when some group members became distressed over the behaviour of their relatives, the group was known to give the members the support they needed, e.g. Walter in Session 115.

As in Group I, so in Group II confirmation was greatly assisted by the attendance of the relatives, by the fact that they were able to learn about the patient and his illness, and rediscover how they should regard him. (This was particularly so with the relatives of Norman, Arthur, and Davis. Perhaps this would have applied also to the other relatives had they been more regular in their attendance. But, in many cases, absence from the group was to be understood rather than criticized. In a way the relatives' group represented a threat to their security; it involved not only a change in the patient, but also a change in the relatives, and since the illness was long-standing, changes in both parties would perhaps inevitably meet with some resistance.)

The question should be raised, however, as to the relation between the sustained confirmation which some patients experienced in the group, and the extent of the concern of their relatives for the relatives' group.

6. THE EXISTENTIAL FOCUS

> 'Man strives ceaselessly to maintain his assumptive world intact. . . . What we have built up as *our* assumptive world is the only universe within which our transactions of living can take place' (Cantril, 1950, p. 91).

The Existential Focus is the meaning and motivating force of a person's existence. It is the assumptions upon which he acts and upon which his world is created, and is experienced by the total being either in awareness or in unawareness. Because of the anxiety and responsibility which are usually associated with it, the Existential Focus is often avoided or intellectualized, and its importance for psychotherapy is sometimes overlooked.

The Existential Focus is significant on two levels, the preliminary and the ultimate.

The preliminary level is that level on which an event does not contribute to any overall configurational pattern, but is short-lived and gives only temporary and intermittent meaning. It seems to be a level of experience in which an event takes place in the present without any awareness of its context in the time-process of present, past, and future. The Existential Focus becomes more a matter of drive-reduction or detensioning. The event has little or no attributed ultimate significance but only an immediate value.

The ultimate level is that level on which an event is experienced in the light of an overall meaning which points the person beyond himself and his situation. Ultimate meaning for a person is that 'which determines his ultimate destiny beyond all preliminary necessities and accidents' (*v.* Tillich, 1951, p. 14). On this level an event or issue may not be immediately or intermittently meaningful, but may nevertheless have significance for the overall and ultimate meaning which the person has attributed to life. Detensioning need not hold satisfaction, but tension may be sustained in the interests of ultimate and perhaps unobtainable goals. Because of my theological frame of reference, the ultimate level of the Existential Focus is regarded as more significant, for it is on this level that the questions of being and non-being are asked.

These questions do not reach their ultimate until man stands with man and apprehends and appropriates the religious, i.e. Christian, Existential Focus such that the ultimate concern is with the constant reception and appropriation of the Christian Message.

Existential therapy attempts to bring an awareness of the manner in which the person grasps and shapes his world, and this should lead to the awareness of the availability and necessity of the ultimate existential focus. The five concepts already discussed are necessarily involved here. It could be said, for example, that out of the encounter, presentness, self-disclosure, participation, and confirmation, a person is led to an ultimate meaning and purpose, and to an ultimate axis around which his life revolves and moves forward. Through the experience of what is subsumed in these concepts, life can take on a purposeful and structured direction representing a decision of the total being. Thus, this Existential Focus can give rise to 'the strength to withstand in openness the confused stream of outer and inner happenings' (Friedman, 1955, p. 36; cf. Wynne *et al.*, 1958, p. 206).

The theologian will benefit in his work and thought if he has some understanding of what is involved in these concepts. In the circumstances of mental illness, and specifically schizophrenia, these are prior to any reception and appropriation of the Christian Message.

There are practical difficulties here for the therapist and theologian. There may be the inclination and tendency to gauge success or failure on whether or not the patient grasps and shapes the therapist's Existential Focus. This may, to some extent, be legitimate, but a difficulty arises in that the assessment is made from the therapist's point of view; and there is the added difficulty that it may be hard to distinguish when the therapist's Existential Focus, which in one sense is his alone, becomes that of the patient. The patient may take over the therapist's Existential Focus by introjecting his world of meanings, or by identifying himself with the therapist. There may also be an intellectual acceptance to please or placate the therapist, or as a means to an end such as to obtain discharge from hospital. In these instances it is difficult to know when and if the new Existential Focus actually belongs to the patient.

In Group I, an attempt was made to bring an awareness of each patient to the availability and necessity of an ultimate Existential Focus. Ususally this was acceptable, but any ultimate concern seemed to turn rapidly to a concern with preliminaries. Instead of the preliminaries leading to the ultimate, the ultimate Existential Focus was reflected on to the preliminaries with the murmur, 'This does not work!' In this group all patients who completed the course of therapy were discharged recovered (psychologically), but only one (Margaret) received and seemed to appropriate a fresh awareness of an ultimate Existential Focus. (This included the reception and appropriation of the Christian Message.) In general, however, there were the recognized trends of estrangement in which any glimpse of the ultimate was lost in the preoccupations with the immediate effect or value. The significance of a quarrel between husband and wife, or the separation of husband from wife, were rarely pursued further than the possible effects on the children, or beyond the statement – 'if only we can get over this one, it'll be all right'.

Although they had experienced one of the most destructive consequences of their estrangement in preliminaries – in the nigh-irredeemable condition of schizophrenia – there was still a preoccupation with these preliminaries. This is not a statement of causality. It does not say that because their Existential Focus was preliminary, schizophrenia developed, nor that if they had an ultimate Existential Focus, schizophrenia would not have developed. We can only say what seems to occur in schizophrenia; beyond this we do not know. The ultimate Existential Focus is wanting, and because of the distortions occurring in the polarities and categories of existence, there is a general absence or distortion in the Existential Focus. If there is any semblance of focus remaining, it obtains on a preliminary level, and if there is any appearance of the ultimate level, this is *only* an appearance.

In Group II no deliberate attempt was made to bring an awareness of the ultimate Existential Focus in terms of the Christian Message, although in this regard it was particularly interesting to witness the almost meaningful enactment of, say, the Crucifixion, or other religious events, e.g. Sessions 104, 105. These enactments (together with written material produced by the patients) suggested that in this state of chronic schizophrenia, the elements of ultimacy *could* be grasped, but not shaped, i.e. they could be apprehended but not appropriated.

Postscript

It is very important to add that schizophrenia, itself a mode of being, can in some cases represent a form of Existential Focus. The condition itself may become the focus giving meaning to the patient's life. In this regard, reference may be made to a patient (aged 51) herself not in my groups but well known to me:

In 1947 she developed schizophrenia, and was admitted to hospital in 1950, where she remained until recently. In 1958 she experienced a spontaneous remission from her illness. She wrote the following letter to her brother (parts of it only are quoted as shown):

> 'A few weeks ago I woke from my delusions . . . I had believed Kingseat [the hospital] to be a training institute for police officers and civil servants. . . . Pay was full board and lodgings and £2 a week pocket money in addition. . . .'

In her letter she proceeded to describe clearly her condition and the hospital situation as she perceived it before she suddenly recovered. Then she added:

> 'Now without any delusions I feel miserable, stripped of all confidence, facing the requirements of life and its problems.'

Thus in losing her schizophrenic condition it appeared that her world of meanings had collapsed.

7. THE RELIGIOUS APPREHENSION

> 'I am come that they might have life, and that they might have it more abundantly.'
>
> (John 10:10)

Generally speaking, in psychotherapy a person's religious belief or his appropriation of the religious revelation is regarded either with suspicion or as something unimportant and peripheral. In this existential therapy, however, the religious apprehension is accepted both for what it is and for its possibilities in the person's living in the world.

Normally the religious apprehension has two aspects:[1] (a) the capacity to grasp the essential nature of the religious teaching and revelation and to express it – the capacity to accept the central

[1] cf. Tillich (1951, p. 76): ' "Grasping" . . . has the connotation of penetrating into the depth, into the essential nature of a thing or an event, of understanding and expressing it. "Shaping" . . . has the connotation of transforming a given material into a Gestalt, a living structure which has the power of being. '

issue of Jesus Christ as a fact of history and of faith, and (b) the capacity to appropriate this teaching or revelation in the person's life, giving it meaning – the capacity to believe and translate the belief into living, such that it brings a new meaning.

These two aspects need not be clearly differentiated but they are interdependent, and the nature of the revelation becomes known by experiencing it as a meaningful structure. Every meaning-structure gathers with it an investment of emotion, and it becomes more than a cognitive or rational system, acknowledging the reality of faith and love.

The religious apprehension is a matter of grasping and shaping both an objective and a subjective reality, i.e. the objective and subjective reality must be appropriated as meaningful structures of Being. There are those who admit the possible validity of the historic event of the Christian revelation and who admit that there is a small minority of people for whom this historic event gathers a certain subjective emotion; but they deny the validity of this subjective reality and deny that the objective event and the subjective reality can become meaningful structures universally. Thus, as there are those who would grasp and shape the religious apprehension with emotional investment, so there are those who, with similar emotion, reject its possibilities.

The religious apprehension, grasped and shaped, fortifies the self and provides for the person an unfailing confirmation of his being, which in turn provides that forward intention by which the person can relate meaningfully to the whole of Being. It thus helps him to deal with his own anxiety and the human predicament generally in a positive and affirmative manner. Every moment becomes a moment of possible fulfilment as he meets God in the other, or as he turns to God in his situation. And at every moment there is an overall proleptic fulfilment which allows him to participate in the human predicament with courage and hope, and with patience as he awaits the final fulfilment.

Paradoxically the religious apprehension is an act of man but fundamentally given by God. One side cannot be accentuated to the detriment of the other. It is in the nature of things that the gift and the act are inter-related. It is neither a solitary gift nor a solitary act. No man comes to this apprehension on his own, for it is within the community of those who have apprehended that he apprehends, and for him that community becomes the medium through which the gift from God comes. The religious apprehension, therefore, is vitally related to man's fulfilment as a man. It is never complete, but it must call man away from his solitary and detached existence into an awareness of his place in community and the necessity of participating in it.

In this study, as in life generally, there were many indications that the grasping and shaping of the religious apprehension were partial; consequently a religious faith was regarded for its instrumental value, for its possibilities as a defence from anxiety and as a prophylactic from further illness.

The attitude among the relatives of the patients was that a religious faith was 'a good thing' so long as it did not entail going to church. In order to discuss the attitude of the patients themselves, we will consider the following examples:

In Group I, Session 47, discussion turned to the stabilizing of the ego-boundaries and to the part that a religious faith could play here. Although it appeared to me that a religious faith was essential, the estrangement and destiny of these patients made the discussion casual and superficial. Stella said, 'Yes, I lost my faith, but that was because I was very sick.' But this did not, in fact, portray her true position. It could be argued that Stella became 'very sick' as a consequence of her loss of faith, as a consequence of her loss of apprehension of ultimate meanings and values, as a consequence of her preoccupation with preliminaries and all the unresolved stress and anxiety which come thereby.

In Sessions 74, 75, the group members became aware of their condition of guilt and scatteredness. In their quest for a unified self, it seemed appropriate to direct their attention to the divine forgiveness and the divine acceptance. Despite their condition it became obvious that their first desire was to please and placate the therapist. It was also evident that there was a definite resistance to any religious apprehension. The reasons for this resistance could be numerous, but it seemed that their estrangement and guilt were so pronounced that the relevance and urgency of a religious faith had been removed from them.

With Desma the position was different, for she had come from a church-going family and she herself was a church member. She told us, however, that when she fell in love with Paul, 'I lost my faith' (Session 82). But there was more involved than was at first apparent. When she was five years old, her father left for war service. For five years her grandfather acted as a foster-father, so it was not surprising to find that when her father returned Desma 'resented' him (Session 88). Up until the time of her breakdown (and even then) she had frequently expressed this resentment in many different ways. Her father made her go to church, but when she became friends with Paul, who was not a church member, she found yet another way to rebel against her father. In rebelling against the Church and the Father of the Church, she also rebelled against her father. 'You are not doing what I brought you up to do,' he told her. But the rebellion against the Church had other components: the presence of unresolved guilt had actualized her further estrangement.

She was guilty over the fact that she had paraded as 'another self' by padding her figure to make her more socially acceptable; she was guilty over her intimacies with Paul; and there was a 'snowballing' guilt over her rebellion against her father. These issues contributed to her resistance to the Church. She seized something she thought she could trust, namely Paul, but even he went off to Borneo and thus presented her with a further threat to an existence which was already unstable. It can be seen here, therefore, that in this breakdown the divine Centre and the religious apprehension were issues for close consideration.

This was no isolated instance. It was evident also in Heather and her husband, who confessed to me that they thought 'all this trouble' began when they stopped attending Church. The significance of this appraisal of their own situation should not be underestimated.

Heather believed that God was punishing her for her misdeeds and her unfortunate past. 'God is making me like this,' she said (Session 102). My assessment of the situation led me at this point to be more directive. I tried to assure her of her forgiveness, and I related her position to the Biblical narrative of the Woman taken in Adultery. It became evident that I had misjudged the situation. It seemed that she thought I was throwing the story at her 'like a stone', and she said, 'Will I have to come through here again? . . . I thought that was the finish.' From this I gathered that she sensed I was giving her a stereotyped answer with all its finality; whereas I might have done better to have said less and 'participated' more. For her this was her guilt, and my easy answer provided no effective solution. It was seen here in Heather (but more so in Margaret to whom this discussion now must turn) that the religious apprehension actually represented a threat.

Note Margaret – Sessions 142 onwards. Margaret's childhood had been associated with rejection and great unhappiness together with the brawling, the harshness, the immorality, and the poverty of her parents. In contrast to this she had been strongly influenced by her grandmother – a staunch member of a religious group.

Margaret, a woman of 22, was admitted to hospital in a distressed condition, saying that her mental torment was only a retribution for her sins. A short time prior to her breakdown she had had pre-marital intercourse (for the first time) with traumatic repercussions. She became delusional and began to hallucinate. The Virgin Mary appeared to her and demanded that she (Margaret) should recite the prayers of the Rosary which were written in gold lettering before her (Margaret was not a Roman Catholic). (See Session 142.) In Session 170, Margaret described how the Virgin Mary 'was pure, I was not. She was a virgin; I was a virgin once, now I'm a virgin no longer.'

On another occasion she saw a pit open in the ground before her, and flames and smoke belched from it. She felt that either she was to be thrown into it or her family would be. Jesus and Judas were both standing above the pit, and Margaret escaped only by doing the penance of walking the streets in her bare feet.

It was little wonder that she was frightened of 'all this heaven and hell business' (Session 163). She thought that she would have to die, but then she said, 'When I thought of dying and going to hell I was scared that you never get out of that place, so I thought it would be better to stick it out here!'

She elaborated the many contradictions she found in the Bible and even more so those found in professing Christians. 'They carry the flag and beat that drum . . . they preach and they pray . . . and the next thing they're in court.' 'As far as religion is concerned,' she said it's 'best left alone.' It was evident that religion had many painful associations for her. It was 'like an ugly fester in my mind, that burst' (Session 185). There were many times when she was extremely resistant to discuss any of the issues relating to it. She was plainly very frightened lest she would have to go through these experiences again; and she was frightened by the reality of the rejection and condemnation which they implied.

As she became aware of my participation in the reality of her world, she seemed to be relieved of the stress, and this relief was even more noticeable when she realized the part which she herself had played in the hallucinations. When she realized, for example, that her one traumatic intercourse with its consequential intense guilt had coloured these hallucinations, she was greatly relieved, for she found that the object of her fear was in herself and not in some external body.

As late as Session 190 she revealed – even at this stage – that she was wearing a cross around her neck out of her fear of going to hell and out of a quest for some assurance that there was some love in the world. Her ambivalence over this cross was perhaps reminiscent of the Gadarene maniac who on the one hand entreated Christ to leave him but on the other hand fell down and worshipped him. In Margaret, this ambivalence was evident in her desire to give the cross to me (and thus to 'lose' herself, for this removal of the cross in a way symbolized her nudism before me) and in her desire to cling to it. 'I get something from it that no minister can give,' she said.

Despite these extremes in her feelings towards religion, it may again be noted that four months after discharge, and after week-by-week supervision, Margaret was able to regard matters of religion in a positive way.

In Group II the cleavage between the capacity to grasp and the capacity to shape the religious apprehension was all the more accentuated, and (as in Group I and life generally) there was a resistance to accept the religious apprehension to the core of their being, and to find there the meaning of all Being. It often appeared that there had been a clear understanding of what had been said regarding these religious issues, but then the picture would become confused and it was difficult to know if this confusion arose from their schizophrenia, their estrangement, or from their background. Note the following examples:

In Session 14 we were concerned with the film of *The Ten Commandments*. Wide disturbances in thought and behaviour were evident, but it was noteworthy that Edward was able to discern the significance of the story. I had told them that the Israelite people in exile had despaired that God no longer cared for them, and I asked the group the significance of Moses coming as a liberator. Edward replied, 'They saw that God *did* care for them.'

Although it was not my policy to impose religious issues on the group, nevertheless, with the passing of the events of the Christian year (Christmas, Easter, Whitsuntide) I attempted to turn these to the group for discussion.

Walter participated eagerly in these issues, though at times his associations seemed disturbed so that when it appeared that he had given a correct statement, care had to be exercised lest this also was a misplaced association. Thus, when he said that the 'origin of Christmas' was in 'the Star of Bethlehem', this could have been a correct statement; but 'The Star of Bethlehem' was the name of a fishing vessel in Aberdeen. Since Walter's remarks were often punctuated with apparently meaningless references to fish (he would interrupt the conversation with: 'Have you got a yellow fish on you?') this remark regarding the origin of Christmas may not be as meaningful as it appears.

Arthur, when asked what he meant by 'the spirit of Christmas' replied with conviction, 'If you don't know, you just don't know. . . .' This seemed to indicate that he regarded it as a feeling well known to those who had it, but otherwise difficult to explain. But when it was suggested that it meant 'goodwill to all men', he rejected this and said, 'That's the English one!' We should note however what Davis said: ' – one gets to believe that when you hear Christmas carols being sung – and you get to listen – and you know it is Christmas carols . . . and you get that feeling inside you that it is Christmas time. You hold your Christmas party, sing carols, sing the hymns, and you think of Jesus Christ, and maybe you know within yourself that it is Christmas.'

In Session 92, Edward was perplexed lest he should meet God or Jesus Christ and not know what to say. Such a remark was perhaps meaningful in itself, but then it was disclosed that he thought Jesus Christ was a patient in the hospital. Care has to be taken lest we who stand outside the schizophrenic world should completely misunderstand these remarks. To Edward's statement Norman replied, 'Here, Edward, it is not the group's opinion, to discuss anybody who is not present.'

In Session 104, Edward and Walter enacted the Crucifixion with considerable feeling and meaning. But in Session 105, Edward confused Good Friday with Man Friday in *Robinson Crusoe*. 'Good Friday is the day Robinson Crusoe met the savage and he was good; and that's why there is a Good Friday.' Fred on the other hand confused Good Friday with Foundation Day, which was also the day on which he was admitted to hospital.

On the issue of Whit Sunday, the group showed a confusion which could have been found in any group. Arthur, who was so knowledgeable on issues relating to the Easter Story, confused Whit Sunday with Druid and pre-Roman times (Session 131.)

In Session 138, reference was made to the Biblical narrative of the Gadarene maniac. Walter read this story meaningfully and explained it to the group. They saw that the story was about a 'schizophrenic', but no attempt was made to apply the story to themselves or to the meaning of their condition. Walter, when he read that the maniac tore himself on the stones, spontaneously said, 'He must have been mad – a madman.' (Walter himself often indulged in this behaviour of self-mutilation.)

We have noted already that Edward sometimes identified himself as God. He was unable to differentiate between the God who gave and the man who received, but the two were embodied in the one person of himself. In Session 61 he said, 'God is getting better', and in Session 161 he said that he was not only Edward, but also God.

A survey of some of the written material produced in Group II showed again the capacity of these patients to grasp what was being said about a religious issue. There were indications, too, of some appropriation of the issue in their lives; but in so far as their lives were the answer to their predicament, the appearance of an appropriation was misleading.

The theologian may ask questions as to what all this means for him. As far as the religious apprehension is concerned, is the schizophrenic different from the so-called normal person? What special approach, if any, should the therapist and pastor employ in order to impart to the schizophrenic this religious apprehension which should reside at the core and centre of his developing and expanding self?

There is little doubt that these questions will eventually become legitimate questions, but at this stage they are somewhat premature and only tentative answers can be given. The present study represents an attempt to lay bare the significance of some of the questions and is itself an embodiment of an early answer to them.

8. EXISTENTIAL VALUE AND EXPERIENCE

'. . . If no value attribute in action is experienced, there is no participation in the on-going process of living and growing' (Cantril, 1950, p. 26).

Experience may be regarded as having the following two aspects:

(a) the overall general experience of reality

(b) the experience where one's perception of the general reality is translated into an event in the person's life, and becomes meaningful to him, or becomes a part of his existential pattern or theme.[1]

The appropriation of the general reality to become a personal experience may be called the *possession-experience*. (In Deuteronomy, Chapter 1, for example, Moses rehearses with the people of Israel how God had told them to go up and 'possess' the land ahead – so, in a symbolic way, the experience of the general reality is to be possessed.) Under different conditions this possession-experience may assume a definite significance which will contribute to the person's standards of value. In addition it may be said that 'we remember the values experienced in life and we store them up, building out of them a standard or pattern of values which we inevitably though generally unconsciously use for later reference' (*v.* Cantril, 1950, p. 26; cf. Allport, 1955, p. 73f.). Some possession-experiences, as they become invested with greater value, will tend to evoke greater participation. Man's capacity to sense the added value in his experience will motivate him to greater endeavour. It follows therefore that the nature of the possession-experience and its value-investment contribute to the person's decision or choice as to whether he will remain secure in his present condition, or whether he will take risks into new experiences 'of emergent qualities' (*v.* Cantril, op. cit., pp. 26, 32).

It may be suggested that this viewpoint places too much emphasis on the individual's appropriation of experience and that value will lose its objectivity. This, however, may be countered by the argument that there can be no existential attitude in isolation from the existential attitude of others, and that the value-

[1] *v.* Wolff (1950, p. 35); cf. Cantril (1950, p. 65); Tillich (1944, p. 62) considers the historical character and the personal decisions of existence.

investment of possession-experiences made by one person will depend on the value-investments made by others. Indeed, even in this matter of existential value and experience, confirmation and its components are not far removed, for as the person finds his experience and value confirmed by others (and theirs confirmed by him) he finds he is able 'to be'.

The schizophrenic, in some cases, seems to lose the capacity to have the possession-experience. Unable to appropriate the general reality to his own experience, he may feel he is merged with the cosmos. He finds that his self is fluid with the universe, and the 'event' in the world is experienced as strange. The possession-experience also tends to take on an excessive value-investment which in turn can greatly influence the existential attitude.

Prior to the schizophrenic episode or breakdown, the value-investments are held in a form of equilibrium, but in the schizophrenic episode one value-investment (or more) may be disturbed and so, too, is the equilibrium. Other value-investments may be accentuated in an attempt to regain the equilibrium or to compensate for the loss in one value-investment, e.g. I found in my patients many *loci* of intense sensitivity, *loci* which by their presence indicated that events in the world of reality had been taken into the patients' experience and contributed their own meaning and significance. On the other hand there were attempts to avoid or escape this experience.

Arthur, in order to avoid the sensitive *locus* of his separation from his wife, would talk on in a way which was often incoherent and incomprehensible (from my point of view). It seemed that for him this was a way by which the world of reality and experience could be avoided, and a way by which the scrutiny of the group could be avoided.

As he encountered the continued group discussion, the issue appeared to take on meaning for Arthur. This did not mean that the issue had no self-attributed meaning before this; it meant that this was the first time in which he disclosed it for the group's endorsement.

A similar example was found in Fred. He often sat with his

head buried in his hands. He found great difficulty in facing the reality of his failure, and his family also seemed to have this difficulty. Fred avoided this sensitive *locus* by withholding his participation, by assuming distant and superior attitudes, by his self-attributions of grandeur. (He lived at a distance and had fantasies of seeing his name written in letters six feet high.) (Session 182.)

It would be expected that a person experiencing a schizophrenic episode would retain something of the possession-experience and value-investment. This was found to be so, but frequently there were changes and distortions in the experience and also in the existential attitude.

e.g. Note the interview with Kerry after Session 95, Group I. Kerry's possession-experience was that she had given her children some Largactil. In the schizophrenic episode, her value-investment took on unreal dimensions. (One might expect that a mother who had done this unintentionally would have been concerned for the welfare of her children and would have contacted her doctor to ensure that there would be no drastic consequences.) With Kerry the value-investment was such that her concern for her children became a concern for the world; her giving of a tablet (which may have produced adverse effects in her children) became a spreading of the 'terrible disease' of cancer. Her other values were also affected. She felt that she was beyond help not only because she had done something about which she felt intolerably guilty (and this was related to her earlier guilt and fear of infecting her children through her masturbation), but because she herself had contracted the 'terrible disease'. She pleaded with me not to expend my energies on her but to turn them to someone whom I *could* help – someone who was worth helping.

These distortions are not confined to the crisis of the episode. Frequently it was found that the episode itself was in the past but the value-investment of the possession-experience was still distorted. (I refer here to Group I, for in Group II, where chronic schizophrenia was present, these distortions, so called, had become part of the person's mode of being.)

> In Group I, Margaret pleaded that her financial needs were so great that she should have her discharge and attend on an out-patient basis. She said, with some arrogance, that she would have no difficulty in obtaining employment. But five weeks after discharge she was still unemployed. As it stands this may not seem unusual, but the change in her existential attitude from one period to the other was so marked that one could only suspect a distortion in value-investment, even at the late stage of five sessions before discharge from hospital.
>
> In Session 185, there were the pressures and cries of great poverty. Five weeks after discharge, faced with the future of unemployment, she calmly discussed the various attempts she had made and the various unsuitable posts which had arisen. The cries of poverty had gone and she said she was satisfied to manage on her Assistance Benefits. Was this only the difference between one who as a patient clamoured for her discharge and one relaxed in her freedom? The medical staff agreed with me that both of these states represented in Margaret distortions in her value-investments.
>
> This can be found also in Desma, in Group I. Four months after her discharge her distortions in value-investment were still evident. This was particularly evident in that she did not or could not communicate that she appreciated the gravity of her mother's deterioration in health. (After Desma's discharge, her mother's heart condition became worse.)

In these groups the capacity of the schizophrenic for the possession-experience was most clearly demonstrated in the group and the group-belonging which developed. At different stages and different times, this possession-experience received different degrees of value-investment, but it was nevertheless an experience which they grasped and shaped. As a consequence of this, existential attitudes underwent certain changes in keeping with the possession-experience of the group. Indeed one of the principles arising from the group was that the person-in-isolation would become aware of the other and turn towards him with the intention of participation and relation. With schizophrenics, this involved a distinctive change in attitude.

The fact that a group developed and that there was a sense of group-belonging and group participation indicated that these changes had taken place.

In Group I there are numerous examples that the group experience had become *their* experience and that their attitude had changed as a result of the encounter in and with the group.

Note, for example, Kerry's perception of the value of the present group experience, Session 45. Stella and Kerry had been given a week's pass from hospital. They were anxious to meet each other socially during that week, but Kerry expressed her concern that she did not know what her husband's attitude would be towards her going away to the other side of the town to see Stella. Stella said, 'Well, . . . I'll come and see you.' I commented as an interpretation that it was satisfying to see they had become such close friends. Kerry replied with feeling, 'It certainly is!'

In Group II, the group experience and group-belonging were also notable and were encouraged at the first opportunity. In Session 3, Walter seemed to recognize that, in order for this group experience to be his, he would have to do something about his neck-tie. When this adjustment was made he was able to posssess the experience which was already possessed by Arthur and Edward, namely, of belonging to a common body. Walter proclaimed his possession-experience by taking his place with the others and saying, 'Meeting of the toffs'.

The term 'group' and their experience of group-belonging became meaningful to them all. Their awareness of the 'presence' of the group and their participation in it became increasingly evident. See for example Edward's reference to the group in Session 113, and his differentiation of the group from 'the outside'.

'If an outsider came in here and asked what the group

was doing, what would we say? What could we say? Well, what could we say, for instance, if I was an outsider and came into the group – but I'm not an outsider, I belong to the group – if you see what I mean, and asked what the group was up to, what would you say?'

Norman's comments in Session 147 are noteworthy. He gave an illustration of how the group was 'like counting from one to ten'. He said that all of the group could count up to ten, and even do this together, but Walter and Edward 'perhaps not so fast'. But they could 'go along with us'. Norman said that this was similar to social welfare. 'We've all not done bad; and are advancing from one to ten, except Edward and Walter are lagging behind sometimes, but we're all advancing. And so we're all happy.'

The value-investment of this possession-experience of the group was also evident. This was seen in Davis's exhortations to the group members to do their best when the group was finally concluded; in Walter's excessive self-mutilations whenever the conclusion of the group was discussed; in Fred's bland acceptance and mechanical expression of sorrow; in Arthur's partial denial of the group's disintegration; in Norman's assertions that there would still be some continuity after I left, so long as he was under the Social Welfare Department; and it was seen in Edward's hitherto unknown behaviour of leaving the hospital (without permission) to go on an extended walk; in his distressed condition, his sudden loss of punctuality, and, latterly, in his absence altogether.

It was clear to me that there was a value-investment here, and I believe that in consequence there was a change in existential attitude which reached out to the other in his attitude. The group itself formed certain standards and this implied that in order for the members to have the possession-experience of the group, their attitude had to undergo some change.

Examples of this may be found in both groups. In Group I, Session 141, it was discovered that Barbara had become friends with a patient who did not belong to the group. The group confronted her with the alternatives – if she continued with the friendship she would have to leave the group, but if she chose to belong to the group she would have to conform to its rules.

In Group II, Session 176, Fred and Norman broke the group rule of punctuality and were forthwith subjected to the group's discipline.

The group experience however did not always evoke what might be regarded as a desirable existential attitude, and the value-investment was sometimes distorted.

This was particularly so with Arthur. At one stage he was prone to see the group experience as warranting the intervention of the police (Session 28); or the intrusion of the town authorities (Session 43). At a later stage he frequently spoke of the group when it seemed that in actuality he meant himself.

He would say, for example, 'They are feeling disgruntled', or 'they are frustrated in their endeavour', and so on.

A different form of distortion arose from Sessions 47, 66. The group had dramatized 'being at sea' in which Walter played the role of captain of the ship. Some weeks later (Session 77) Walter signed his letter, 'Captain Walter W———'. He then reminded me that he was the captain. It seemed that the role-playing had become reality; a distortion of value-investment had taken place, and in turn this had influenced the existential attitude to become one with a tendency toward grandiosity.

As far as the therapy adopted in this work was concerned, the fact that the group experience was not in keeping with reality or with what might be considered desirable, was not of fundamental importance. Fundamentally, the patient was having a 'group experience', and fundamentally it was *his*.

9. EXISTENTIAL SHOCK

'The question of being is produced by the "shock of non-being"' (Tillich, 1951, p. 186).

The existential shock as it is regarded here has three aspects, and as each of these is discussed its overall meaning should become clear.

(a) *There is the gradual or sudden awareness of my predicament, my finitude, of my place in the world, of my death.*

This is a statement which can obtain for every man and is not specifically pertinent to schizophrenia. Existential therapy as adopted here, however, is particularly concerned about this awareness or shock, for there cannot be an adequate appreciation of the polarities of existence without it.

We have already noted that, generally, man lives in a state of unawareness of his existential predicament or, being aware of it, is inclined to disregard or avoid it. In many ways this is understandable. By reason of man's character and capacities he can be involved in an extreme predicament yet be able to transcend it. At one moment he may be struck aware of his finitude, but in the next he experiences an awareness of his expanding unlimitedness. There seems to be an unwillingness to recognize that there is no escape from this predicament, and in this unwillingness he contrives to find an escape. He may turn to drunkenness, which leads to a distortion of value-investments and likewise of the existential attitude. He becomes possessed of a sense of power and significance of which normal life might have deprived him. He finds licence to make himself the centre of his world 'to a degree which normal reason with its consciousness of the ego's insignificance makes impossible' (*v.* Niebuhr, R., 1941, pp. 233–36).

He may turn to sexuality and sexomania; to excessive entertainment; to overactivity in business or other pursuits; or he may turn to suicide, though even here the escape is only partially successful. In all, he is attempting, in the totality of his being and thus perhaps in unawareness, to suppress the existential shock. Although he succeeds to some extent in avoiding the impact of his finitude, this existential shock is always present (albeit in unawareness). It disturbs him in his dreams, confuses his thoughts when he stops to think, leads his life to what it is (retiring, self-conscious, alcoholic, monastic, etc.), driving him into neurosis, perhaps into psychosis.

Existential therapy attempts to bring an awareness of this existential shock (the awareness of being and non-being, the awareness of loss or distortion in the encounter, presentness, self-disclosure, participation, and confirmation, the awareness of estrangement). Awareness of the existential shock is not in itself sufficient, so therapy attempts to lead the patient into a positive and open attitude towards this shock, and to the courage by which it may be met and its impact overcome.

It was found in this work that the sudden awareness of the existential predicament (the shock) could become a precipitating factor of schizophrenia if the resources to handle the shock were absent.

> e.g. Margaret (Group I) had been aware of the guilt and estrangement which she shared with the world. She could be compared with any person of her age in her attempt to avoid the existential question. She became partially intoxicated and this produced a distortion of value-investment such that she permitted sexual intercourse with her boy-friend. When she had recovered from her intoxication she was suddenly 'brought back' from the oblivion in which it was possible to feel free from cultural value-investments. She became aware of the extent to which her own value-investments had been distorted through intoxication, and there followed the painful awareness of her own guilt. The shock was so disturbing, and her resources so lacking, that the only solution her total being could bring to this situation was temporary psychosis.

(b) *The shock of the existential prototype*

The existential prototype occurs in the life of the young child and forms a dynamic node around which is gathered an inarticulated configuration of experiences leading him 'to be', or threatening him in his attempts 'to be'.

The prototype can become the nucleus for the individual's forward or regressive existential attitude.[1] It can create 'the plot'

[1] Wolff (1950, p. 41) adopts the term 'primary scene'. This term is not employed in the present work because of the confusion which may arise from its Freudian connotation.

for his life although need not be a causative factor in what his life becomes. R. D. Laing writes (unpublished MS.):

> '... the basic existential position originally arrived at does not *determine* the subsequent course of life; but ... it does constitute the *Anlage* for what will be the setting of the adult's hopes, disappointments, anxiety, love, hate, in short the setting in which his joy and suffering will be encountered, and the terms in which they will be lived.'

But in addition to having this forward-significance for the person's life, the existential prototype has the further character of drawing about it all similar experiences and of continually producing (or playing some part in producing) counter-reactions as protective mechanisms. It thus seems to set the situation for regressive behaviour, namely, to return to the existential level which prevailed before this shock occurred.

Again, this does not mean that the existential prototype tightly pre-conditions later development – this would disregard man's potentialities of freedom and transcendence. These potentialities are highly significant but are often neglected by those who are involved in therapy. Perhaps one reason for this neglect is that therapists are generally concerned for a sick population, i.e. their patients, in whom these potentialities are lacking. Existential therapy, in attempting to find the ontological structures or patterns of existence, sees these potentialities as part of man's being-in-the-world.

The existential prototype need not be negative in its influence, but in its development as a nodal point in the child's life, the family situation is profoundly important. The child must experience the confirmation of his being. Although all other personal encounters (teacher, associates) may or may not contribute to this confirmation, it is necessary for him to experience it within his family. Here, the situation of the 'double-bind' enunciated by Bateson, Jackson, Haley, and Weakland (1956), is important and relevant. It seems possible that the existential prototype plays a significant part in the development of schizophrenia, and the failure to be aware of it or to adjust to it in some way can be a prerequisite for schizophrenia.

Existential therapy seeks this awareness in the patient and, although the elements involved in the shock of this prototype cannot be erased, the patient's attitude to the shock may be changed, and certain events may be introduced into the patient's life which may reduce its impact. The patient can experience an 'existential birth'. As in biological birth, the child encounters the physical elements of his world, so in the existential birth he is 'born again' in that he encounters the existential realities of his world.

The significance of the existential prototype can be seen in Kerry, Group I. In Sessions 29 and 31, she told the group of her 'shock'. Her parents died. She went to live with a foster-mother, who in turn gave her to her mother, i.e. the foster-mother's mother. The latter ill-treated Kerry, subjecting her to what seemed to be ruthless physical punishment.

Kerry was deprived of her dolls; she was not allowed to visit her brothers and sisters (even today she does not know who they are); she was refused any information about her actual parents except that they were farmers. Kerry told the group of the pain she experienced in not being loved or wanted, and of having no home. Her existential attitude was affected in that, prohibited from making expression of her life and feelings, she turned herself towards herself. The masturbation (self-love) which followed became distorted in its value-investment, the acts of self-love were translated into self-hate and self-punishment, and she believed that this action had brought about some transmissible disease.

This change of existential attitude and the psychosis which followed in later life were related to the shock of the existential prototype.

The existential prototype in its attraction of similar experiences was also evident. When she was in hospital, her relatives-in-law visited her. On the one hand she felt the need to express her outward feelings by weeping (here was someone taking an interest in her), but she stifled her response. She then thought that they saw her as an object (an echo of the existential prototype), so she behaved as an object.

In Session 25, Kerry revealed the pathetic story of the fears that she would become a windmill – 'something that somebody used', and in Session 29 she disclosed how she felt that her husband had withdrawn his love, and that while she hoped she would still have her children, even their love seemed to be waning. Here again were the echoes of the existential prototype.

Her early masturbation represented a protective mechanism as well as an attempt to return to an experience prior to that of the existential prototype. With the accumulation of echoes of the prototype and with her lack of resources to transcend or to take further protective measures (other than suicide), it seemed that her being could only provide the way of a schizophrenic breakdown. It became evident that the Existential Focus (discussed earlier) could play a significant part in the life of this person who seemed to stand subsumed to the onward march of all that was other.

In existential therapy her attitude to the prototype and its echoes was ventilated. An attempt was made to help her to understand the significance of the prototype and the echoes. When the value-investment of the protective and regressive measures was disclosed and brought into a realistic focus, her existential attitude changed. As she became aware of the influences of the prototype, its value-investment diminished. It was as if she knew its name (she knew it was there) and in this knowledge commanded power over it. It was to some extent divested of its crippling and pre-conditioning effects, and she became aware of her freedom to shape her life within its destiny. She became aware of her potentiality to transcend the impact of the shock of the prototype and its echoes.

The change which came over this woman was largely due to what happened in the encounter with the group and with me; to what happened in the presentness, the self-disclosure, the participation, and the confirmation. Here she was loved, and this gave her courage, temporarily at least, to meet herself and others. It was this love that contributed to the courage by which she was able to address herself to the existential shock.

(c) *The shock of the existential redress*

Arising out of the existential prototype, its shock and its echoes, the person's being undergoes a change, an 'existential switch' (*v.* Wolff, 1950, p. 102). This change represents the precursor of what I have called the existential redress. The existential shock is not limited to the individual in whom its impact is concentrated, but involves this individual in his meeting with others and more particularly his immediate family. Thus the existential redress, arising to some extent out of the existential prototype, has three aspects:

(i) the collapse of the secure configurational patterns; and the existential attitude with which the person was once satisfied is temporarily or permanently confused, fragmented, or changed.

> e.g. Suppose I am an exponent of pacifism and the abolition of capital punishment. Suppose also that some man crept into my house in the night and committed an atrocity on my child, and she died. For me the secure patterns may suddenly collapse, and I may be tempted to change my attitude.

(ii) The collapse having occurred there follows either a negative acceptance of this collapse or an attempt to reorganize one's existence around a different Existential Focus.

> e.g. If my wife died, I could either fall into a negative and morbid existence, or I could begin to reorganize my life to make something of it without her.

(iii) The redress not only concerns the shock as it occurs to the person, but concerns also the reverberation of this shock between the person and those whom he meets. It thus has significance for the meeting of the one and the other; it is something that concerns man and man.

For the example of the existential redress in the groups, I turn to Group II, although examples are equally prevalent in Group I.

> In Group II we find the existential shock of redress in Fred when he was diagnosed as mentally ill. Ten years later, when he was still in hospital, some relief seemed to be gained in both himself and his family if they could qualify the illness by saying

it was not 'serious'; or if instead of facing the reality of the diagnosis of schizophrenia they could use the term 'nervous breakdown'. It seemed that these circumnavigations helped to cushion the shock and relieve them from the necessity of changing the configurational patterns or the existential attitudes. Fred came from a family in which there must have been many conflicts. Some of these conflicts would have been present in the family long before Fred was born. Social aspirations and educational and vocational achievements cannot help but colour appraisals of our situation. Thus it was in Fred's family. The mother and all of her children except Fred had received very good education. But his mother had many difficulties with the marriage, and the locale of the family home possibly contributed to these difficulties. The family home was situated in one of the small townships outside the city of Aberdeen; it was a large tenement dwelling in an unattractive street. Fred's father – compared with the mother's outstanding educational record – was a working man who lived close to his feelings. Outwardly he showed little desire to understand Fred or Fred's condition.

There was no doubt about the mother's concern for Fred's welfare, and equally there was no doubt about Fred's devotion to his mother. But there were anomalies which must have disturbed Fred from time to time. There was, for example, his clothing. He always appeared as a sad spectacle, with clothes rarely matching his size. There was also the mother's obvious reluctance over attending the relatives' group. Fred, like all the other patients, had very tender feelings about this group. The lack of appreciation by the relatives of the importance of such small events only added pain to pain for the patient. Fred's mother said she had a 'bad back' and therefore could not attend the group. One day I saw her in the street in Aberdeen. I mentioned this to Fred, commenting that I was pleased her back was better. Fred took this to his mother who sent back the message that I could not have seen her in the street, for she had not been into Aberdeen for years. Perhaps she had already forgotten that she had been to see me twice within the previous six months, and this necessitated coming into Aberdeen. She had also been to see Fred in hospital and this also entailed passing through Aberdeen. In the midst of such subtle contradictions, I imagine Fred was reared.

There would be few mothers who would not make every effort to see their son recover from this schizophrenic condition. Thus, no one would criticize Fred's mother for refusing to accept local expert advice on his condition. She took him to a consultant in London for a second opinion. In her position, we would all do the same. But nobody really knows why we do these things: is it to make sure we do everything for the patient? – or to escape the painful shock of redress in ourselves and for the family? – or why?

In addition to this avoidance arising from Fred's actual illness, the mother possibly saw in Fred her own complete failure. This added fact made her involvement more enclosed, and the possibility of changes in her configurational patterns all the more difficult. All this is not said to condemn the woman, for under any circumstances it must be extremely distressing to accept into one's configurational pattern the fact that there is a chronic schizophrenic in the family. The distress is accentuated in this woman's case in view of the family circumstances, and in view of the fact that the other children of her family had already been so successful.

For Fred himself, the shock involved in the redress was grasped but could not be appropriated. He knew he was a schizophrenic; he knew he was not meant to feed among the swine, and he knew he wanted 'to get out of this asylum'. But his being could not respond to this articulated desire. The shock involved in the redress restricted his being into acceptance.

Inevitably we are confronted by those questions which are so deeply relevant to the existential redress: What is the purpose and destiny of the schizophrenic? Why should this condition be at all? Why should it be one and not the other? Why him and not me? Why now and not later?

As we consider these complex issues we may come to see that at this stage, and for some people, schizophrenia is a necessary mode of being. How else can these people live in a schizophrenic age where men and women are often inaccessible and keep their genuine thoughts concealed; where men and women avoid the encounter with existential reality, and try to find fulfilment among preliminaries; where the divine Centre is displaced and religion is dismissed as peripheral and unnecessary? In the long run we may come to see that this condition of schizophrenia participates in the overall tragedy of mankind and has its peculiar part in the divine economy. Thus, although it may appear to be a hideous and freakish event of our human existence, we may yet meet its reality with hopeful acceptance.

POSTSCRIPT

Although at times there is the tendency to adopt an attitude of philosophical detachment or speculation regarding the condition of schizophrenia, we can never overlook the diabolical nature of the condition and the great impoverishment which is associated with it. In Group II these features were particularly evident; and in this regard we may note the written appraisal made of each of the patients by the Physician Superintendent of the hospital.

For Edward, he wrote, 'A schizophrenic, who at times is almost inaccessible. The prognosis is very poor.'

Walter, 'He presents the picture of a typical chronic schizophrenic, and the prognosis is very poor.'

Davis, 'He suffers from chronic simple schizophrenia and the outlook is not at all good.'

Norman, 'A schizophrenic – superior in attitude, not at all sociable, often behaves strangely. He has been known to lie in a chair with a handkerchief over his face, or to stand in a corner and talk to the wall. Conversation has always been difficult; he cannot keep to the point and often interrupts with irrelevant comments. The prognosis is poor.'

Fred, 'A very awkward man with a frightened look. When alone he takes up strange postures, laughs and grimaces without apparent reason. He suffers from chronic schizophrenia, and the prognosis is very poor.'

> Arthur, 'His symptoms are clearly those of chronic paranoid schizophrenia. The prognosis is definitely very poor.'

In view of examples given earlier in this chapter it is unnecessary to elaborate on the statements given above, but reference to two or three instances will help to show how this poverty was manifest.

> In the face of pathos, the schizophrenic may laugh uproariously. In session 72, Edward sobbed to great excess over the fact that he had taken a flea 'by the wings' and burnt it alive. (It may be significant that he sometimes felt that he, himself, would be burnt alive.) His tears turned rapidly to a great burst of laughter in which Walter joined.
>
> We have noted how Fred distanced himself from every object of participation. He would bury his head in his hands, and sometimes he would put his head and his hands down between his knees, and in this posture he would grind his teeth loudly. His participation in the group was mechanical and often he would memorize parrot-fashion what his contribution was to be. On some occasions he would speak in stereotypes such as 'I have nothing to say', or such-and-such 'is hopelessly out of date'. On the other hand – as if to compensate for this poverty – he would experience fantasies of grandeur: he wanted to see his name written in letters six feet high; he repeatedly told us he was handsome; he was convinced that he could handle the group more efficiently than I could, and be a better therapist than I was. (See Session 182.)
>
> Note also the impoverishment in Davis – to a pathetic extent. He was a very friendly and congenial man and often spoke of 'doing my best' to get out of hospital when already he had been seventeen years there. In written communications to me he would state: 'Life is sweet – '.

It was noteworthy that in spite of the poverty and the dimensions of the existential shock, there was a general negation of the possibility of suicide (except where the schizophrenia was coloured with depressive components). This suggested that there was a preference (of the total being) for a social death rather than a physical death and that some satisfaction was to be derived from such a mode of being. In this existence-at-a-distance with its impoverishment, concealment, and diffusion, it seemed that the schizophrenic was afraid, afraid even of his own identity, and he was set on fabricating an immunity to the threats of any responsible relatedness to the world.

In contrast to this need to live at a distance, the present work attempted to bring the schizophrenic into a situation where he (in the totality of his being) could apprehend that he could now afford to abandon his psychotic mode of existence. We set out to discover a situation which would approach that in which man was *meant* to live, hence the relevance of the study of the fundamental structures of existence. It was thought that if the schizophrenic could experience such a situation, he might experience also the possibilities of courage to turn to a sustained and genuine relation with the world. Although it may have been too ambitious to hope that he would suddenly emerge from his disturbance and deterioration to accept the ultimate values involved in sanity and salvation, it is nevertheless suggested that this present study may represent some progress towards this remote goal.

The foregoing pages point to the fact that although schizophrenia has wide and tragic manifestations, the possibilities of relation and fulfilment are never completely lost. Distancing may become encounter and participation, diffusion and concealment may become presentness and self-disclosure, non-mutuality and pseudo-mutuality may become confirmation. There are clear indications that the schizophrenic can experience a fresh awareness of the claim and address of the world, and can be helped towards a sense of forward self-fulfilment. Thus, it is evident that there *is* 'a pearl at the bottom of the sea', but we must be prepared to go 'deep' enough to find it.

A COMMENT IN CONCLUSION

A concluding word might be spoken to the theologian. He may ask why he should be involved in this type of work and what relevance it has for preaching, communication of the Gospel, and salvation. Indeed, it may be thought that the present study, in its concern for the extreme condition of schizophrenia, is relevant only to a small number and open to a yet smaller one.

But this work stresses, implicitly and explicitly, that these extreme conditions can reveal possibilities of ordinary conditions and that, regardless of whether the conditions are ordinary or extreme, the theologian should be involved in them. The work acknowledges that the theologian's task is threefold, and that each aspect should receive its full accentuation: He must understand the Christian Message; he must communicate it to the world; and he must become involved in the human predicament. Clearly, communication and involvement are related, for if the communication is to be meaningful, it is necessary that there should be understanding, and this will depend to some extent on the involvement with the person in his situation.

The situation of schizophrenia – or mental illness generally – presents no exception. More than any other person, the schizophrenic has foundered in the unresolved dilemma: To be or not to be. To be, for him, means more than a psychiatric cure (though plainly this is of great importance) – it means the rebuilding of his world of assumptions and the rediscovery of hope and courage. In this long and extremely difficult process, it seems to me that the theologian has a clear and vital mandate. He in no way underestimates the psychiatric cure, but actually embraces it as a possible step towards a self-fulfilment in which the patient is led to a new awareness of the self-world relation, to a new discovery of ultimate values, and to a new experience of the divine determining Centre of all being.

No one need labour the fact that the schizophrenic lives in a strange world, but in view of the urgent universality of the Christian Message, the theologian cannot rest until he has found some way of reaching the man in this condition. Clearly no solution will emerge so long as the theologian stands apart from it.

It becomes increasingly evident, therefore, that the only positive answer which is at present available to us to meet this condition is the way of participation. For my part, this participation is not fully understood until there is an awareness that our participation in this human predicament is derived from the divine participation, and that through this we all experience a fundamental unity, one with the other, in which we move together towards our shared and corporate destiny. Under these circumstances the predicament and suffering and inequality of others necessarily strike at the foundations of our security, but instead of drawing us into ourselves we are drawn out beyond ourselves 'to understand, to give, to share, to help'.

> 'The awareness that others who *could* have become fully developed human beings and never *have*, changes my state of full humanity. Their early death, their early or late disintegration, makes my life and my health a continuous risk, a dying which is not yet death, a disintegration which is not yet destruction. In every death which we encounter, something of us dies, in every disease which we encounter, something of us tends to disintegrate' (Paul Tillich: a private communication).

This, then, is a corporate participation which is not only derived from God, but is actually drawn towards God. It could be that the schizophrenic is so far from knowing the divine participation that he must first experience the human participation; that before he can accept the divine acceptance he must experience a genuine human acceptance. Thus so much depends on the meeting in the midst of this disturbance. It may be only a meeting one with the other, but in this meeting a man may move towards the meeting with the Eternal Other and rediscover his possibilities of community and self-fulfilment. It will be seen, therefore, that although the present work is not the theologian's exclusive realm, it has implications which could hold immense significance for him.

Appendix

The events of Group II aroused such widespread interest that Professor Millar brought the group to his rooms at Foresterhill Medical School, where a recording of the session was made. The recording was transcribed and is reproduced below. It was Session 171.

The group entered the playroom at Foresterhill. Norman, who had been there before, drew back the curtains to display the children's toys.

FRED: You don't have children at Foresterhill, do you?

PROFESSOR: We have children up here.

FRED: I thought all the children were at the Sick Children's.

PROFESSOR: Yes, but they do come up here from the Sick Children's Hospital. I see occasionally children with nervous trouble – and take them up here. This is really a play bath that Mr Macnab is sitting on.

NORMAN: Does it come up? (He began to lift the cushions on which I was sitting.) Yes. The bath in there. A good idea eh?

FRED: Yes.

PROFESSOR: So they can sail their boats there and we have a little sand tray here.

NORMAN: There's the right idea now isn't it – see, sand.

PROFESSOR: That's the job.

NORMAN: Maybe find some money in there eh, you never know.

PROFESSOR: Would you like to play with the sand? Would you like to play with the boats?

WALTER: No thank you (laughed).

FRED: Is this where you have your meetings of our families, Mr Macnab?

I: This is where I have the meetings, yes.

FRED: Why is it all sound-proofed?

PROFESSOR: Well because when we give any demonstrations or make recordings and so on, we like to get the voice as soft as possible. You'll notice when I am speaking, it's soft; there is no echo –

FRED: You're recording us today?

PROFESSOR: Yes. And there was another suggestion I had that you might like to do what you did some months ago and record a message to your people again. Would you like to?

WALTER: Oh yes, that's a good idea. We did that last Christmas, remember?

PROFESSOR: You did that very nicely. What do you feel about that, Edward?

EDWARD: That's all right, that's fine, yes, I'd like that.

Walter and I began to play with toys. Walter began to use a hammer on one of the toys. He laughed loudly.

PROFESSOR: Ah, that's it . . . do you see how it works?

(There was a pause while we looked for the piece which Walter had hit across the room.)

Now look at this – give that a bash. (Walter gave it a bash. There was an immediate effect.) (Laughter.) Right, now give that a bash – another one. (Laughter.) You don't need to hit it quite so hard. You're a good shot. Isn't he? (There was a loud crash followed by laughter.)

WALTER: That's finished it.

PROFESSOR: That's broken the handle, no the head, off it – it's not broken, it's just fallen off – it's there some place. We'll get it mended. That's it. Are you good at cowboys, Walter?

(There were noises of Walter shooting with a gun. Fred dressed him as a cowboy.)

PROFESSOR: Which one would you prefer – would you like this one – that bobby's hat; see what you look like in it now. Oh yes. Aye, we are scared of you now. (Walter laughed.) These are little puppets. Have you ever played puppets?

NORMAN: Well, it's very good of you Professor to return the

invitation. (Referred to the fact that they had invited the Professor out to see them; now he had invited them to see him.)

PROFESSOR: Not at all, I'm very glad.

EDWARD: Thanks for the tea.

NORMAN: It's most acceptable.

PROFESSOR: Enjoyed the tea?

EDWARD: Yes.

NORMAN: Edward here is going to make a speech. (Claps.) Come on then, Edward!

EDWARD: Well, I'll just say it was a fine tea and very nice of you to pay for it, and thank you for the motor ride too. It's been good coming here.

DAVIS: Very nice.

EDWARD: And I got a nice piece of heather on my way.

FRED: Beautiful countryside. I've never been out that road before.

EDWARD: Bell heather, and it was very nice of you to invite us to Foresterhill.

PROFESSOR: Well, you are very welcome and you'll come back again.

EDWARD: Yes, oh yes.

DAVIS: We'll be glad to.

PROFESSOR: Thank you very much, Edward.

I said to Walter: You don't want to keep talking about Norman's mother because you think we are going to talk about your mother.

WALTER: Yes.

I: Why not let's talk about *your* mother. (Silence.)

NORMAN: Come on Walter, say something about visiting day or something. How would that do?

WALTER: Do I smoke a cigarette on visiting days, then?

NORMAN: Well, if you get cigarettes you can smoke them, that's what I'm on just now.

WALTER: You are on sweets, are you? Hh! (Chuckles.)

PROFESSOR: He didn't offer you one then, did he?

NORMAN: It's the last one. . . .

NORMAN: Come on Walter, you have your mother out on Sunday.

WALTER: I do not talk to her.

FRED: You must talk to your mother – you are not at loggerheads with her are you? (Silence.)

WALTER: I only talk to her sitting at the table.

NORMAN: Well, you still speak to her, then!

FRED: And do you like your brother?

WALTER: Yes.

FRED: He brings you out oranges and apples, doesn't he?

WALTER: Mmm. (Silence.)

NORMAN: I'll tell you what we'll do. If you change seats with me and one doesn't talk we'll change round. How would that do? You change this seat then, now you've to talk about your mother, right?

WALTER: (Immediately) My mother is a woman of 56.

NORMAN: 56, oh well, that's not bad.

WALTER: There's nine of a family.

NORMAN: Nine, the same as me. (Silence.)

WALTER: Which I am the seventh one and she stays in Garth Dee (a suburb of Aberdeen).

NORMAN: Garth Dee. Well, well.

WALTER: In a two-roomed house.

NORMAN: Beside the sea, eh?

WALTER: Yes.

I: Your mother has not been well lately.

WALTER: But she goes her messages; she goes to the pictures.

I: Where does she stay now?

WALTER: She stops in 4 Robertson Place.

I: That's not Garth Dee is it?

WALTER: No.

I: No . . . she lived in Garth Dee the last time you were home.

WALTER: Yes.

I: And that's why you were thinking Garth Dee?

WALTER: Yes.

PROFESSOR: I'm interested in what Walter is telling us about his mother. Am I right in thinking that he has not been keen to talk about her before?

NORMAN: O definite, yes.

PROFESSOR: Has he talked about her before? Or has he not wanted to talk about her?

NORMAN: Well the second part.

DAVIS: He didn't want it to be talked about.

PROFESSOR: But he did seem to want to talk.

DAVIS: Uhuh.

PROFESSOR: Is there anything else you want to tell us about her?

WALTER: No, no, nothing else.

ARTHUR: We were talking to Fred about influences and how you get your opinions, and we were discussing when we were at home, how your opinions were greatly influenced by your mother.

I: Now before you go on, there was something really important about Fred that brought this all on – have you noticed?

EDWARD: His beard, he shaved it all off.

I: Did you notice that, Edward?

EDWARD: He had a beard. I can see he has no beard now.

FRED: My mother didn't like it.

I: Well, Arthur, would you please go on.

ARTHUR: We were discussing it and he was giving the opinion that he gave his own private opinion to us and later on he gave us the impression that he was inclined to discuss them with his mother and he did admit that his mother somewhat influenced his opinion. Well he discussed it at great length and impressed on everybody that she definitely impressed Fred.

I: Would you recall what the group decided about this beard?

ARTHUR: Yes, that's how it came out a few days before you asked that particular question and we had to vote whether the beard became Fred and we disagreed; but Fred of course thought it did become him and he was quite pleased because of his beard, and he gave us his opinion that he would ask his mother whether he was to keep it or not.

FRED: She disapproved.

ARTHUR: She had disapproved, she didn't like his beard. He gave me the impression that he would shave it off. When it came to a vote whether he should keep it or whether he should shave it off and the majority did disagree with you – it did not become you – he shaved it off – I still think that his mother *did* influence him, nobody else, he shaved his beard off.

DAVIS: Quite so.

FRED: Where's the nurse gone?

I: What about your mother?

FRED: Well, she can't come out to see me just now, she's got a bad back.

I: What about the influence your mother has on you?

FRED: Oh, she has a great influence on me. I always take advice from her.

I: Before you took any notice of the group?

FRED: Before I met the group.

I: No, but even when the group gave a decision, you didn't worry about them did you?

FRED: I sometimes took advice from her – she often helped me in my letters, the things we often used to do at nights, she often helped me.

I: So it was your mother's influence before the group, was it?

FRED: Yes.

PROFESSOR: You've got a good head on you.

FRED: Yes, sir.

PROFESSOR: Have you kept up any of your studies?

FRED: No, I let them fall, sir.

PROFESSOR: You are aiming to get out of hospital?

FRED: Yes, sir.

PROFESSOR: And what will you do when you get out of hospital?

FRED: Try and get a job as a clerk.

PROFESSOR: I wonder if we could go round and ask the same question of the other lads – what they would like to do when they leave hospital. Walter, what would you like to do – or where would you like to be? Where would you like to stay or whom would you like to stay with, if you weren't in hospital?

WALTER: I'd like to be a steward on the *Queen Mary*.

PROFESSOR: There's a job.

NORMAN: That's a big enough job, anyway.

PROFESSOR: Norman?

NORMAN: Oh, a shop assistant of some kind or whatever employment is obtainable in Aberdeen. It depends on the situation.

PROFESSOR: And how about Davis?

DAVIS: I would like to get my old job back in the Co-operative.

PROFESSOR: That's in the dairy.

DAVIS: Yes. If I could get a steady job too, where I left off. Most of all I would like to get my health back again and feel fit and everything. I would be fit enough for work then. I would be quite happy.

PROFESSOR: And how long is it since you worked?

DAVIS: Seventeen years now.

PROFESSOR: And Arthur?

ARTHUR: If I got a job that appeals to one, gives one quite a responsibility and constant change spread out in your own particular way of thoughts; responsibility and a liking for the job, one that appeals to you, gives you a sense of being something.

PROFESSOR: Mmm. Anything in particular you have in mind?

ARTHUR: No.

Professor Millar asked Edward what job he would like when he leaves hospital.

EDWARD: I won't be getting a job when I get out of hospital.

PROFESSOR: Oh?

EDWARD: I'll be going into Foresterhill – Woodend.

PROFESSOR: Oh, what are you going to do there?

EDWARD: Eh? (Chuckles.) Well, I hope to die, sir.

PROFESSOR: You hope to die?

EDWARD: Yes.

PROFESSOR: Oh, but that's a long way away.

EDWARD: But that's what's going to happen anyhow when I leave the hospital.

PROFESSOR: Well, maybe you are *wrong*, supposing you are

wrong. Supposing you leave the hospital and you can work, let's just pretend for fun.

EDWARD: I would get a job at the fish.

PROFESSOR: Ah, that's the job.

NORMAN: That's a healthy job, eh Edward – away in the morning at 5 o'clock.

Paintings: Discussion turned to some of their best paintings, e.g.:

PROFESSOR: Well, Norman, let's have yours, would you?

NORMAN: This one was of Edward.

PROFESSOR: Hold it up and let the boys see it.

NORMAN: This painting is of Edward as best suited, seated. This painting means of Edward as what comments at times he is likely to give.

PROFESSOR: What do you mean by that, now?

NORMAN: Mr Macnab suggested, Professor, that I draw Edward and also him as God, as comments you see. (This refers to the fact that in one session Edward said he was not only Edward, but also God.) There's Edward on the left and there's Edward and his comments – just the same – that he is God.

PROFESSOR: He is God now.

NORMAN: Yes, I gave him a nice purple suit for the definition and comparison.

PROFESSOR: Yes.

NORMAN: White handkerchief and all. Now what comments at times he is likely to give. Well, that's about all there is to it because I was only listening to him you see. But what Mr Macnab wanted was 'give us a proper idea of Edward, his personality, as he is, he thinks he is Edward, we know that – but at the same time he thinks he is God too.'

PROFESSOR: Oh yes, you think you are God sometimes.

EDWARD: Oh no.

NORMAN: Well, not this time – anyway. . . .

NORMAN: So for a background I says, well give him robot signals, that's the easiest of the lot, so I asked you Edward, remember, to agree with this, it's quite suitable for you, remember that?

EDWARD: Aye.

NORMAN: And you were thoroughly delighted? Get the idea now. So Edward is himself is at say, go, and at the same time, just the same as robot signals stopped, you canna go by signals, any ordinary sort of person – so the next time it's at go, God.

PROFESSOR: So there are some times that Edward is himself and that's when it stops and then some times he is God and then it's go.

NORMAN: Just like that – just like that. Well that was my experience. We canna just go on when it said stop. But Edward can do it. He's Edward one minute and explaining himself, and the next minute he's God.

PROFESSOR: Yes, so that this really stands also for what we might call convention – laws of the land and. . . .

NORMAN: Yes, the ordinary person and what his point would be in comparison with Edward. In other words I used that as an easy way out for myself and yet explain the subject.

PROFESSOR: But isn't that just what art means – what you call an easy way out for yourself, it's a way of putting down on a piece of paper a whole collection of very complicated ideas just in one drawing.

Walter had spoken about the sea.

PROFESSOR: When did you last see the sea?

WALTER: 1946.

I: Fred, could you tell Walter some of his experiences on the sea that he doesn't like to talk about?

FRED: You had an accident when you were diving, hadn't you, Walter? You slipped on the bottom of the pool or something like that and you got such a shock you couldn't stand up again, wasn't it; that was your trouble wasn't it? Something to do with diving, I know that.

NORMAN: Well, what probably would be, Walter – was the air out of your lungs, Walter? They put a rope round you and you grabbed it – you grabbed the rope and went up yourself.

WALTER: You see I was going over this tight rope and I fell into the water.

PROFESSOR: Oh, I see.

NORMAN: Oh, it was a tight rope you were going over.

PROFESSOR: And you fell into a tank, is that right, and they fished you out.

WALTER: I don't know what happened.

PROFESSOR: Aye, can you swim?

WALTER: A wee bit, yes.

PROFESSOR: Had you been knocked out in the water?

WALTER: I wasn't familiar with the place, you see.

PROFESSOR: I see – well would you like to see the sea-side?

WALTER: Very much. (Quickly.)

PROFESSOR: Will we go back by the sea-side? Will we go back to Kingseat by the sea-side?

WALTER: Yes – yes, if it's advisable.

PROFESSOR: We can easily do that. Fine, we can stop and just have a wee look at it.

PROFESSOR: How long have you been in, Walter – since 1946?

WALTER: 1947 – 17 November 1947.

PROFESSOR: Who has been in Kingseat the longest?

DAVIS: I think I have.

NORMAN: Davis, is it?

I: What was your first date of admission, Davis?

DAVIS: 41, 41 sir.

PROFESSOR: 1941. And then, Norman?

NORMAN: Well, I'd be 47, round about there, or 49.

PROFESSOR: And Fred?

FRED: I've been in off and on, January 1946 I came in.

PROFESSOR: Arthur?

ARTHUR: 1950.

PROFESSOR: And Edward?

EDWARD: 1951, sir.

PROFESSOR: You'll be wearied to get out.

EDWARD: Oh, yes.

PROFESSOR: And where would you go when you come out?

EDWARD: To my home, sir. I would work at the fish.

PROFESSOR: Yes, and if you didn't?

EDWARD: Well, there would be an ambulance at the door for me to take me to Foresterhill.

PROFESSOR: And then?

EDWARD: Well, they'd put me in bed and thoroughly examine me. They would take me through on a trolley you see, and examine me through in the other room. They would give me chloroform or gas. Of course everything would be really finished to me you see, until the two gentlemen come along and put a needle in one arm and a needle in the other arm and that would be the end of me.

PROFESSOR: That would be the *end* of you?

EDWARD: Yes.

PROFESSOR: Uhuh – they would do this?

EDWARD: Yes.

PROFESSOR: And who are these chaps that would do that?

EDWARD: Oh, just hospital authorities I suppose.

PROFESSOR: And do you believe in an after-life, do you think you would live on afterwards?

EDWARD: No, I don't believe in an after-life.

PROFESSOR: Do you think you would really be finished?

EDWARD: Yes.

PROFESSOR: Would you believe – well I'm a doctor, do you believe that I would do that sort of thing?

EDWARD: No sir, no you wouldna do that.

PROFESSOR: Well, do you think I could stop him?

EDWARD: No sir, I don't think so.

We made arrangements to send recorded messages to the relatives:

EDWARD: Well, Mr Macnab means to say that we have to meet here again, that we'll be coming back here some day again, so he wants us to send messages home to our parents saying that we will be coming back here.

I: That's not quite right.

NORMAN: Get the idea, Edward. At a later date your parents will be coming by here, *we hope*. However, when they come by they'll have a recorded message from us that we have already been here, at the invitation of Professor Millar in return visit to what he paid us at Kingseat, you see? So that's what I'm going to do. We are going to say 'hello' again to the folks when they arrive here; it will be a sort of surprise and make them feel at home, see. They're not accustomed to this sort of atmosphere in the houses of Aberdeen.

I: Do you follow now, Edward?

PROFESSOR: There may be one bit that Edward is still puzzled about; he probably doesn't know whether the group is coming back here. But I'll invite you back here as well as you see, so that's all right, got it?

EDWARD: Yes.

Walter stood up and rubbed his stomach. He then said: 'Oh pish, I'm bustin' again.'

I: Oh, I think you can wait this time, can't you? (Walter puffed and then chuckled.)

PROFESSOR: For this thing, for today, what I would like from Mr Macnab is for you to say a wee message to your folk into the recorder and we'll have it ready for them when they come in the next week or so; is that O.K.?

EDWARD: Yes. Well, Professor Millar means to say we have to talk into here and our parents should come along after we have gone, of course, and hear the recording, you see, of what we were saying. And he wants to have our parents back again or something to see about the other recordings.

NORMAN: That's right, Edward, we'll maybe get a reply from them, you never know. It's a long time till the 23rd October.

PROFESSOR: Yes, the next time you come you may get a recording from them.

I: Edward, you are having a bit of trouble I think, aren't you, because you haven't got any parents to send your message to, but you send yours to Bill and Susan, will you?

EDWARD: Yes. That's right.

I: Before you send your message, Edward, would you explain that this is a group meeting here, and that we are going to talk to them; imagine that we are talking to them in the next room.

EDWARD: Yes. Well, this is Kingseat. I'm from Kingseat along with the other lads, that's Walter, Norman, Fred, Davis, and Arthur, and Professor Millar, and last of all comes Mr Macnab, and so we have come here to Foresterhill along with Professor Millar and Mr Macnab and the rest of the group and I'd like to say 'hello' to Bill and 'hello' to Susan and Margaret, so that's all for just now, thank you.

ARTHUR: I've just to say that I enjoyed it today very well, I enjoyed it and I do believe they have behaved in exactly the same way as they do with Mr Macnab at his own discussions and I hope you enjoy them as I do, thank you.

DAVIS: Well, folks, we come here today and I've had a very pleasant time and I ken I've enjoyed it anyway, a pleasant day and we couldn't have had a better time, so I'm just trying to make the best of it, so I hope that I'll benefit by it.

FRED: Well, Mum, it's been a very, very nice meeting that we have had today. Professor Millar stood us to a small coffee morning at the Gates Café, the weather is beautiful and we had a lovely run in through Persley from Kingseat.

NORMAN: Well Miss ——, my sister Marion, if you are here again it will be a case that we'll have to pay the bus fare this time just for a novelty, that's good enough, because you will be busy enough at home, as far as I know, but should you be here again, you'll be quite welcome either by say October, by Mr Macnab or if not, by Professor Millar, should the need arise, but I doubt that – however, for any news we'll wait and see, thank you.

WALTER: We have enjoyed ourselves very much in the tea room and I'm looking forward to the discussion group again, some time. I could do with a day in town. (Laughed.)

Edward began to bring the meeting to a close: Well, we were coming by the roadside, we stopped, we came in by car you see, Professor Millar's car, and we stopped by the roadside to get some heather, that was Mr Macnab and the group and of course there was an attendant there with us, but when we came back here, like, to Foresterhill, we had our tea in a café, and I think that's about all I have to say, thank you. (Pause.) Well, thank you, Professor Millar for inviting us to Foresterhill and the rest of the group for coming to see Professor Millar at the hospital, I thank you sir.

Session 172 contained a discussion about their trip to see Professor Millar on the previous day.

NORMAN asked: No black marks towards yourself as far as Professor Millar was concerned, Mr Macnab?

There was a discussion of their impressions of the trip, the city, etc. I asked Walter what was his most pleasurable experience on the trip. He replied: 'Coming out of the car at the beach.' Questioned further, he said, 'Seeing the sea.'

I: What was the most unpleasant experience?

WALTER: When we were turning into Craigie Road again. (Craigie Road is the last turning toward the hospital gate.) I don't know . . . it was not long enough . . . was it, Arthur?

Walter suggested that the only thing he did not like about Professor Millar was his moustache: 'It should be more fully grown,' he said. He then turned to Fred and said, 'He should have a bigger car though, shouldn't he . . . do you think he should have given us a better tea than that?'

EDWARD: I *did* object to him asking me where I was going after I leave Kingseat Mental Hospital.

Asked about this, Edward said, 'I thought it put too much of a strain on me.' Asked further: 'I thought he was being personal. I could see no other place that I *could* go to.'

Works Consulted

ABRAHAMS, J. (1948). 'Preliminary report on the Group Psychotherapy of Schizophrenics.' *Amer. J. Psychiat.* **104**, 613–617.

ACKERMAN, H. W. (1944). 'Dynamic Patterns in Group Psychotherapy.' *Psychiatry* **7**, 341–348.

ALEXANDER, F. (1959). 'Impressions from the Fourth International Congress of Psychotherapy.' *Psychiatry* **22**, 89–95.

ALEXANDER, L. (1953). *Treatment of Mental Disorders.* London & Philadelphia: W. B. Saunders.

ALEXANDER, L., and MOORE, M. (1958). 'Multiple Approaches to Treatment in Schizophrenia and Discussion of Indications.' *Amer. J. Psychiat.* **114**, 577–582.

ALLEN, E. L. (1953). *Existentialism from Within.* London: Routledge & Kegan Paul.

ALLERS, R. (1961). *Existentialism and Psychiatry.* Springfield, Ill.: C. C. Thomas.

ALLPORT, G. W. (1943). 'The Ego in Contemporary Psychology.' *Psychol. Rev.* **50**, 451–478.

ALLPORT, G. W. (1950). *The Individual and his Religion.* New York: Macmillan.

ALLPORT, G. W. (1951). 'Prejudice. A Problem in Psychological and Social Causation.' In Parsons, T., and Shils, E. (eds.), *Toward a General Theory of Action.*

ALLPORT, G. W.(1955). *Becoming. Basic Considerations for a Psychology of Personality.* New Haven, Conn.: Yale University Press.

ALPERT, B., and SMITH, P. A. (1949). 'How Participation Works.' *J. soc. Issues* **4–5**, 3–13.

ANON. (1955). 'An Autobiography of a Schizophrenic Experience.' *J. abnorm. soc. Psychol.* **51**, 677–689.

ARIETI, S. (1948). 'Special Logic of Schizophrenic and Other Types of Autistic Thought.' *Psychiatry* **11**, 325–338.

ARIETI, S. (1950). 'New Views in the Psychology and Psychopathology of Wit and of the Comic.' *Psychiatry* **13**, 43–62.

ARIETI, S.(1955). *Interpretation of Schizophrenia.* New York: Brunner.

ASCH, S. E. (1952). *Social Psychology.* New York: Prentice-Hall.

AYD, F. J. (1957). 'A Critique of Tranquilizing Drugs.' In Garattini, S., and Ghetti, V. (eds.), *Psychotropic Drugs.* Amsterdam: Elsevier, pp. 548–555.

AZIMA, H., and WITTKOWER, E. D. (1956). 'Gratification of Basic Needs in Treatment of Schizophrenics.' *Psychiatry* **19**, 121–129.

AZIMA, H., CRAMER-AZIMA, F., and WITTKOWER, E. D. (1957). 'Analytic Group Art Therapy.' *Int. J. Gp. Psychotherap.* **7**, 243–260.

AZIMA, H., WITTKOWER, E. D., and LA TENDRESSE, J. (1958). 'Object Relations Therapy in Schizophrenic States.' *Amer. J. Psychiat.* **115**, 60–62.

BACH, G. R. (1957). 'Observations on Transference and Object Relations in the Light of Group Dynamics.' *Int. J. Gp. Psychotherap.* **7**, 64–76.

BAK, R. C. (1954). 'The Schizophrenic Defence against Aggression.' *Int. J. Psycho-Anal.* **35**, 129–134.

BAKER, A. A., and THORPE, J. G. (1956). 'Deteriorated Psychotic Patients – Their Treatment and its Assessment.' *J. ment. Sci.* **102**, 780–789.

BAKER, A. A., and THORPE, J. G. (1956). 'Some Simple Measures of Schizophrenic Deterioration.' *J. ment. Sci.* **102**, 838–846.

BALES, R. F. (1951). *Interaction Process Analysis.* Cambridge, Mass.: Addison-Wesley, 2nd edition.

BALES, R. F. (1953). 'A Theoretical Framework for Interaction Process Analysis.' Cartwright and Zander, pp. 29–38.

BALES, R. F., and GERBRANDS, H. (1948). 'The "Interaction Recorder".' *Hum. Relat.* **1**, 456–463.

BATESON, G., JACKSON, D. D., HALEY, J., and WEAKLAND, J. (1956). 'Toward a Theory of Schizophrenia.' *Behav. Sci.* **1**, 251–264.

BAYNES, H. G. (1949). *Mythology of the Soul.* London: Methuen.

BEAGLEHOLE, E. (1950). 'Interpersonal Theory and Social Psychiatry.' In Mullahy, P. (ed.), *A Study of Interpersonal Relations*, pp. 50–79.

BECKETT, P. G., ROBINSON, D. B., FRAZIER, S. H., STEINHILBER, R. M., DUNCAN, G. M., ESTES, H. R., LITIN, E. M., GRATTAN, R. T., LORTON, W. L., WILLIAMS, G. E., and JOHNSON, A. M. (1956). 'Studies in Schizophrenia at the Mayo Clinic, I. – The Significance of Exogenous Traumata in the Genesis of Schizophrenia.' *Psychiatry* **19**, 137–142.

BEHYMER, A. F., CANIDA, J., COOPER, S., FADEN, P. D., and KAHNE, M. J. (1957). 'Mental Health Films in Group Psychotherapy.' *Psychiatry* **20**, 27–38.

BELLAK, L. (ed.) (1958). *Schizophrenia – A Review of the Syndrome.* New York: Logos Press.

BERGMAN, P. (1958). 'The Role of Faith in Psychotherapy.' *Bull. Mennin. Clin.* **22**, 92–103.

BINDELGLAS, P. M., and GOSLINE, E. (1957). 'Differential Reactions of Patients Receiving Group Psychotherapy with Concomitant Somatic and Drug Therapies.' *Int. J. Gp. Psychotherap.* **7**, 215–280.

BINSWANGER, L. (1956). *Existential Analysis and Psychotherapy.* In Fromm-Reichmann, F., and Moreno, J. L. (eds.), pp. 114–148.

BINSWANGER, L. (1958). 'The Existential Analysis School of Thought.' In May, R. *et al.*, *Existence*, ch. 7.

BINSWANGER, L. (1958). 'Insanity as Life-Historical Phenomenon and as Mental Disease. The Case of Ilse.' In May, R. *et al.*, *Existence*, ch. 8.

BINSWANGER, L. (1958). 'The Case of Ellen West.' In May, R. *et al.*, *Existence*, ch. 9.

BION, W. R. (1948). 'Experiences in Groups: I.' *Hum. Relat.* **1**, 314–320.

BION, W. R. (1948). 'Experiences in Groups: II.' *Hum. Relat.* **1**, 487–496.

BION, W. R. (1949). 'Experiences in Groups: III.' *Hum. Relat.* **2**, 13–22.

BION, W. R. (1949). 'Experiences in Groups: IV.' *Hum. Relat.* **2**, 295–303.

BION, W. R. (1950). 'Experiences in Groups: V.' *Hum. Relat.* **3**, 3–14.

BION, W. R. (1950). 'Experiences in Groups: VI.' *Hum. Relat.* **3**, 395–402.

BION, W. R. (1951). 'Experiences in Groups: VII.' *Hum. Relat.* **4**, 221–227.

BION, W. R. (1954). 'A Note on the Theory of Schizophrenia.' *Int. J. Psycho-Anal.* **35**, 113–118.

BION, W. R. (1955). See: KLEIN, M., HEIMANN, P., MONEY-KYRLE, R. E. (eds.), *New Directions in Psycho-analysis*, chs. 9, 19. London: Tavistock Publications; New York: Basic Books.

BLAU, A. (1957). 'Benign Schizophrenia.' *Arch. Neurol. & Psychiat.* **78**. 605–611.

BLEULER, E. (1908). *Dementia Praecox or the Group of Schizophrenias.* (Trans. Joseph Zinkin.) New York: International Universities Press, 1950.

BLEULER, M. (1955). 'Research and Changes in Concepts in the Study of Schizophrenia, 1941–1950.' *Bull. Isaac Ray Med. Libr.* **3**, Nos. 1 & 2.

BOISEN, A. T. (1936). *The Exploration of the Inner World. A Study of Mental Disorder and Religious Experience.* New York: Harper & Bros. 2nd edition, 1952.

BOISEN, A. T. (1952). 'The Genesis and Significance of Mystical Identification in Cases of Mental Disorder.' *Psychiatry* **15**, 287–296.

BORGATTA, E. F. (1955). 'Analysis of Social Interaction: Actual, Role-playing, and Projective.' *J. abnorm. soc. Psychol.* **51**, 394–405.

BOSS, M. (1949). *Meaning and Content of Sexual Perversions: An Existentialist Account.* New York: Grune & Stratton.

BOSS, M. (1957). *The Analysis of Dreams.* (Trans. A. J. Pomerans.) London: Rider.

BOVARD, E. W. (1953). 'Group Structure and Perception.' In Cartwright and Zander, pp. 177–189.

BRECKIR, N. J. (1950). 'Hospital Orientation and Training Program for Group Psychotherapy of Schizophrenic Patients.' *Psychiat. Quart.* **24**, 131–143.

BRIGHTMAN, E. S. (1943). 'Values, Ideals, Norms and Existence.' *Phil. & Phenomenol. Res.* **4**, 219–224.

BRODY, E. (1952). 'The Treatment of Schizophrenia' – Review. In Brody and Redlich, pp. 39–88.

BRODY, E. B., and REDLICH, F. C. (eds.) (1952). *Psychotherapy with Schizophrenics.* New York: International Universities Press.

BROWN, C. W., and GHISELLI, E. E. (1955). *Scientific Method in Psychology.* New York and London: McGraw-Hill.

BROWN, G. W., CARSTAIRS, G. M., and TOPPING, G. (1958). 'Post Hospital Adjustment of Chronic Mental Patients.' *Lancet*, ii, 27 Sept., pp. 685–689.

BROWN, J. A. C. (1955). *Subject and Object in Modern Theology.* London: S.C.M. Press.

BRUNNER, E. (1937). *The Divine Imperative.* London: Lutterworth.

BRUNNER, E. (1939). *Man in Revolt.* London: Lutterworth.

BRUNNER, E. (1954). *Eternal Hope.* London: Lutterworth.

BUBER, M. (1937). *I and Thou.* (Trans. R. Gregor Smith.) Edinburgh: T. & T. Clark.

BUBER, M. (1946). *Mamre.* (Trans. G. Hort.) University of Melbourne Press.

BUBER, M. (1947). *Between Man and Man.* (Trans. R. Gregor Smith.) London: Routledge & Kegan Paul.

BUBER, M. (1951). 'Distance and Relation.' (Trans. R. Gregor Smith.) *Hibbert J.* **49**, 105–113.

BUBER, M. (1953). *Eclipse of God.* London: Victor Gollancz.

BUBER, M. (1957a). The William Alanson White Memorial Lectures, Fourth Series. (i) Distance and Relation, pp. 97–104. (ii) Elements of the Interhuman, pp. 105–113. (iii) Guilt and Guilt Feelings, pp. 114–129. *Psychiatry* **20**, 95–129. (Introduction by L. H. Farber, pp. 95–96.)

BUBER, M. (1957b). *Pointing the Way: Collected Essays.* (Trans. and edited by Maurice Friedman.) London: Routledge & Kegan Paul.

BULTMANN, R. (1930). 'Die Geschichtlichkeit des Daseins und der Glaube.' *Zeitschrift für Theologie und Kirche* **10**, 339ff.

BURNHAM, D. L. (1956). 'Misperception of Other Persons in Schizophrenia.' *Psychiatry* **19**, 283–303.

BYCHOWSKI, G. (1952). *Psychotherapy of Psychosis.* New York: Grune & Stratton.

BYCHOWSKI, G. (1954). 'On Handling Some Schizophrenic Defence Mechanisms and Reaction Patterns.' *Int. J. Psycho-Anal.* **35**, 147–153.

CAIRNS, D. (1953). *The Image of God in Man.* London: S.C.M. Press.

CAIRNS, D. (1959). An unpublished Outline and Summary of Martin Heidegger's *Sein und Zeit.*

CAIRNS, D. (1960). *Gospel without Myth.* London: S.C.M. Press.

CAMERON, J. L. (1957). 'Some Implications of Ego Psychology for Group Psychotherapy of Chronic Schizophrenia. *Int. J. Gp. Psychotherap.* **7**, 355–362.

CAMERON, J. L., LAING, R. D., and MCGHIE, A. (1955). 'Patient and Nurse Effects of Environmental Changes in the Care of Chronic Schizophrenics.' *Lancet*, ii, 31 Dec., pp. 1384–6.

CAMERON, J. L., FREEMAN, T., and MCGHIE, A. (1956). 'Clinical Observations on Chronic Schizophrenia.' *Psychiatry* **19**, 271–281.

CANTRIL, H. (1950). *The 'Why' of Man's Experience.* New York: Macmillan.

CAPLAN, G. (ed.) (1961). *Prevention of Mental Disorders in Children.* New York: Basic Books; London: Tavistock Publications.

CARSTAIRS, G. M. (1958). 'Preventive Psychiatry – is there such a thing? *J. ment. Sci.* **104**, 63–71.

CARTER, L., HAYTHORN, W., MEIROWITZ, B., and LANZETTA, J. (1951). 'The Relation of Categorizations and Ratings in the Observation of Group Behaviour.' *Hum. Relat.* **4**, 239–254.

CARTWRIGHT, D. (1951). 'Achieving Change in People: Some Applications of Group Dynamics Theory.' *Hum. Relat.* **4**, 381–392.

CARTWRIGHT, D., and ZANDER, A. (1953). *Group Dynamics – Research and Theory*. Evanston, Ill.: Row Peterson; London: Tavistock Publications.

CARTWRIGHT, D., and LIPPITT, R. (1957). 'Group Dynamics and the Individual.' *Int. J. Gp. Psychotherap.* **7**, 86–102.

CASSIRER, E. (1944). *An Essay on Man*. New Haven, Conn.: Yale University Press. 2nd edition 1945.

CHEIN, I., COOK, S. W., and HARDING, J. (1948). 'The Use of Research in Social Theory.' *Hum. Relat.* **1**, 497–511.

COHEN, B. (1956). 'Motivation and Performance in Schizophrenia.' *J. abnorm. soc. Psychol.* **52**, 186–190.

COHEN, R. A. (1950). 'The Management of Anxiety in a Case of Paranoid Schizophrenia.' In Mullahy, P., *A Study of Interpersonal Relations*, pp. 480–507.

COLM, H. (1953). 'Healing as Participation.' Comments based on Paul Tillich's Existential Philosophy. *Psychiatry* **16**, 99–111.

COSER, L. A. (1956). *The Functions of Social Conflict*. London: Routledge & Kegan Paul.

CREEGAN, R. F. (1954). *The Shock of Existence. A Philosophy of Freedom*. Cambridge, Mass.; Sci-Art Publ.

DASTUR, D. (1959). 'The Pathology of Schizophrenia.' *Arch. Neurol. & Psychiat.* **81**, 601–614.

DAVID, H. P., and VON BRACKEN, H. (eds.) (1957). *Perspectives in Personality Theory*. New York: Basic Books.

DAX, E. C. (1953). *Experimental Studies in Psychiatric Art*. London: Faber & Faber.

DREIKURS, R. (1957). 'Group Psychotherapy from the point of view of Adlerian Psychology.' *Int. J. Gp. Psychotherap.* **7**, 363–375.

DUGAN, J. B. (1957). 'One Aspect of the Psychotic Episode in the Psychotherapy of Schizophrenic Patients.' *Psychiatry* **20**, 177–180.

DURKIN, H. E. (1955). 'Acting Out in Group Psychotherapy.' *Amer. J. Orthopsychiat.* **25**, 644–652.

DURKIN, H. E. (1957), 'Toward a Common Basis for Group Dynamics.' *Int. J. Gp. Psychotherap.* **7**, 115–130.

EISSLER, K. R. (1952). 'Remarks on the Psychoanalysis of Schizophrenia.' In Brody and Redlich, pp. 130–167.

EISSLER, K. R. (1954). 'Notes upon Defects of Ego Structure in Schizophrenia.' *Int. J. Psycho-Anal.* **35**, 141–146.

EKSTEIN, R. (1958). 'Faith and Reason in Psychotherapy.' *Bull. Mennin. Clin.* **22**, 104–108.

ELLENBERGER, H. F. (1958). 'A Clinical Introduction to Psychiatric Phenomenology and Existential Analysis.' In May, R. *et al.*, *Existence*, ch. 3.

ERIKSON, K. T. (1957). 'Patient Role and Social Uncertainty – A Dilemma of the Mentally Ill.' *Psychiatry* **20**, 263–274.

EZRIEL, H. (1950). 'Psychoanalytical Approach to the Treatment of Patients in Groups.' *J. ment. Sci.* **96**, 774–779.

EZRIEL, H. (1952). 'Notes on Psychoanalytic Group Therapy: II. Interpretation and Research.' *Psychiatry* **15**, 119–126.

FABIAN, A. A. (1954). 'Group Treatment of Chronic Patients in a Child Guidance Clinic.' *Int. J. Gp. Psychotherap.* **4**, 243–252.

FAIRBAIRN, W. R. D. (1952). *Psychoanalytic Studies of the Personality*. London: Tavistock Publications.

FALES, W. (1943). 'The Phenomenology of Questions.' *Phil. & Phenomenol. Res.* **4**, 60–74.

FARBER, L. H. (1956a). 'Martin Buber and Psychiatry.' *Psychiatry* **19**, 109–120.

FARBER, L. H. (1956b). 'Secrets of the Universe.' *Psychiatry* **19**, 408–415.

FARBER, L. H. (1958). 'The Therapeutic Despair.' *Psychiatry* **21**, 7–20.

FEDERN, P. (1953). *Ego Psychology and the Psychoses.* (Ed. E. Weiss.) London: Imago Publg. Co.

FENICHEL, O. (1945). *The Psychoanalytic Theory of Neurosis.* London: Routledge & Kegan Paul.

FESTINGER, L. (1947). 'The Role of Group Belongingness in a Voting Situation.' *Hum. Relat.* **1**, 154–180.

FESTINGER, L. (1949). 'The Analysis of Sociograms using Matrix Algebra.' *Hum. Relat.* **2**, 153–158.

FESTINGER, L. (1950). 'The Role of Group Belongingness.' In Miller, J. G., ch. 3.

FESTINGER, L. (1953). 'Informal Social Communication.' In Cartwright and Zander, pp. 190–203.

FINNEY, BEN. C. (1954). 'A Scale to Measure Interpersonal Relationships in Group Psychotherapy.' *Gp. Psychotherap.* **7**, 52–66.

FISH, F. J. (1958). 'A Clinical Investigation of Chronic Schizophrenia.' *J. ment. Sci.* **104**, 34–54.

FISH, F. J. (1958). 'Leonhard's Classification of Schizophrenia.' *J. ment. Sci.* **104**, 943–971.

FITCH, R. E. (1957). 'The Social Philosophy of Paul Tillich.' *Rel. in Life* **27**, 247–256.

FLAVELL, J. N. (1956). 'Abstract Thinking and Social Behavior in Schizophrenia.' *J. abnorm. soc. Psychol.* **52**, 208–211.

FLECK, S., CORNELISON, A. R., NORTON, N., and LIDZ, T. (1957). II. 'Interaction between Hospital Staff and Families.' *Psychiatry* **20**, 343–350.

FLESCHER, J. (1957). 'The Economy of Aggression and Anxiety in Group Formations.' *Int. J. Gp. Psychotherap.* **7**, 31–39.

FOLKARD, M. S. (1956). 'A Sociological Contribution to the Understanding of Aggression and its Treatment.' Reprint from *Proc. Roy. Soc. Med.* **49**, 1030–1034.

FORD, R. S. (1959). 'Existentialism: Philosophy or Theology.' *Rel. in Life* **28**, 433–442.

FOULKES, S. H. (1957). 'Group Analytic Dynamics with Special Reference to Psychoanalytic Concepts.' *Int. J. Gp. Psychotherap.* **7**, 40–52.

FOULKES, S. H., and ANTHONY, E. J. (1957). *Group Psychotherapy – The Psychoanalytic Approach.* Harmondsworth: Penguin Books.

FRANK, J. D. (1952). 'Group Therapy and Chronic Hospitalized Schizophrenics.' In Brody and Redlich, pp. 216–230.

FRANK, J. D. (1957). 'Some Determinants, Manifestations and Effects of Cohesiveness in Therapy Groups.' *Int. J. Gp. Psychotherap.* **7**, 53–63.

FRANKL, V. (1954). 'Group Therapeutic Experiences in a Concentration Camp.' *Gp. Psychotherap.* **7**, 81–90.

FREEMAN, T., CAMERON, J. L., and MCGHIE, A. (1958). *Chronic Schizophrenia.* London: Tavistock Publications; New York: International Universities Press.

FRENCH, J. R. P. (1953). 'The Disruption and Cohesion of Groups.' In Cartwright and Zander, pp. 121–134.

FREUD, ANNA (1948). *The Ego and the Mechanisms of Defence.* London: Hogarth Press. (3rd impression.)

FREUD, S. (1921). 'Group Psychology and the Analysis of the Ego.' In *Complete Psychological Works of Sigmund Freud*, Vol. XVIII. London: Hogarth Press, 1955.

FREUD, S. (1949). *Collected Papers.* Volume IV. London: Hogarth Press.

FREUDENBERG, R. K., and ROBERTSON, J. P. S. (1956). 'Personal Stress in Relation to Psychiatric Illness.' Reprint from *Proc. Roy. Soc. Med.* **49**, 1034–1040.

FREUDENBERG, R. K. *et al.* (1957). 'The Relative Importance of Physical and Community Methods in Schizophrenia.' A Paper: 7 September.

FREYHAN, F. A. (1958). 'Eugen Bleuler's Concept of the Group of Schizophrenias at Mid-Century.' *Amer. J. Psychiat.* **114**, 769–779.

FRIED, E. (1955). 'Combined Group and Individual Therapy with Passive-Narcissistic Patients.' *Int. J. Gp. Psychotherap.* **5**, 194–203.

FRIEDEMANN, A. (1956). 'Psychotherapy in Switzerland.' In Fromm-Reichmann & Moreno, pp. 318–323.

FRIEDMAN, M. S. (1955). *Martin Buber – The Life of Dialogue.* London: Routledge & Kegan Paul.

FRIEDMAN, M. S. (1958). ' "I-Thou" and "I-It".' In *Handbook of Christian Theology.* New York: Meridian Books, pp. 173–176.

FROMM, E. (1939). 'Selfishness and Self-Love.' *Psychiatry* **2**, 507–523.

FROMM-REICHMANN, F. (1939). 'Transference Problems in Schizophrenics.' *Psychoanal. Quart.* **8**, 412–426.

FROMM-REICHMANN, F. (1946). 'Remarks on the Philosophy of Mental Disorder.' *Psychiatry* **9**, 293–308.

FROMM-REICHMANN, F. (1952). 'Some Aspects of Psychoanalytic Psychotherapy with Schizophrenics.' In Brody and Redlich, pp. 89–111.

FROMM-REICHMANN, F. (1953). *Principles of Intensive Psychotherapy*. London: Allen & Unwin.

FROMM-REICHMANN, F. (1959). 'Loneliness.' *Psychiatry* **22**, 1–15.

FROMM-REICHMANN, F., and MORENO, J. L. (eds.) (1956). *Progress in Psychotherapy*. New York: Grune & Stratton.

GERARD, D. L., and SIEGAL, J. (1950). 'The Family Background of Schizophrenia.' *Psychiat. Quart.* **24**, 47–73.

GILDEA, M. C-L., DOMKE, H. R., MENSH, I. N., BUCHMUELLER, A. D., GLIDEWELL, J. C., and KANTOR, M. B. (1958). 'Community Mental Health Research. Findings after Three Years.' *Amer. J. Psychiat.* **114**, 970–976.

GLATZER, H. T. (1952). 'Transference in Group Therapy.' *Amer. J. Orthopsychiat.* **22**, 499–509.

GLICKSMAN, M. (1938). 'A Note on the Philosophy of Heidegger.' *J. Philos.* **35**, 93–104.

GLOVER, E. (1939). *Psychoanalysis*. London: Staples Press.

GLOVER, E. (1955). *The Technique of Psychoanalysis*. London: Baillière, Tindall & Cox.

GOFFMAN, E. (1961). *Asylums – Essays on the Social Situation of Mental Patients and Other Inmates*. New York: Anchor Books, Doubleday.

GOLDMAN, G. D. (1957). 'Some Applications of Harry Stack Sullivan's Theories to Group Psychotherapy.' *Int. J. Gp. Psychotherap.* **7**, 385–391.

GOLDSTEIN, K. (1947). *Human Nature – In the Light of Psychopathology*. Cambridge, Mass.: Harvard University Press.

GORLOW, L., HOCH, E. L., and TELSCHOW, E. F. (1952). *The Nature of Non-Directive Group Psychotherapy. An Experimental Investigation*. New York: Columbia University Press.

GRIMSLEY, R. (1955). *Existentialist Thought*. University of Wales Press.

GROTJAHN, M. (1950). 'The Process of Maturation in Group Psychotherapy and in the Group Therapist.' *Psychiatry* **13**, 63–67.

GRYGIER, P., and WATERS, M. A. (1958). 'Chlorpromazine Used with an Intensive Occupational Therapy Program.' *Arch. Neurol. & Psychiat.* **79**, 697–701.

HACKER, F. (1955). 'Psychiatry and Religion.' *J. Rel.* **35**, 74–84.

HADDEN, S. B. (1951). 'Dynamics of Group Psychotherapy.' *Arch. Neurol. & Psychiat.* **65**, 125.

HADDEN, S. B. (1955). 'Historic Background of Psychotherapy.' *Int. J. Gp. Psychotherap.* **5**, 162–168.

HARE, A. P., BORGATTA, E. F., and BALES, R. F. (1962). *Small Groups – Studies in Social Interaction.* New York: Alfred A. Knopf.

HEATH, R. G. (ed.) (1954). *Studies in Schizophrenia. A Multi-disciplinary Approach to Mid-Brain Relationships.* Cambridge, Mass.: Harvard University Press.

HEIDEGGER, M. (1949). *Existence and Being – An Appreciation by Stefan Schimanski.* London: Vision Press.

HEIDEGGER, M. (1953). *Sein und Zeit.* Tübingen: Niemeyer.

HEIDEGGER, M. (1958). *What is Philosophy?* (Trans. with an introduction by William Kluback & Jean T. Wilde.) London: Vision Press.

HEIDEGGER, M. (1959). *The Question of Being.* (Trans. with an introduction by William Kluback and Jean T. Wilde.) London: Vision Press.

HEINEMANN, F. H. (1953). *Existentialism and the Modern Predicament.* London: Adam & Charles Black.

HENDERSON, D. K., and GILLESPIE, R. D. (1946). *A Textbook of Psychiatry.* London: Oxford University Press. 6th edition.

HILL, L. B. (1955). *Psychotherapeutic Intervention in Schizophrenia.* Chicago: University of Chicago Press.

HOCH, P. H., and PENNES, H. H. (1958). In Bellak.

HOROWITZ, M. J. (1963). 'Graphic Communication.' *Amer. J. Psychotherapy* **17**, 230–239.

HULSE, W. C. (1958). 'Psychotherapy with Ambulatory Schizophrenic Patients in Mixed Analytic Groups.' *Arch. Neurol. & Psychiat.* **79**, 681–687.

HUSTON, P. E., and PEPERNIK, M. C. (1958). In Bellak.

HYDE, R. W., and LESLIE R. C. 'Introduction to Group Therapy for Graduate Theological Students.' (A pamphlet, undated.)

ILLING, H. A. (1957). 'Jung's Theory of Group as a Tool in Therapy.' *Int. J. Gp. Psychotherap.* **7**, 392–397.

JACKSON, D. D. (1957). 'A Note on the importance of Trauma in the Genesis of Schizophrenia.' *Psychiatry* **20**, 181–184.

JACKSON, D. D., BLOCK, JACK, BLOCK, JEANNE, and PATTERSON, V. (1958). 'Psychiatrists' Conceptions of the Schizophrenogenic Parent.' *Arch. Neurol. & Psychiat.* **79**, 448–459.

JASPERS, K. (1938). *Existenzphilosophie.* Berlin & Leipzig: Waller de Gruyter.

JOHNSON, A. M., GIFFIN, M. E., WATSON, E. J., and BECKETT, P. G. S. (1956). 'Studies in Schizophrenia at the Mayo Clinic, II – Observations on Ego Functions in Schizophrenia.' *Psychiatry* **19**, 143–148.

JONES, M. (1957). 'Treatment of Personality Disorders in a Therapeutic Community.' *Psychiatry* **20**, 211–220.

JONES, M. *et al.* (1952). *Social Psychiatry.* London: Tavistock Publications.

JUNG, C. G. (1906). *The Psychology of Dementia Praecox.* (Trans. by A. A. Brill, 1936.) New York: Nerv. & Ment. Dis. Publg. Co.

KANT, O. (1942). 'The Problems of Psychogenic Precipitation in Schizophrenia.' *Psychiat. Quart.* **16**, 341–350.

KATAN, M. (1954). 'The Importance of the Non-Psychotic Part of the Personality in Schizophrenia.' *Int. J. Psycho-Anal.* **35**, 119–128.

KATZENELBOGEN, S. (1942). 'Dementia Praecox – Formulation by Kraepelin, Bleuler, and Meyer.' *Psychiat. Quart.* **16**, 439–453.

KEGLEY, C. W., and BRETALL, R. W. (eds.) (1952). *The Theology of Paul Tillich.* New York: The Macmillan Co.

KELNAR, J., and SUTHERLAND, J. D. (1956). 'Some Current Developments in Psychotherapy in Great Britain.' In Fromm-Reichmann & Moreno, pp. 277–283.

KIERKEGAARD, S. (1846). *Concluding Unscientific Postscript to the Philosophical Fragments.* (Trans. by D. F. Swenson, 1941.) London: Humphrey Milford.

KIERKEGAARD, S. (1847). *Purify Your Hearts.* (Trans. by A. S. Aldworth and W. S. Ferrie, 1937.) London: C. W. Daniel.

KIERKEGAARD, S. (1849.) *The Sickness Unto Death.* (Trans. by Walter Lowrie, 1941.) London: Humphrey Milford.

KITAGAWA, J. M. (1957). 'Joachim Wach and Sociology of Religion.' *J. Rel.* **37**, 174–184.

KLAPMAN, J. W. (1946). *Group Psychotherapy.* London: Heinemann.

KLEH, J., EHRMANTRAUT, W., and FAZEKAS, J. F. (1957). 'The Choice of Psychotropic Drugs in the Treatment of Neuropsychiatric Disorders.' In Garattini and Ghetti (eds.), *Psychotropic Drugs.* Amsterdam: Elsevier.

KLEIN, D. B. (1951). *Abnormal Psychology.* New York: Henry Holt.

KLEIN, M., HEIMANN, P., and MONEY-KYRLE, R. E. (eds.) (1955). *New Directions in Psycho-analysis,* chs. 9, 19. London: Tavistock Publications; New York: Basic Books.

KLUCKHOHN, C. (1951). 'Values and Value – Orientation in the Theory of Action.' In Parsons and Shils, pp. 388–433.

KNIGHT, ROBERT P. (1946). 'Determinism, "Freedom", and Psychotherapy.' *Psychiatry* **9**, 251–262.

KNIGHT, ROBERT P. (1952). 'An Introduction.' In Brody and Redlich, pp. 11–17.

KORS, P. C. (1961). 'The Existential Moment in Psychotherapy.' *Psychiatry* **24**, 153–162.

KRAEMER, H. (1956). *Religion and the Christian Faith.* London: Lutterworth.

KRECH, D., and CRUTCHFIELD, R. S. (1948). *Theory and Problems of Social Psychology.* New York: McGraw-Hill.

KUHN, H. (1951). *Encounter with Nothingness – An Essay on Existentialism.* London: Methuen.

KUHN, R. (1958). 'The Attempted Murder of a Prostitute.' In May, R. *et al.*, *Existence,* ch. 10.

KUNKEL, F. (1938). *Character, Growth, Education.* New York: Lippincott.

LAING, R. D. (1960a). *The Divided Self.* London: Tavistock Publications; Chicago: Quadrangle Books.

LAING, R. D. (1960b). 'The Development of Existential Analysis.' Lecture given to the Royal Medico-Psychological Association.

LAING, R. D. (1961). *The Self and Others*. London: Tavistock Publications; Chicago: Quadrangle Books.

LAING, R. D. 'Infancy and Ontological Insecurity' (Unpublished Manuscript).

LAING, R. D., and ESTERSON, A. (1964). *Sanity, Madness, and the Family*, Volume I. London: Tavistock Publications.

LANGER, S. K. (1951). *Philosophy in a New Key*. Chap. 1. London: Oxford University Press.

LEARY, T. (1955). 'The Theory and Measurement Methodology of Interpersonal Communications.' *Psychiatry* **18**, 147–161.

LEARY, T., and COFFEY, H. S. (1954). 'The Prediction of Interpersonal Behaviour in Group Psychotherapy.' *Gp. Psychotherap.* **7**, 7–51.

LECERF, A. (1949). *An Introduction to Reformed Dogmatics*. London: Lutterworth.

LEMKAU, P. V., and CROCETTI, G. M. (1958). In Bellak.

LESLIE, R. C. (1948). 'Group Therapy as a Method for Church Work.' An Abstract of a Dissertation, Ph.D., Boston University.

LESLIE, R. C. (1950). 'Pastoral Group Psychotherapy.' In *Gp. Psychotherap.* **3**, a Reprint.

LESLIE, R. C. (1950). 'Growth Through Group Interaction.' A Reprint of an Address at Silver Anniversary of Clinical Pastoral Training. Chicago, Oct.

LESLIE, R. C. (1955). 'Group Experience and Communication in Interpersonal Relationships.' *Religious Ed.* **2**, a Reprint.

LEVIN, M. (1957). 'Wit and Schizophrenic Thinking.' *Amer. J. Psychiat.* **113**, 917–923.

LEWIN, K. (1952). *Field Theory in Social Science*. (Edited by D. Cartwright.) London: Tavistock Publications.

LICHTENBERG, J. D. (1963). 'The Return to Reality As A Critical Phase in The Treatment of Schizophrenic Patients.' *Psychiatry* **26**, 26–38.

LIDZ, R. W., and LIDZ, T. (1952). 'Therapeutic Considerations

Arising from the Intense Symbiotic Needs in Schizophrenic Patients.' In Brody and Redlich, pp 168–178.

LIDZ, T., PARKER, B., and CORNELISON, A. (1956). 'The Role of the Father in the Family Environment of the Schizophrenic Patient.' *Amer. J. Psychiat.* **113**, 126–132.

LIDZ, T., CORNELISON, A. R., FLECK, S., and TERRY, D. (1957). 'The Intrafamilial Environment of the Schizophrenic Patient, I: The Father.' *Psychiatry* **20**, 329–342.

LIDZ, T., CORNELISON, A. R., TERRY, D., and FLECK, S. (1958). 'The Intrafamilial Environment of the Schizophrenic Patient, VI: Transmission of Irrationality.' *Arch. Neurol. & Psychiat.* **79**, 305–316.

LIDZ, T., FLECK, S., ALANEN, Y. O., and CORNELISON, A. (1963). 'Schizophrenic Patients and their Siblings.' *Psychiatry* **26**, 1–18.

LIMENTANI, D. (1956). 'Symbiotic Identification in Schizophrenia.' *Psychiatry* **19**, 231–236.

LIPPITT, R. (1950). 'The Strategy of Sociopsychological Research.' In J. G. Miller, ch. 2.

LIPPMAN, H., GERTY, F., and BOYD, D. A. (1958). 'Pastoral-Psychiatric Workshops: St John's Mental Health Institute.' *Amer. J. Psychiat.* **115**, 529–534.

LOESER, L. H. (1957). 'Some Aspects of Group Dynamics.' *Int. J. Gp. Psychotherap.* **7**, 5–19.

LORENZ, MARIAN (1957). 'Expressive Form in Schizophrenic Language.' *Arch. Neurol. & Psychiat.* **78**, 643–652.

LOWITH, K. (1948). 'Heidegger: Problem and Background on Existentialism.' *Soc. Res.* **15**, 345–369.

LUCHINS, A. S. (1955). 'A Social Experimental Approach to Group Psychotherapy.' *J. soc. Psychol.* **42**, 121–127.

MALAMUD, W., and OVERHOLSER, W. (1958). 'Multidisciplinary Research in Schizophrenia.' *Amer. Psychiat.* **114**, 865–872.

MARCEL, G. (1952). *Men Against Humanity.* (Trans. by G. S. Fraser.) London: Harvill Press.

MARQUIS, D. G. (1950). 'Scientific Methodology in Human Relations.' In J. G. Miller, ch. 1.

MARTIN, E. A., and HILL, W. F. (1957). 'Toward a Theory of Group Development. Six Phases of Therapy Group Development.' *Int. J. Gp. Psychotherap.* **7**, 20–30.

MARTIN, P. W. (1955). *Experiment in Depth.* London: Routledge & Kegan Paul.

MAVES, P. B. (ed.) (1953). *The Church and Mental Health.* London & New York: Charles Scribner's Sons.

MAY, A. R. (1957). 'An Attempt to Counter "Institutionalization" in Chronic Schizophrenic Patients.' *Lancet,* i. 1294–1295.

MAY, ROLLO (1950). *The Meaning of Anxiety.* New York: The Ronald Press.

MAY, ROLLO (ed.) (1961). *Existential Psychology.* New York: Random House.

MAY, R., ANGEL, E., and ELLENBERGER, H. F. (1958). *Existence – A New Dimension in Psychiatry and Psychology.* New York: Basic Books.

MAYER-GROSS, W., SLATER, E., and ROTH, M. (1954). *Clinical Psychiatry.* London: Cassell.

MEDALIA, N. Z. (1955). 'Authoritarianism, Leader Acceptance, and Group Cohesion.' *J. abnorm. soc. Psychol.* **51**, 207–213.

MENNINGER, K. A. (1947). *The Human Mind.* London: Allen & Unwin.

MENZER, D., STANDISH, C. T., and MANN, J. (1950). 'Some Observations on Individual Psychotherapy with Psychotics.' *Psychiat. Quart.* **24**, 144–152.

MEREI, F. (1949). 'Group Leadership and Institutionalization.' *Hum. Relat.* **2**, 23–39.

MILLAR, W. M., and BEDDARD, F. D. (1958). Memorandum of Visit to Graylingwell Hospital, Chichester, and Mapperly Hospital, Nottingham.

MILLER, A. (1956). *The Renewal of Man.* London: Victor Gollancz.

MILLER, A. (1958). 'Man.' In *Handbook of Christian Theology.* New York: Meridian Books Inc., pp. 223–226.

MILLER, J. G. (ed.) (1950). *Experiments in Social Progress.* New York: McGraw-Hill.

MINKOWSKI, E. (1958). 'Findings in a Case of Schizophrenic Depression.' In May, R. *et al., Existence*, ch. 4.

MONEY, J. (1948). 'Delusion, Belief, and Fact.' *Psychiatry*. **11**, 33–38.

MONRO, A. B. (1956). 'Behavior Patterns in Mental Disorders.' *J. ment. Sci.* **102**, 742–752.

MORAN, L. J. (1953). 'Vocabulary Knowledge and Usage among Normal and Schizophrenic Subjects.' *Psychol. Monogr.*, No. 370, **67**, No. 20.

MORENO, J. L. (1951). *Sociometry, Experimental Method, and the Science of Society*. New York: Beacon House.

MORENO, J. L. (1953). *Who Shall Survive? Foundations of Sociometry, Group Psychotherapy and Psychodrama*. New York: Beacon House. Rev. edn.

MULLAHY, P. (1950). 'A Philosophy of Personality.' *Psychiatry* **13**, 417–437.

MULLAHY, P. (ed.) (1950). *A Study of Interpersonal Relations*. New York: Hermitage Press Inc.

MULLAHY, P. (1956). 'Interpersonal Psychiatry versus the Philosophy of I-Thou and I-It.' *Psychiatry* **19**, 401–408.

MUNZER, J., and GREENWALD, H. (1957). 'Interaction Process Analysis of a Therapy Group.' *Int. J. Gp. Psychotherap.* **7**, 175–190.

MURRAY, H. A. (1951). 'Toward a Classification of Interaction.' In Parsons & Shils, pp. 434–464.

MCCORD, W., PORTA, J., and MCCORD, J. (1962). 'The Family Genesis of Psychoses.' *Psychiatry* **25**, 60–71.

MCDOUGALL, W. (1920). *The Group Mind*. London: Cambridge University Press.

MCKNIGHT, W. K. (1958). 'Historical Landmarks in Research on Schizophrenia in the United States.' *Amer. J. Psychiat.* **114**, 873–881.

MACMILLAN, D. (1956). 'An Integrated Mental Health Service.' *Lancet*, ii, pp. 1094–1095.

MACMILLAN, D. (1958). 'Community Treatment of Mental Illness.' *Lancet*, ii, pp. 201–204.

MACMILLAN, D. (1958). 'Mental Health Services of Nottingham.' Reprint from *Int. J. Soc. Psychiat.* **4**, 5–9.

MACQUARRIE, J. (1955). *An Existential Theology – A Comparison of Heidegger and Bultmann.* London: S.C.M. Press.

NAUMBURG, M. (1950). *Schizophrenic Art – Its Meaning in Psychotherapy.* New York: Grune & Stratton.

NEWBURGER, H., and SCHAUER, G. (1953). 'Sociometric Evaluation of Group Psychotherapy.' *Gp. Psychotherap.* **6**, p. 7–20.

NIEBUHR, H. RICHARD (1952). *Christ and Culture.* London: Faber & Faber.

NIEBUHR, REINHOLD (1940). *Europe's Catastrophe and the Christian Faith.* London: Nisbet & Co.

NIEBUHR, REINHOLD (1941). *The Nature and Destiny of Man.* Volume I. New York: Charles Scribner's Sons.

NIEBUHR, REINHOLD (1943). *The Nature and Destiny of Man.* Volume II. London: Nisbet.

OVERHOLSER, W., and WERKMAN, S. L. (1958). In Bellak.

PARRISH, M. M. (1953). 'Psychodrama. Description of Application and Review of Techniques.' *Gp. Psychotherap.* **6**, p. 63–89.

PARSONS, T., and SHILS, E. A. (eds.) (1951). *Toward a General Theory of Action.* Cambridge, Mass.: Harvard University Press.

PATTERSON, E. S. (1958). 'Effectiveness of Insulin Coma in the Treatment of Schizophrenia.' *Arch. Neurol. & Psychiat.* **79**, 460–467.

PERRY, J. W. (1953). *The Self – In the Psychotic Process. Its Symbolization in Schizophrenia.* University of California Press.

PFUETZE, P. E. (1954). *The Social Self.* New York: Bookman Associates (an assessment of G. H. Mead and Martin Buber).

POWDERMAKER, F. B., and FRANK, J. D. *et al.* (1953). *Group Psychotherapy. Studies in Methodology of Research and Theory.* Cambridge, Mass.: Harvard University Press.

REDL, F. (1948). 'Resistance in Therapy Groups.' *Hum. Relat.* **1**, 307–313.

REDLICH, F. C. (1952). 'The Conception of Schizophrenia and its Implication for Therapy.' In Brody and Redlich, pp. 18–38.

REICHARD, S., and TILLMAN, C. (1950). 'Patterns of Parent-Child Relationships in Schizophrenia.' *Psychiatry* **13**, 247–257.

REVIEW – 'Rehabilitation Methods for Long-Stay Patients. Netherne Hospital.' (A paper.)

RICKMAN, J. (1950). 'The Role and Future of Psychotherapy within Psychiatry.' *J. ment. Sci.* **96**, 181–189.

RICKMAN, J. (1950). 'The Factor of Number in Individual and Group Dynamics.' *J. ment. Sci.* **96**, 770–773.

ROGERS, C. R. (1951). *Client-Centered Therapy. Its Current Practice, Implications and Theory.* Boston: Houghton Mifflin.

ROGERS, C. R. (1955). 'Persons or Science? A Philosophical Question.' *Amer. Psychologist* **10**, 267–278.

ROBERTS, D. E. (1950). *Psychotherapy and a Christian View of Man.* New York: Charles Scribner's Sons.

ROBERTS, D. E. (1957). *Existentialism and Religious Belief.* (Ed. by R. Hazleton.) New York: Oxford University Press.

ROSE, S. (1957). 'Horney Concepts in Group Psychotherapy.' *Int. J. Gp. Psychotherap.* **7**, 376–384.

ROSEN, I. M., and CHASEN, M. (1949). 'Study of Resistance and its Manifestations in Therapeutic Groups of Chronic Psychotic Patients.' *Psychiatry* **12**, 279–283.

ROSEN, J. (1953). *Direct Analysis.* New York: Grune & Stratton.

ROSENFELD, H. (1954). 'Considerations Regarding the Psycho-analytical Approach to Acute and Chronic Schizophrenia.' *Int. J. Psycho-Anal.* **35**, 135–140.

ROSENTHAL, L., and GARFINKEL, A. (1957). 'Group Therapy Literature – 1956.' *Int. J. Gp. Psychotherap.* **7**, 196–211.

ROSENZWEIG, S. (1942). 'An Hypothesis Regarding Cycles of Behavior in a Schizophrenic Patient.' *Psychiat. Quart.* **16**, 463–468.

ROSS, W. D. (1948). 'Group Psychotherapy with Patients' Relatives.' *Amer. J. Psychiat.* **104**, 623–626.

RUESCH, J. (1953). 'Synopsis of the Theory of Human Communication.' *Psychiatry* **16**, 215–243.

RUESCH, J., and BATESON, G. (1949). 'Structure and Process in Social Relations.' *Psychiatry* **12**, 105–124.

RUESCH, J., and BATESON, G. (1951). *Communication. The Social Matrix of Psychiatry.* New York: W. W. Norton.

RUESCH, J., and PRESTWOOD, A. R. (1949). 'Anxiety – Its Initiation, Communication and Interpersonal Management.' *Arch. Neurol. & Psychiat.* **62**, 527–550.

SARGANT, W. (1957). *Battle for the Mind. A Physiology of Conversion and Brain Washing.* London: Heinemann.

SAVAGE, C., and DAY, J. (1958). 'Effects of a Tranquilizer (Reserpine) on Psychodynamic and Social Processes.' *Arch. Neurol. & Psychiat.* **79**, 590–596.

SCHACHTER, S., ELLERTON, N., MCBRIDE, D., and GREGORY, D. (1951). 'An Experimental Study of Cohesiveness and Productivity. *Hum. Relat.* **4**, 229–238. *v.q.* Cartwright and Zander, ch. 27.

SCHEIDLINGER, S. (1953). 'Freudian Concepts of Group Relations.' In Cartwright and Zander, pp. 52–61.

SCHILDER, P. (1942). *Mind. Perception and Thought in their Constructive Aspects.* New York: Columbia University Press.

SCHINDLER, R. (1956). 'The Development of Psychotherapy in Austria since 1945.' In Fromm-Reichmann and Moreno, pp. 267–276.

SCHNADT, F. (1955). 'Techniques and Goals in Group Psychotherapy with Schizophrenics.' *Int. J. Gp. Psychotherap.* **5**, 185–193.

SCHNEIDER, L. I. (1955). 'A Proposed Conceptual Integration of Group Dynamics and Group Therapy.' *J. soc. Psychol.* **22**, 173–191.

SCHWARTZ, D. P. (1959). 'The Integrative Effects of Participation.' *Psychiatry* **22**, 81–86.

SCHWING, G. (1954). *A Way to the Soul of the Mentally Ill.* (Eng. edn. by R. Ekstein & B. H. Hall.) New York: Int. Universities Press.

SEARLES, H. F. (1958). 'Positive Feelings in the Relationship between the Schizophrenic and His Mother.' *Int. J. Psycho-Anal.* **39**, 569–586.

SEARLES, H. F. (1958). 'The Schizophrenic's Vulnerability to the Therapist's Unconscious Processes.' *J. nerv. & ment. Dis.* **127**, 247–262.

SEARS, R. R. (1951). 'Social Behavior and Personality Development.' In Parsons and Shils, pp. 465–478.

SECHEHAYE, M. (1956). *A New Psychotherapy in Schizophrenia.*

Relief of Frustrations by Symbolic Realization. (Trans. by G. Rubin-Rabson.) New York: Grune & Stratton.

SELYE, H. (1950). *Physiology and Pathology of Exposure to Stress.* Montreal: Acta Inc.

SENF, R., HUSTON, P. E., and COHEN, B. D. (1956). 'The use of Comic Cartoons for the Study of Social Comprehension in Schizophrenia.' *Amer. J. Psychiat.* **113**, 45–51.

SHEA, J. E. (1954). 'Differentials in Resistance Reactions in Individual and Group Psychotherapy.' *Int. J. Gp. Psychotherap.* **4**, 253–261.

SHERIF, M. (1948). *An Outline of Social Psychology.* New York: Harper & Bros.

SIMEY, T. S. (1957). 'Social Investigation. Past Achievments and Present Difficulties.' *Brit. J. Sociol.* **8**, 121–129.

SINGER, J. L., and GOLDMAN, G. D. (1954). 'Experimentally Contrasted Social Atmospheres in Group Psychotherapy with Chronic Schizophrenics.' *J. soc. Psychol.* **40**, 23–37.

SLAVSON, S. R. (ed.) (1956). *The Fields of Group Psychotherapy.* New York: Int. Universities Press.

SLAVSON, S. R. (1957). 'Are there "Group Dynamics" in Therapy Groups?' *Int. J. Gp. Psychotherap.* **7**, 131–154.

SMITH, P. B. (1959). 'A Sunday with Mescaline.' *Bull. Mennin. Clin.* **23**, 20–27.

SOMMER, R., and OSMOND, H. (1962). 'The Schizophrenic No-Society.' *Psychiatry* **25**, 244–255.

SONNEMANN, U. (1954). *Existence and Therapy.* New York: Grune & Stratton.

SOROKIN, P. A. (1956). *Fads and Foibles in Modern Sociology and Related Sciences.* Chicago: Henry Regnery Co.

SPEROFF, B. J. (1955). 'Empathy and Role-Reversal as Factors in Communications.' *J. soc. Psychol.* **41**, 163–165.

SPOTNITZ, H. (1957). 'The Borderline Schizophrenic in Group Psychotherapy.' *Int. J. Gp. Psychotherap.* **7**, 155–174.

STANDISH, C. T., MANN, J., and MENZER, D. (1950). 'Some Aspects of the Psycho-pathology of Schizophrenia.' *Psychiatry* **13**, 439–445.

STAUFFER, E. (1955). *New Testament Theology.* (Trans. by John Marsh.) London: S.C.M. Press.

STEINZOR, B. (1949). 'The Development and Evaluation of a Measure of Social Interaction.' *Hum. Relat.* **2**, 103–121.

STORCH, A. (1924). *The Primitive Archaic Forms of Inner Experiences and Thought in Schizophrenia.* (Trans. by Clara Willard.) New York: Nerv. & Ment. Dis. Publishing Co.

STRAIGHT, B., and WERKMAN, S. L. (1958). 'Control Problems in Group Therapy with Aggressive Adolescent Boys in a Mental Hospital.' *Amer. J. Psychiat.* **114**, 998–1001.

STRAUS, E. W. (1958). 'Aesthesiology and Hallucinations.' In May, R. *et al., Existence,* ch. 5.

SULLIVAN, H. S. (1947). *Conceptions of Modern Psychiatry.* New York: Norton; London: Tavistock Publications.

SULLIVAN, H. S. (1948). 'The Theory of Anxiety in Psychiatry and in Life.' *Psychiatry* **11**, 1–13.

SULLIVAN, H. S. (1949). 'The Theory of Anxiety and the Nature of Psychotherapy.' *Psychiatry* **12**, 3–12.

SULLIVAN, H. S. (1950a). 'The Illusion of Personal Individuality.' *Psychiatry* **13**, 317–332.

SULLIVAN, H. S. (1950b). 'Psychiatry. An Introduction to the Study of Interpersonal Relations.' In Mullahy, P., *A Study of Interpersonal Relations,* pp. 98–121.

SULLIVAN, H. S. (1950c). 'Notes on Investigation, Therapy, and Education in Psychiatry and their Relations to Schizophrenia.' In Mullahy, P., *Study,* pp. 192–210.

SULLIVAN, H. S. (1950d). 'Therapeutic Investigations in Schizophrenia.' In Mullahy, P., *Study,* pp. 446–470.

SUTTIE, I. D. (1948). *The Origins of Love and Hate.* London: Kegan Paul, Trench, Trubner & Co. 4th impression.

SUTHERLAND, J. D. (1952). 'Notes on Psychoanalytic Group Therapy, I: Therapy and Training.' *Psychiatry* **15**, 111–117.

TAYLOR, F. KRÄUPL (1950). 'The Therapeutic Factors of Group Analytic Treatment.' *J. ment. Sci.* **96**, 976–998.

TAYLOR, F. KRÄUPL (1954). 'The Three Dimensional Basis of Emotional Interaction in Small Groups.' *Hum. Relat.* **7**, 441–471.

THIBAUT, J. (1950). 'An Experimental Study of the Cohesiveness of Underprivileged Groups.' *Hum. Relat.* **3**, 251–278. *v.q.* Cartwright and Zander, ch. 9.

THORA, T. (1957). 'Group Psychotherapy in the Rehabilitation Process of the Borderline Patient.' *Int. J. Gp. Psychotherap.* **7**, 406–413.

TILLICH, P. (1944). 'Existential Philosophy.' *J. Hist. Ideas* **5**, 44–70.

TILLICH, P. (1951). *Systematic Theology, Volume I.* Chicago: University of Chicago Press.

TILLICH, P. (1952). *The Courage to Be.* London: Nisbet. Reprinted 1955.

TILLICH, P. (1957). *Systematic Theology, Volume II.* Chicago: University of Chicago Press.

TILLICH, P. (1959). 'The Riddle of Inequality.' A Sermon. Private Communication.

TÖNNIES, F. (1955). *Community and Association.* (*Gemeinschaft und Gesellschaft*). (Trans. by C. P. Loomis.) London: Routledge & Kegan Paul.

TOWER, S. S. (1950). 'Management of Paranoid Trends in Treatment of a Post-Psychotic Obsessional Condition.' In Mullahy (ed.), *A Study of Interpersonal Relations*, pp. 471–479.

TWEEDIE, D. F. (1961). *Logotherapy and The Christian Faith.* Michigan: Baker.

ULMAN, E. (1953). 'Art Therapy at an Outpatient Clinic.' *Psychiatry* **16**, 55–64.

UNGERSMA, A. J. (1961). *The Search for Meaning.* U.S.A.: Allen and Unwin.

VON GEBSATTELL, V. E. (1958). 'The World of the Compulsive.' In May, R. *et al.*, *Existence*, ch. 6.

VON WITZLEBEN, H. D. (1958). 'On Loneliness.' *Psychiatry* **21**, 27–43.

VARLEY, B. K. (1959). '"Reaching out" Therapy with Schizophrenic Patients.' *Amer. J. Orthopsychiat.* **29**, 407–416.

WAHL, J. (1943-4). 'Religion, Dialectic, and Transcendent.' *Phil. & Phenomen. Res.* **4**, 496–505.

WALLACE, M. (1956). 'Future Time Perspective in Schizophrenia.' *J. abnorm. soc. Psychol.* **52**, 240–245.

WEAKLAND, J. K., and JACKSON, D. D. (1958). 'Patient and Therapist Observations on the Circumstances of a Schizophrenic Episode.' Reprint from *Arch. Neurol. & Psychiat.* **79**, 554–574.

WEIGERT, E. (1949). 'Existentialism and its Relation to Psychotherapy.' *Psychiatry* **12**, 399–412.

WEIGERT, E. (1958). 'Problems of Communication between Doctor and Patient.' *Psychiatry* **21**, 241–248.

WELLS GOODRICH, D., MAZER, J., and CLINE, B. (1958). 'Fostering the Involvement of the Psychiatric Patient in Group Activities.' *Psychiatry* **21**, 259–268.

WEXLER, M. (1952). 'The Structural Problem in Schizophrenia. The Role of the Internal Object.' In Brody and Redlich, pp. 179–201.

WHITMAN, R., and STOCK, D. (1958). 'The Group Focal Conflict.' *Psychiatry* **21**, 269–276.

WILKINS, L. T. (1955). 'Some Developments in Prediction Methodology in Applied Social Science.' *Brit. J. Sociol.* **6**, 348–363.

WILL, O. A. (1959). 'Human Relatedness and the Schizophrenic Reaction.' *Psychiatry* **22**, 205–223.

WILMER, H. A. (1958). 'Towards a Definition of the Therapeutic Community.' *Amer. J. Psychiat.* **114**, 824–834.

WINKLER, W. T. (1956). 'The Present Status of Psychotherapy in Germany.' In Fromm-Reichmann and Moreno, pp. 288–305.

WINNICOTT, D. W. (1958). *Collected Papers: Through Paediatrics to Psycho-analysis.* London: Tavistock Publications; New York: Basic Books.

WISEBORD, N., DENBER, R. C. D., CHARATAN, F. B., and TRAVIS, J. H. (1958). 'Patients' Reaction to the "Open-Door".' *Amer. J. Psychiat.* **115**, 518–521.

WOLFF, W. (1950). *Values and Personality. An Existential Psychology of Crisis.* New York: Grune & Stratton.

WYNNE, L. C., RYCOFF, I. M., DAY, J., and HIRSCH, S. I. (1958). 'Pseudo-Mutuality in the Family Relations of Schizophrenics.' *Psychiatry* **21**, 205–220.

WYSCHOGROD, M. (1954). *Kierkegaard and Heidegger. The Ontology of Existence.* London: Routledge & Kegan Paul.

ZIMET, C. E., and FINE, H. J. (1955). 'Personality Changes with a Group Therapeutic Experience in a Human Relations Seminar.' *J. abnorm. soc. Psychol.* **51**, 68–73.

Index